# College Preparatory Mathematics 1

## (Algebra 1)
## Second Edition
## version 6.1

**Managing Editor:**
Leslie Dietiker
    Phillip and Sala Burton High

**Contributing Editors:**
Susan Baskin
    Oakland Unified
Elizabeth Coyner
    Bear River Elementary
Brian Hoey
    Christian Brothers High
Pat King
    Holmes Junior High
Dina Luetgens
    Andros Karperos Middle
Micheal Marsh
    Culver City High
Bob Petersen
    Sacramento High

**Illustrator:**
Eric Ettlin
    Menlo-Atherton High

**Technical Assistance:**
Dean Hickerson
    Consultant
Thu Pham
    The CRESS Center
    University of California, Davis

**Program Directors:**
Tom Sallee
    Department of Mathematics
    University of California, Davis
Judy Kysh
    Northern California Mathematics Project
    The CRESS Center
    University of California, Davis
Elaine Kasimatis
    Department of Mathematics
    California State University, Sacramento
Brian Hoey
    CPM Educational Program

# Credits for the First Edition

## Editors
Scott Holm, Cloverdale High
Elaine Kasimatis, UC Davis
Bob Petersen, Sacramento High

## Consultant
Joel Teller, College Preparatory School

## Technical Assistance
Thu Pham, UC Davis
Crystal Mills, Consultant

## First Edition Contributors

| | |
|---|---|
| Annette Bartos | Churchill Middle School |
| Duane Blomquist | Roseville High |
| Beverly Braverman | C. K. McClatchy High |
| Nancy Clark | Woodland Senior High |
| James Friedrich | Valley High |
| Carol Grossnicklaus | Oxnard High |
| Maria Herndon | Valley High |
| Ted Herr | Roseville High |
| Brian Hoey | Christian Brothers High |
| Scott Holm | Cloverdale High |
| Gail Holt | El Camino Fundamental High |
| Sylvia Huffman | Del Campo High |
| Yury Lokteff | San Juan High |
| Grant McMicken | San Juan High |
| Richard Melamed | El Camino Fundamental High |
| Crystal Mills | Sacramento Waldorf High |
| Bob Petersen | Sacramento High |
| Brad Schottle | Elk Grove High |
| Jeanne Shimizu-Yost | San Juan High |
| Bonnie Sieber | Valley High |
| Pat Stowers | O. W. Holmes Junior High |
| Sharon Swanson | John F. Kennedy High |
| Clark Swanson | Sacramento High |
| Linda Tucker | Bear River High |
| Joe Veiga | Elk Grove High |
| Michael White | Temecula Valley High |
| Malcolm Wong | Luther Burbank High |

8  9  10     04  03

Printed in the United States of America     ISBN 1-885145-67-5

## A Note to Parent(s) and Guardian(s)

Hello. My name is Chris Ott. While I am not an author of the College Preparatory Mathematics (CPM) textbook series, I have tutored dozens of CPM students. Based on this experience, I have written a study guide for CPM Algebra 1 that is incorporated into the student text. If you want an extended overview of this course, read all the PZL problems in the first five units (Units 0-4). They are easy to find, since each PZL problem has a puzzle piece (like the one above) around the problem number in the left margin. These problems will explain the goals of CPM Algebra 1, its methods, the structure of the textbook, the role and duties of the teacher, and the responsibilities of the student. It has numerous practical suggestions for students to maximize the prospect for success in this course.

The authors have also written a more extensive unit by unit *Parent's Guide with Review for Math 1 (Algebra 1)*. This document contains annotated solutions for important problems that help you and your child understand the core ideas of each unit. Most of these sections are followed by a few additional sample problems and their solutions and/or answers. The guide also makes suggestions about how to help your child in this course. At the end of each unit there are several dozen additional practice problems to supplement the textbook. The guide concludes with a brief outline of how the five content threads of the course--graphing, writing equations, ratios, solving equations, and manipulating symbols--are developed through the fourteen units in this textbook. Some schools make the guide available through the classroom teacher or school library. You may order the guide online at www.cpm.org, get an order form there, or mail your request for the *Parent's Guide with Review for Math 1 (Algebra 1)*. 2nd. ed., **version 6.0/6.1,** with a check payable to "CPM Educational Program" for $20 plus local tax (CA only) and $3 shipping and handling, to 1233 Noonan Drive, Sacramento, CA 95822-2569. Allow ten days for delivery.

# College Preparatory Mathematics 1: Second Edition
## (Algebra 1)

# Table of Contents
## Volume 1

# Volume 2

# Unit Seven
# The Big Race
## Slopes and Rates of Change

# Unit 7 Objectives
## *The Big Race:*  SLOPES AND RATES OF CHANGE

We will strengthen our understanding of lines and equations in this unit with a focus on slope. When someone asks "What is the bank's interest rate?" they are referring to a **rate of change, or slope**. Slope is not only an important concept, it is also a useful tool. It will help us graph lines faster and will be used to predict future events.

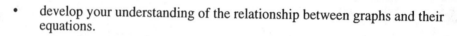

Our work with systems of equations will continue to focus on substitution and graphing. Our understanding of slopes, graphing, and systems of equations will help us determine the winner of the Big Race.

In this unit you will have the opportunity to:

- develop your understanding of the relationship between graphs and their equations.

- formalize the notion of the steepness and direction of a line (slope) in terms of rate of change.

- continue learning how to solve systems of linear equations, especially expanding your understanding of algebraic solutions by substitution.

- learn how to graph linear equations using the slope-intercept method (y = mx + b).

- work with distance, rate and time relationships in context.

This unit typically starts the second semester of the course. You will continue to have opportunities to practice skills and concepts you encountered during the first semester, especially graphing, ratios, and solving equations. You will be expected to keep an organized notebook and continue your tool kit for Units 7 - 13.

---

**BR-0.**    THE BIG RACE

One of the annual events at school during Spirit Week is a tricycle race held in the gym. Leslie, a member of your class, has won the race each of the last three years and is starting to brag about it. The rest of the class is annoyed by this attitude and wants to end this winning streak. The race will be held at the end of this unit. Since you will also compete, you need to size up the competition.

---

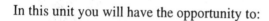

Problem Solving
Graphing
Writing and Solving Equations
Ratios
Geometry
Symbol Manipulation

# Unit 7

## *The Big Race:* SLOPES AND RATES OF CHANGE

## LINEAR EQUATIONS

BR-1. You will receive information every day in this unit about different competitors who will try to beat Leslie in the Big Race. On the resource page provided by your teacher, carefully graph all the given information to help you decide who might win. **BE SURE TO BRING THIS RESOURCE PAGE WITH YOU TO CLASS EVERY DAY.** Without it, following the Big Race will be difficult.

Leslie rides at a constant rate of 2 meters per second. On the resource page provided by your teacher, neatly graph and write an equation in terms of x and y that shows the distance Leslie travels. Let x represent time in seconds and y represent the distance in meters. We do not know how long the race will be, so extend your graph appropriately.

Find Leslie's equation and label her line appropriately. Keep this resource page in a safe place. We will use it every day during this unit.

BR-2. Write a rule using x and y for a line or curve that uses the following coordinates. Look for patterns to help find the rule.

a)  (4, 2), (8, 4), (-10, -5), (16, 8)

b)  (1, 6), (4, 9), (-1, 4), (10, 15)

c)  (3, 9), (4, 16), (7, 49), (-2, 4)

---

### SCALING AXES

Before setting up a graph, it its important to analyze if both positive and negative numbers are needed. Then you must decide how to scale the x- and y-axes. On <u>each</u> axis, one unit of graph paper must represent the same increment, but each axis can have different scales.

---

BR-3.    SLEEPY TIME

An equation used to relate the age of a person to the number of
hours of sleep required each day is shown at right, where H
represents the number of hours of sleep required and A
represents the age in years.

$$H = \frac{34 - A}{2}$$

a)    Graph this equation with H on the vertical
axis and A on the horizontal axis. What is the
smallest and largest number of hours you will
need on this axis? What is the youngest age?
The oldest age? Mark your axes clearly to
reflect these values. Discuss the range of H
and A with your study team.

b)    Plot the point on the graph that represents your
age and your typical number of hours of sleep.
Are you on the line? Label each of your study
team members on the graph with their name to
see if they are on or off the line.

c)    Does this formula work for you? Does it work for babies? Does it work for older
people? For what ages does the formula seem to work best? Is there a point on
this graph that makes no sense? Explain.

BR-4.    On graph paper draw and label △ABC.

a)    Write the ratio of $\frac{\text{the vertical side of } \triangle ABC}{\text{the horizontal side of } \triangle ABC}$ .

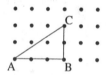

b)    Enlarge △ABC so that the new triangle, △DEF, has
corresponding sides twice as long. Draw and label △DEF.

c)    Write the ratio of $\frac{\text{the vertical side of } \triangle DEF}{\text{the horizontal side of } \triangle DEF}$ . Simplify if possible.

d)    What do you notice about the ratios for parts (a) and (c) ?

e)    Use similar figures to justify your findings about the ratios.

BR-5.    Suppose you multiply the sides of △ABC in BR-4 by four and call the new triangle
△GHI. Draw and label △GHI. Write the ratio:

$$\frac{\text{vertical side of } \triangle GHI}{\text{horizontal side of } \triangle GHI}$$

Compare its ratio to the ratios in the previous problem.

BR-6.    Transform (change) each of the following equations into y-form and then graph them using the two-point y-form method. Refer to your tool kit if necessary.

a)    $y - 4x = -3$                    c)    $3y - 3x = 9$

b)    $3x + 2y = 12$                  d)    $2(x - 3) + 3y = 0$


BR-7.    Write the coordinates of the y-intercept of each line in **BR-6.**


BR-8.    Solve each equation below for x. Show all steps.

a)    $5 + 4(x + 1) = 5$              d)    $4(x + 5) - 3(x + 2) = 14$

b)    $\frac{2x}{3} - 5 = -13$       e)    $\frac{2x}{7} = \frac{4}{5}$

c)    $4(2x - 1) = -10(x - 5)$


BR-9.    Which of the following points are on the graph of the equation? Try to answer this question <u>without</u> a graph.

a)    $(8, 4)$, $(4, 0)$, $(4, 3)$, $(3, 4)$   for $y = \frac{1}{4}x + 2$

b)    $(0, -7)$, $(2, -1)$, $(4, 5)$, $(6, 11)$   for $y = 3x - 7$


BR-10.    Look at the graphs below and answer the following questions.

a)    Compare and contrast lines l, m, n, & k. Be as detailed as possible.

b)    Which line appears steepest?

c)    Which lines appear to have the same steepness?

d)    How is line k different from the other lines?

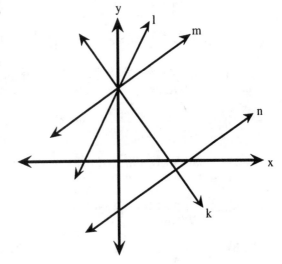

BR-11.

Dina wants to see if she could win the Big Race with a 3 meter head start. If she can ride her tricycle 1 meter per second, can she beat Leslie? Using her speed and her head start, add Dina to your graph on the BR-0 resource page. Label her graph with her name and equation. Be sure to extend her line as far as possible. Using different colors or markings will help to keep each competitor identified.

a) Compare both Leslie and Dina's lines.

b) How is Dina's head start represented on the graph?

BR-12. MONEY MATTERS, Part One

Six cousins were each given $20.00 in a new bank account for the Lunar New Year. On the same set of axes, graph their bank account balances. Use a different marking (or different color pen or pencil) for each person. Let x represent time in days and y represent money in the bank. You should look for the comparative steepness (or slope) of the lines as you graph the different financial scenarios. We will formally define slope on another day. For the purposes of this problem, slope is how steeply the line slants across the graph.

a) May saves two dollars every day. Graph her situation. Label the line with her equation and name.

b) Ling saves five dollars every day. Graph her situation. Label the line with her equation and name.

c) Tuan saves fifty cents each day. Graph his situation. Label the line with his equation and name. Hint: Do not forget the starting balance.

d) Compare May's, Ling's and Tuan's graphs and equations. How are they alike? Different?

e) Minh spends two dollars a day. Graph his situation. Label the line with his equation and name.

f) Tam spends three dollars every day. Graph her situation. Label the line with her equation and name.

g) Compare Minh's and Tam's graphs. How are they the same? How are they different?

h) Now compare May's, Ling's and Tuan's graphs to Minh's and Tam's. How are they different?

i) Kim is not going to spend or save any money. Graph her situation. What does this graph look like? What is her equation?

BR-13.    Add this definition to your tool kit, if you have not done so already:

---

### X- and Y-INTERCEPTS

Recall that the **X-INTERCEPT** of a line is the point where the graph crosses the x-axis; that is, where $y = 0$. To find the x-intercept substitute 0 for y and solve for x. Its coordinate is $(x, 0)$.

Similarly, recall that the **Y-INTERCEPT** of a line is the point where the graph crosses the y-axis, which happens when $x = 0$. Its coordinate is $(0, y)$.

---

BR-14.    In Unit Six, you used the y-form two point method to graph lines. Often the quickest and easiest two points to choose are the x- and y-intercepts. When you use the intercepts, the equation does not need to be in y-form. Find the x- and y-intercepts for the two lines below and use them to graph each line. Write the coordinates of the x- and y-intercepts on your graph.

a)    $x - 2y = 4$                    b)    $3x + 6y = 24$

*(handwritten: $x - 2 = 4$)*          *(handwritten: $3x + 6(3.5) = 24$)*

BR-15.    The graph of the equation $2x - 3y = 7$ is a line.    *(handwritten: $y = 3x + 6 = 24$)*

a)    Find the x- and y-intercepts and graph the line using these two points.

b)    If a point on this line has a x-coordinate of 10, what is its y-coordinate?

BR-16.    MONEY MATTERS, Part Two

a)    May's, Ling's and Tuan's graphs have a **positive slope**. Minh's and Tam's graphs have a **negative slope.** Explain why this makes sense. What would Kim's graph represent?  Explain.

b)    Who is spending money at the fastest rate?  How does the graph show this?  How does the equation show this?

c)    How does May's line differ from Minh's?  How does the equation show this?

d)    Where would you expect the line for Kai, who <u>saves</u> $10 per day to be?  Where would you expect his line to be if he <u>spent</u> $10 per day?

e)    Predict what would happen to Ling's line if she had started with $10 instead of $20. What would happen to Tam's line if she started with $30 instead of $20?

f)    Beside each graph, write the rate of savings or spending for each cousin. For example, May saves at a rate of $2 per day. This can be written as $2/day. Write these rates on the graph. Is there a relationship between the rates and the equations?

**BR-17.** In each part below, find the length of side BC if △ABC is similar to △DEF. Write your answer for the length as a fraction.

a) 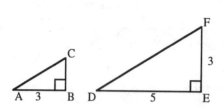 b)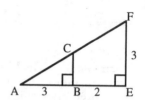

c) For the drawing in part (b), if the coordinates of point A were (0, 0), what would be the coordinates of points C and F ?

**BR-18.** Use the graph at right to answer the following questions: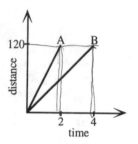

a) Which car is traveling at the greater rate?

b) Find the coordinates of point A and point B.

c) What is the average rate in miles per hour for car A? For car B ?

**BR-19.** Write a rule using x and y for the following coordinates. Look for patterns.

a) (2, 4), (4, 8), (-5, -10), (8, 16)      b) (1, 4), (2, 3), (6, -1), (10, -5)

**BR-20.** Graph the point P: (4, -2).

a) Find the point 5 units up and 2 units to the left of P. Label it Q. Write the coordinates of Q.

b) Go back to P and now find the point 5 units up and 2 units to the right. Label it W. Write the coordinates of W.

c) Draw lines PQ and PW. How are those lines alike?  How are they different?

d) **Extension**: Find the area of triangle PQW.

# POSITIVE AND NEGATIVE SLOPE

**BR-21.** Look at Leslie's and Dina's graphs on your BR-0 Resource Page.

a) What happens to Leslie and Dina at the point of intersection?

b) Where is the point of intersection of the two lines?

c) Use substitution and your equations for Leslie and Dina to verify your point of intersection.

**BR-22.** Some of the lines below are quite steep; others are not. Below each line there is a ratio that describes how steep it is. This ratio is called the **slope** of the line. With your study team, discuss and compare the following graphs and ratios to discover how to determine the slope of a line.

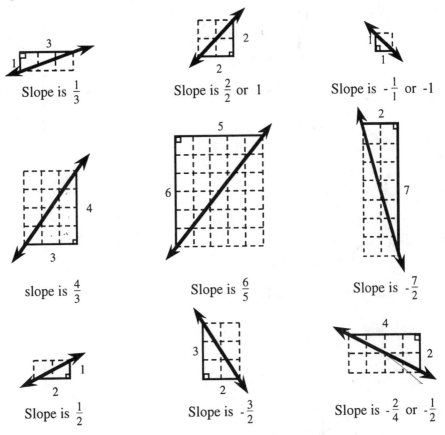

Slope is $\frac{1}{3}$

Slope is $\frac{2}{2}$ or 1

Slope is $-\frac{1}{1}$ or -1

slope is $\frac{4}{3}$

Slope is $\frac{6}{5}$

Slope is $-\frac{7}{2}$

Slope is $\frac{1}{2}$

Slope is $-\frac{3}{2}$

Slope is $-\frac{2}{4}$ or $-\frac{1}{2}$

a)  Use your observations of the preceding lines to find the slope for the following three lines.

1)          2)          3)

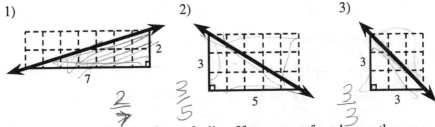

$\frac{2}{7}$          $\frac{3}{5}$          $\frac{3}{3}$

b)  Describe how to find the slope of a line. If your team found more than one method, describe each method. Your descriptions should be clear enough for other teams to understand. Be ready to share your descriptions with the class.

c)  How can you determine if the slope is positive or negative?

d)  Does it matter if the triangle is above or below the line? Why or why not?

**BR-23.** On the Resource Page provided by your teacher, draw slope triangles and find the slope of the line segments below. Be sure to examine the scale carefully. Write the slope as a ratio. Compare your answers in your study team.

a)
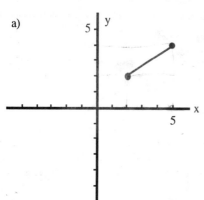

c)
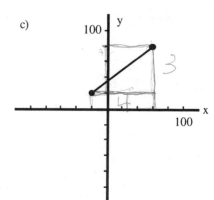

b)
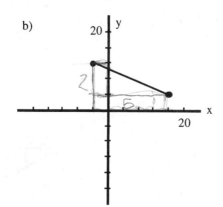

d)
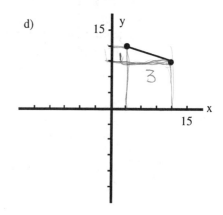

**BR-24.** Graph each to the following pairs of points on graph paper. Draw the slope triangle and determine the slope.

a) (1, 2) and (4, 5)

b) (3, 8) and (5, 4)

c) (-6, 8) and (-4, 5)

d) (7, 3) and (5, 4)

e) (-4, 5) and (5, 4)

f) (5, 0) and (0, 1)

g) Jim got "1" for the slope of the line through points (1, 2) and (4, -1). Explain to Jim the mistake he made and how to correctly find the slope.

~1

BR-25.    Include this information in your tool kit.

---

### THE SLOPE OF A LINE

The **SLOPE** of a line is a measure of the rate at which something changes. It represents both "steepness" and direction.

$$\textbf{slope} = \frac{\text{vertical change}}{\text{horizontal change}} = \frac{\text{change in y-values}}{\text{change in x-values}}$$

Note that lines that go **upward** from left to right have **positive** slope, while lines that go **downward** from left to right have **negative** slope. The slope of a line is often denoted by the letter "m." Some texts refer to the vertical change as the "rise" and the horizontal change as the "run."

To calculate the slope of a line, graph two points on the line, draw the slope triangle (as shown in the examples), write the ratio, and lastly check to see if the slope is positive or negative.

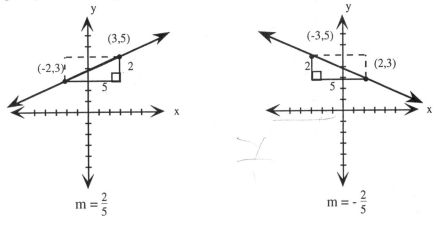

---

BR-26.    Use the scale graph at right of the three points
A (12, 334), B (288, 334), and C ( 288, 934) to answer
the following questions:

a)    What kind of triangle is triangle ABC?

b)    What is distance AB?

c)    What is distance BC?

d)    What is the slope of the line AC, that contains
(12, 334) and ( 288, 934)?

e)    What is the area of the triangle?    600

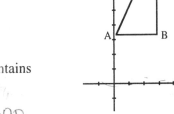

BR-27.    Solve the following systems of equations to find both x and y.

a)    $y = 3x - 5$
      $y = 4x + 11$

b)    $y = \frac{2}{3}x$
      $y = x + 15$

BR-28.    Refer to your BR-0 Resource Page.

a)    What is the minimum distance the Big Race needs to be in order for Leslie to win?  Explain your answer.

b)    Under what condition would Dina win?

BR-29.    Use the two-point method to graph $y = -3x + 4$.

a)    What is the y-intercept?

b)    What is the x-intercept?

c)    Draw a slope triangle on your line and find its slope.

BR-30.    Copy these generic rectangles on your paper. Multiply or factor to rewrite these expressions.

a)

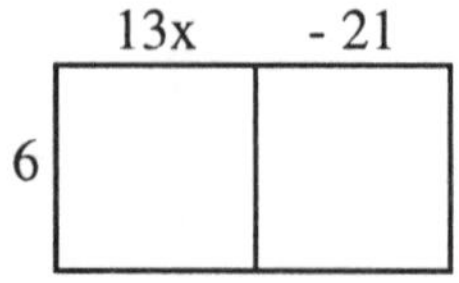

| | 13x | - 21 |
|---|---|---|
| 6 | | |

c)

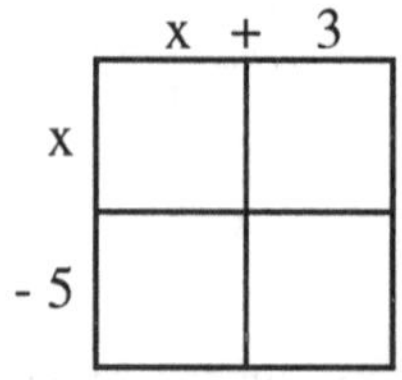

| | x + | 3 |
|---|---|---|
| x | | |
| - 5 | | |

b)

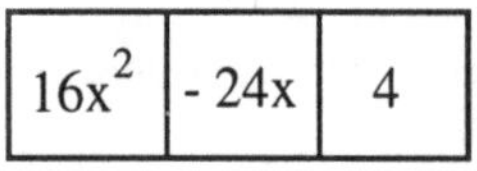

| $16x^2$ | - 24x | 4 |
|---|---|---|

d)

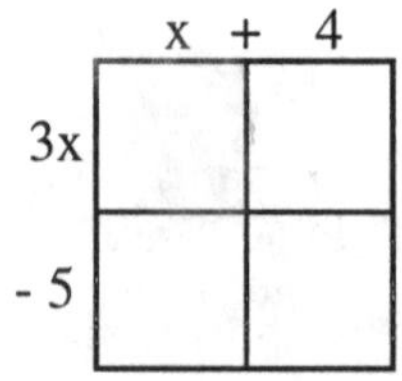

| | x + | 4 |
|---|---|---|
| 3x | | |
| - 5 | | |

BR-31.    Solve each of the following equations.

a)    $2x + 8 = 3x - 4$

b)    $8(x + 6) + 23 = 7$

c)    $1.5(w + 2) = 3 + 2w$

d)    $3(2x - 7) = 5x + 17 + x$

BR-32. The length of a certain rectangle is five times its width. Use this information to sketch and label a rectangle. Write an expression to represent the perimeter. Find the rectangle's dimensions if its perimeter is 30 centimeters.

## SLOPE: RELATING THE EQUATION TO ITS GRAPH

BR-33. Study these slopes: $-\frac{2}{5}$, $\frac{-2}{5}$, $\frac{2}{-5}$, and $\frac{-2}{-5}$.

a) Which of the slopes above are negative?

b) Which of the slopes above are positive?

c) Does the sign of the ratio depend on the position of the negative sign? Explain.

BR-34. Place a sheet of graph paper over these lines to estimate the slope of each line below. Remember to describe each slope with a positive or negative ratio.

BR-35. Graph the line $y = \frac{1}{2}x$.

a) Mentally verify that this line goes through the points $O = (0, 0)$, $A = (2, 1)$, $B = (4, 2)$, $C = (10, 5)$, $D = (-6, -3)$, $E = (-8, -4)$ and $F = (2000, 1000)$. Explain how you verified point F.

b) If you use points A and B to compute the slope and points A and D to compute the slope, how will the answers compare?

c) Describe how to move (slide) from the y-intercept to point A.

MATCH-A-GRAPH, Part Three

With your study teams, match the following graphs with their equations. Record the clues your team used to match each graph with its equation.

1) $y = \frac{1}{4}x + 4$           3) $y = \frac{1}{2}x + 4$

2) $y = 2x + 4$           4) $y = -\frac{2}{3}x + 4$

a)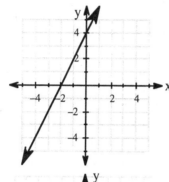

c)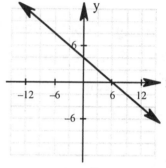

b)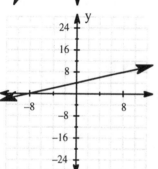

d)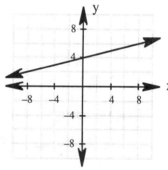

BR-37. Refer back to your Money Matters graph, BR-12. Determine the slope for each person's line. Determine the y-intercept for each line. How do these relate to the equations for each person? Be sure to consider whether the slope is positive or negative.

BR-38. Graph the line $y = -2x + 3$.

a) Mentally verify that this line goes through the points $O' = (0, 3)$, $A' = (2, -1)$, $B' = (3, -3)$, $C' = (-1, 5)$, $D' = (-2, 7)$ and $E' = (1000, -1997)$.

b) Compute the slope of this line.

c) What is the y-intercept of $y = -2x + 3$ ?

d) How do the answers to parts (b) and (c) compare with the original equation?

BR-39. Find the slope of the line $y = \frac{5}{3}x - 2$. How did you determine the slope?

BR-40.　Ms. Speedi is planning on starting at the finish line and walking toward the starting line when the race starts. If she walks one meter per second and meets Dina 11 seconds after the start of the race, how long is the race?

BR-41.　Sketch and label an example of a line with positive slope. Sketch and label an example of a line with negative slope. Graph paper may be helpful.

BR-42.　Refer back to your graph of the race so far. Determine the slope of both Dina's and Leslie's lines. How do these slopes relate to the equations of the lines?

BR-43.　Express each number below as a ratio of two integers. For example, $2.7 = \frac{27}{10}$.

a)　1.2

d)　-4

b)　0.003

e)　50%

c)　5

f)　1250%

BR-44.　In 35 minutes, Suki's car goes 25 miles.

a)　If she continues at the same speed, how long will it take Suki to drive 90 miles?

b)　How far will Suki go in 60 minutes?

c)　Determine the car's average speed in miles per hour.

BR-45.　Arnold is juggling four bowling balls and two seedless watermelons which amount to 66 pounds in all. Each watermelon weighs three pounds more than half of the weight of one bowling ball. How much does each watermelon weigh?

BR-46.　Solve this system for the point of intersection.

$$x = 2y - 1$$
$$x = -5y + 10$$

# SLOPE-INTERCEPT FORM OF LINEAR EQUATIONS

BR-47.     Dean has decided he will enter the race. He estimates that he rides 3 meters every 4 seconds and wants a 2 meter head start.

    a)     On the Resource Page, graph a line representing Dean's distance from the starting line. Label his graph with his name.

    b)     How many meters does Dean ride each second?

    c)     Compare your answer to part (b) with the slope of the line.

BR-48.     On a sheet of graph paper, draw a set of coordinate axes. Draw a line through the origin that has a slope of 1. Remember that the origin is the point (0, 0).

    a)     Write the coordinates of three points that are on the line.

    b)     Write an equation that describes these points.

BR-49.     UNDERSTANDING THE EQUATION OF A LINE

    Obtain a resource page from your teacher. With your study team, investigate each family of graphs. Compare the graphed solid lines to $y = x$, which is dotted.

    1)

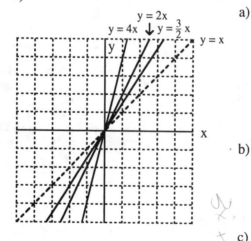

    a)     Copy and complete the table below and fill it in with the equation, slope, and y-intercept of each line. The first entry is done for you.

| equation | slope | y-intercept |
|----------|-------|-------------|
| $y = x$  | 1     | 0           |

    b)     Examine the graph carefully and compare the slope of the lines to the slope of the line $y = x$. Describe your observations in complete sentences.

    c)     Examine the equations of the lines. What relationship does the slope have to the equation of the line?

**>>Problem continues on the next page.>>**

UNIT 7

2)

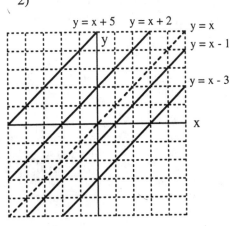

a) Copy and complete the table below and fill it in with the equation, slope, and y-intercept of each line. The first entry is done for you.

| equation | slope | y-intercept |
|---|---|---|
| y = x | 1 | 0 |

b) Examine the graph carefully and compare the slope of the lines to the slope of the line y = x. Describe your observations in complete sentences.

c) Compare the y-intercepts of the lines. What relationship does the y-intercept have to the equation of the line?

3)

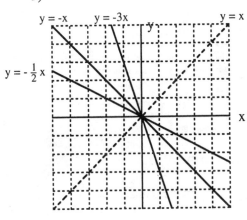

a) Copy and complete the table below and fill it in with the equation, slope, and y-intercept of each line. The first entry is done for you.

| equation | slope | y-intercept |
|---|---|---|
| y = x | 1 | 0 |

b) What is different about the lines in graph (3) at left and the lines in graphs (1) and (2) above?

c) Examine the equations of the lines. What makes these slopes different than the those in graphs (1) and (2) ?

**>>Problem continues on the next page.>>**

The Big Race: Slopes and Rates of Change

4)

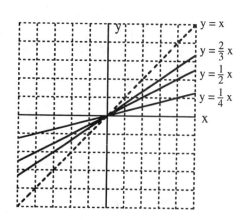

a) Copy and complete the table below and fill it in with the equation, slope, and y-intercept of each line. The first entry is done for you.

| equation | slope | y-intercept |
|----------|-------|-------------|
| y = x | 1 | 0 |

b) Examine the graph carefully and compare the slope of the lines to the slope of the line y = x. These lines are also different than those in graph (1) above. Describe your observations in complete sentences.

c) If the slope is less than one, describe the line.

BR-50. Without graphing, identify the slope and y-intercept of the following equations:

a) $y = 3x + 5$

b) $y = -6x + 3$

c) $y = -\frac{3}{4}x - 1$

d) $y = \frac{5}{-4}x$

e) $y = 7 + 4x$

f) $y = \frac{-x}{5} + 6$

BR-51. Explain to a student who was absent today how to find the slope and y-intercept of a line written in the y-form.

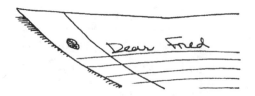

BR-52. Add this information to your tool kit.

---

**SLOPE-INTERCEPT FORM**

Any line can be described by an equation in the form of **y = mx + b**. The "m" represents the slope (it is the coefficient of x). The "b" represents the y-value of the y-intercept (where x = 0). Ordered pairs (x , y) that make the equation true are coordinates of points on that line.

---

BR-53. Interesting patterns occur when graphing several equations on one coordinate grid.

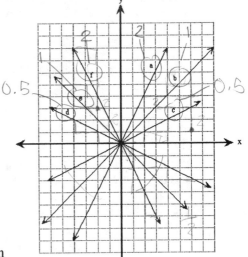

a) Find the slope of each of the lines at right.

b) Write the equation of each line.

c) What is the slope of the x-axis?

d) If the slope of a line were $\frac{-3}{2}$, between which two lines would the graph lie?

e) If the slope of a line were 100, between which two lines would the graph lie? (Hint: one of the lines may be one of the axes.)

f) If the slope of a line were $\frac{1}{6}$, between which two lines would the graph lie?

BR-54. Draw a line with the slope of $\frac{3}{4}$. Draw another line with the slope of $-\frac{3}{4}$.

BR-55. Use your explanation from BR-51 to state the slope and y-intercept of each of the following lines.

a) $y = 2x - 5$

b) $y = -3x + 10$

c) $y = \frac{3}{4}x + \frac{7}{4}$

d) $y = -\frac{5}{2} + 2x$

e) $4y = 3x + 6$
(Hint: first solve for y.)

f) $y + 2x = 4$
(Hint: first solve for y.)

g) Two pairs of lines above are parallel. Name them.

BR-56. Simplify the following. (Hint: $3x = \frac{3x}{1}$ .)

a) $3x \cdot \frac{4}{x}$

b) $25 \cdot \frac{x}{5}$

c) $x \cdot \frac{1}{x}$

BR-57. Find the point of intersection for the two lines: $y = 6x - 9$ and $y = -\frac{1}{3}x - 2$.

## GRAPHING USING SLOPE-INTERCEPT FORM

BR-58. Do you think it is always possible to draw a line given only one point and its slope?

The Big Race: Slopes and Rates of Change

**BR-59.** When first graphing a line in Unit Three, you set up a table and used many points to graph the line. In Unit Six, we developed the two-point method. Now, with your study team, you will explore a way to graph a line using one point and a slope.

a) Plot the point (2, 3).

b) Draw a line through that point with a slope of $\frac{1}{2}$. Discuss with your study team how to do this accurately. Is there more than one way to do this?

c) Find the equation of the line using the slope and y-intercept.

**BR-60.** Use the slope and the given point on the line to graph the following lines. Use a ruler and draw carefully so you can accurately find the y-intercept for:

a) a line through (8, 2), with a slope of $\frac{3}{4}$. Write the equation of the line.

b) a line through (8, 2), with a slope of $-\frac{3}{4}$. Write the equation of the line.

c) a line through (-4, 3), with a slope of -2. Write the equation of the line.

**BR-61.**

Elizabeth and Bob are considering joining the race. Bob usually rides 3 meters in 2 seconds and will get a 5 meter head start. Elizabeth rides 1 meter in 4 seconds and wants a 6 meter head start. Add lines for Elizabeth and Bob to the Big Race graph and label their lines with each equation and its name. Use a different color pen, pencil or highlighter if you can.

a) Who rides faster, Elizabeth or Bob? How does the graph show this?

b) When does Dean pass Elizabeth? How can you tell by examining the graph?

**BR-62.** Kyle made this sketch to find the slope of a line through ( -15, 39) and (29, -2). Use his sketch to finish the problem. Remember to check whether the slope is negative or positive.

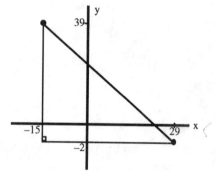

**BR-63.** Draw sketches similar to Kyle's to find the slope of the lines through the given points. We call this sketch a **slope triangle**.

a) (10, 2) and (2, 24)

b) (-3, 5) and (2, 12)

c) (-6, 5) and (8, -3)

d) (-6, -3) and (2, 10)

BR-64.    Refer to your BR-0 resource page for the Big Race.

   a)    Find the equation for Dean.

   b)    If the race were 8 meters long, who would be first, second and third? Explain
         your answer.

   c)    If the race were held today, how long does Dean's advantage over Leslie last?
         Use substitution to find the exact time that Leslie passes Dean.


BR-65.    MORE OR LESS

   Judy has $20 and is saving at the rate of $6 per week. Ida has $172 and is
   spending at the rate of $4 per week. After how many weeks will each have the same
   amount of money? Use your observations from Money Matters, problem BR-12, to
   answer the following questions.

   a)    Write an equation for Judy and Ida. Draw the graphs to estimate the solution.
         What will x represent? What will y represent? What scales will you use for
         each axis? Label your graphs completely. Carefully decide what scales to use.

   b)    Solve this problem using substitution.

   c)    Compare your answers from (a) and (b). Which answer is more accurate?


BR-66.    Solve each of the following equations for x.

   a)    $\frac{x}{6} = \frac{7}{3}$                     c)    $3x + 2 = 7x - 8$

   b)    $\frac{6}{x} = \frac{4}{x + 1}$                  d)    $6(x - 4) = 42$


BR-67.    Write a shorter expression for each of the following polynomials by simplifying.

   a)    $3x^2 + 2x - 2 + 4x^2 + 6 - 5x$        d)    $(-5x^2 + 2) - (6x^2 + x)$

   b)    $(4x^2 + 12x - 5) - (3x^2 + 6)$         e)    $3(x + 1) + 2(x + 1) + (x + 1)$
                                                          $3x+3 \qquad 2x+2 \qquad x+1$

   c)    $2(x^2 + 3) - 5(x^2 + 3)$
         $2x^2+6 \quad -5x^2-15$

BR-68.    Multiply. You may find the sketch of a generic rectangle useful.

   a)    $(x + 2)(x + 8)$                       d)    $(x - 2)(x + 8)$

   b)    $(x - 2)(x - 8)$                       e)    $3x(2x + 4)$

   c)    $(x + 2)(x - 8)$                       f)    $-5x(4x - 8)$


BR-69.    Miguel bragged that he saved $12.60 by buying his
          new sneakers on sale at 30% off. How much did the
          sneakers cost originally?

# SOLVING SYSTEMS OF LINEAR EQUATIONS BY SUBSTITUTION

**BR-70.** Use the recipe below, right and answer the questions below.

a) Copy the following sentence, but substitute the word "test" with "assignment".

There will be a test on Friday, and tests are worth 25% of your grade.

b) In the recipe at right, $\frac{1}{2}$ cup of apple sauce can be substituted for one egg and $\frac{1}{4}$ cup of butter. Rewrite the new recipe for Ms. Speedi's Brownies by replacing all the eggs and butter with applesauce.

> **Ms. Speedi's Brownies**
> 4 squares of Chocolate
> 2 cups sugar
> 1 teaspoon vanilla
> 1 cup flour
> 3 eggs
> $\frac{3}{4}$ cups butter

c) If $x = -2$, and $4x - 3y = -11$, then what is y? Explain what you do to solve for y and do it.

d) If $x = -3y + 1$ and $4x - 3y = -11$, discuss with your study team and write a complete sentence to explain why $4(-3y + 1) - 3y = -11$.

**BR-71.** Add this information to your tool kit.

---

### MORE ON THE SUBSTITUTION METHOD

In Unit Six, we used Substitution to algebraically find the point of intersection for two linear equations. In those problems, the two equations were always in y-form. However, substitution can be used even if the equations are <u>not</u> in y-form.

Given:
$$x = -3y + 1$$
$$4x - 3y = -11$$

Use substitution to rewrite the two equations as one:

We can then write: $4(-3y + 1) - 3y = -11$ by replacing x with $(-3y + 1)$.

$x = (-3y + 1)$

$4(\quad) - 3y = -11$

$4(-3y + 1) - 3y = -11$

a) Solve the equation for y.

b) Substitute your answer from part (a) into $x = -3y + 1$. Write your answer for x and y as an ordered pair.

c) Substitute y = 1 into $4x - 3y = -11$ to verify that <u>either</u> original equation may be used to find the second coordinate.

d) Why is this method called substitution?

---

254

BR-72. Use substitution to find the point of intersection $(x, y)$ for each pair of linear equations below.

a) $y = -3x$
$4x + y = 2$

c) $x = y - 3$
$x + 3y = 5$

b) $2x + 3y = -17$
$y = x - 4$

d) Verify that your solution to (c) works in BOTH equations.

BR-73. The graphs for $y = -\frac{1}{2}x + 5$ and $y = \frac{3}{2}x + 1$ appear at right.

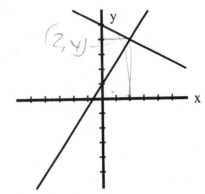

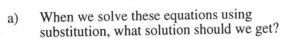

a) When we solve these equations using substitution, what solution should we get?

b) Solve using substitution to verify your answer. How is this solution represented on the graph?

c) The graphs for $y = \frac{1}{2}x + 3$ and $y = \frac{1}{2}x - 2$ appear at right. When we solve using substitution, what solution should we get?

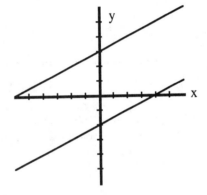

d) Use substitution and solve this system of equations. What happens? Why?

BR-74. The points $(1, 2)$ and $(7, 12)$ lie on a line. Find the coordinates of a third point on the line. How can you use the idea of slope?

$$\frac{12 - 2}{7 - 1} = \frac{10}{6} = \boxed{\frac{5}{3}}$$

BR-75. Eventually everybody passes Elizabeth in the Big Race.

a) Write the order in which people passed her.

b) Ignoring head starts, make a list of the competitors going from fastest to slowest.

c) How do you know this from the graph?

d) How do you know this from the equations?

e) What is the slope of each line? How does this relate to their speed?

BR-76. Without making a table, graph each line. Start with the y-intercept, then use the slope.

a) $y = \frac{2}{3}x - 2$

c) $y = 3x$

b) $y = -\frac{2}{3}x + 2$

d) $y = 4 - 2x$

BR-77. Complete the following percentage problems using the method of your choice.

a) Eighteen is what percent of 25 ?

b) Eighteen percent of 25 is what?

c) Twenty-five is what percent of 18 ?

BR-78. Find the area of a rectangle with one side 10,000 millimeters long and the other side 20 meters long. (Hint: the answer is not 200,000)

## LINES WITH EQUAL SLOPES AND MORE SUBSTITUTION

BR-79. If Brian starts 3 seconds late and catches up with Dina 7 seconds after the race begins, add Brian's line to the graph.

a) What is the x-intercept for Brian's line?

b) Find Brian's speed.

BR-80.    Simplify the following expressions. Check your results with your team. Making sense of the negative in front of the parentheses is important.

a)    $-1(4x - 6)$    *-4x + 6*    c)    $4x - (5 - 2x)$

*-4x*                        *6ᵤ*
*-6*                        *-5 + 2x*

b)    $- (2x + 5)$

BR-81.    Joe learned substitution yesterday and solved the following system of equations.

$$\left. \begin{array}{l} x = 4 - 2y \\ 3y - x = 6 \end{array} \right\}$$

$$3y - (4 - 2y) = 6 \qquad x = 4 - 2(10)$$

$$3y - 4 - 2y = 6 \qquad x = 4 - 20$$

$$y - 4 = 6 \qquad x = -16$$

$$y = 10$$

a)    Joe got an answer of y = 10 and x = -16. Check his answer.

b)    Solve the problem and find the correct answer.

c)    What did he do wrong?

BR-82.    Solve the following systems. Remember to check your solution in both equations to make sure it is the point of intersection.

a)    $y = 2x - 3$
      $x - y = -4$

b)    $y = x - 2$
      $2x - 3y = 14$

BR-83.    Use the figure at right for these questions.

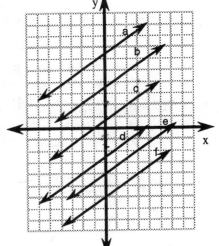

a)    Estimate the y-intercept of each line.

b)    What do all the lines have in common?

c)    Between which two lines would the graph of $y = \frac{2}{3}x + 2$ lie?

d)    Between which two lines would the graph of $y = \frac{2}{3}x - \frac{12}{7}$ lie?

e)    Explain what happens to the graph of $y = \frac{2}{3}x$ when a positive number is added to the right side of the equation. What happens when a negative number is added there?

f)    Write an equation for each of lines *a* through *f*.

BR-84.    Solve the following systems. Remember to check your solution in both equations to make sure it is the point of intersection.

a)    $5x - 4y = 8$
       $y = x - 3$

b)    $4y - x = 6$
       $x = 12 - 2y$

BR-85.    Use generic rectangles to multiply.

a)    $(x + 12)(x - 11)$

c)    $2x(6x - 7)$

b)    $(2x - 1)(x + 5)$

d)    $(4x - 11)(5x + 7)$

BR-86.    Graph the lines:    $y = -\frac{1}{3}x + 1$   and   $y - 2x = 8$

a)    Where do they intersect?

b)    Name the y-intercepts for each line.

c)    Find the area of the triangle formed by the two lines and the y-axis.

BR-87.    Elizabeth is trying to choose her Internet Service Provider (ISP). She has three different companies competing for her business, and each has sent her some information, summarized below:

WEBCom        $4.95 per month, plus $1.95 per hour
Ameri-Net     $19.95 per month, unlimited hours

a)    Analyze this information carefully. Create an equation to represent each company. Explain to Elizabeth which service you advise her to use.

b)    Another company, CPMOnline, will soon be in business and is planning to offer 5 free hours each month, but then charge $2.49 for each hour thereafter. Add this company to your graph and find when CPMOnline is the best deal.

BR-88.    Multiply or factor to rewrite the following expressions.

a)    $4x(9x - 5)$

c)    $12m^2 - 8m$

b)    $9(3m^2 - 11m + 16)$

d)    $15x^2 - 60x + 75$

BR-89.    Draw a graph similar to the Big Race to solve this problem.

Mia started pedaling along the bike trail at 10 miles per hour. Lucy left the same place one hour later going 15 miles per hour. How long does it take before Lucy catches up with Mia?

BR-90.    THE BIG RACE, Part One

Today is finally the Big Race. Obtain a fresh BR-0
Resource Page for this problem. You and the rest
of your study team will compete against Leslie
and Elizabeth at today's rally in the gym.
Determine who will win the race.

**Rules**:
- Your study team must work cooperatively to
  answer all the questions on the cards.
- Each member of the team will select rider A,
  B, C, or D.
- You may not show your card to your team. You may only communicate the
  information contained on the card.
- Elizabeth's and Leslie's cards will be shared by the entire team.

Remember your guidelines for study teams. Be sure everyone on your team discusses
the entire problem and its solution.

---

BR-91.    THE BIG RACE, Part Two

a)    Use a table to organize your information. Find the slope for each rider. Find the
      y-intercept for each rider. Write the equation for each rider.

b)    Who won the race?  What was the speed of this rider?

c)    In what order did the participants finish the race?  List their names (or letters)
      with the time it took them to finish.

d)    After 8 seconds, which tricyclist had traveled the shortest distance from the
      starting line?  Who had traveled the farthest distance?

e)    Locate and label three times when one rider passed another rider. Is there a point
      where more than two tricyclists are tied?

f)    If the race were only 20 meters long, does the order of the winners change?  How?

g)    After 16 seconds, how far had each rider traveled from the starting line?

h)    Extension:  How long does the race have to be for "C" to be able to win?

i)    Extension:  If the race is 22 meters long, how much of a head start does Elizabeth
      need to beat "D"?

**BR-92.** Before the Big Race, the track needs to be resurfaced. The price of the work depends on the area to be resurfaced. Use the dimensions of the track given at right to find the area of the track. (Assume the ends of the track are circular.)

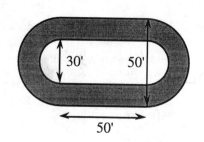

**BR-93.** Betty's Diner makes 15% profit on its lunches and 22% profit on its dinners. If the diner took in $2,700 on Tuesday and made $524 profit, how much was spent at lunch? Let $x$ represent the sales at lunch and $y$ represent the sales at dinner, write two equations, then solve.

**BR-94.** Use generic rectangles to multiply:

a) $(12x - 2)^2$

c) $(4x - 3)(x - 2)$

b) $(5a + 4)(2a - 7)$

d) $(y - 11)(y + 11)$

**BR-95.** Solve for x:

a) $2 - 12x = 14$

c) $3.1x - 58 = 20.69x - 71.2$

b) $9(x - 2) = 81$

d) $5(x + 1) - 2(x + 1) = 3$

**BR-96.** Two passenger trains started toward each other at the same time from towns 288 miles apart and met in three hours. The rate of one train was six miles per hour slower than that of the other. Find the rate of each train.

# UNIT SUMMARY AND REVIEW

**BR-97.** UNIT SEVEN SUMMARY

With your study team, list 3 or 4 big ideas that you feel best represent Unit 7. Write a description of each main idea. For each topic, choose a problem that best demonstrates your understanding. Explain your solution as in previous unit summaries. Show all your work.

**BR-98.** Write the equations in the form y = mx + b for the following graphs:

a)

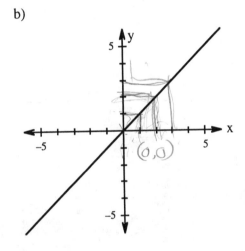

$(0,-2)=y$
$(0,4)=x$

c)

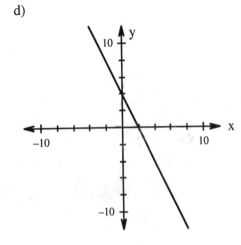

b)

$(0,0)$

d)

**BR-99.** GETTING IN SHAPE

Frank weighs 160 pounds and is on a diet to gain two pounds a week so that he can make the football team. John weighs 208 pounds and is on a diet to lose three pounds a week so that he can be on the wrestling team in a lower weight class. If they can meet these goals with their diets, when will Frank and John weigh the same, and how much will they weigh?

a) Solve the problem.

b) Clearly explain your method.

BR-100.  Use generic rectangles to multiply:

a)  $(x + 3)(x + 2)$

c)  $(x + 7)(x - 5)$

b)  $(x - 9)(x - 4)$

d)  $(2x + 5)(x - 8)$

BR-101.  Points $(-9, 3)$ and $(1, 1)$ are two points on a line.

a)  Find the coordinates of a third point on the line.

b)  Find the slope of the line.

BR-102.  Use substitution to solve the following systems for x and y.

a)  $3x + 7y = 71$
    $y = 4x + 50$

b)  $y = 4.5 - x$
    $y = -2x + 6$

BR-103.  Graph the lines and find the x-intercepts.

a)  $y = -2x + 4$

b)  $y = \frac{2}{3}x - 6$

BR-104.  TOOL KIT CHECK-UP

Your tool kit contains reference tools for algebra. Return to your tool kit entries. You may need to revise or add entries.

Be sure that your tool kit contains entries for all of the items listed below. Add any topics that are missing to your tool kit NOW, as well as any other items that will help you in your study of algebra.

- X- and Y-intercepts
- Slope of a Line

- Substitution Method
- Slope-Intercept Form

*NOTE:* *A question similar to GM-13 is asked at job interviews at a major computer software firm.*

GM-13.   CROSSING OVER

Elizabeth, Brian, Dean, and Leslie want to cross a bridge. They all begin on the same side and have only 17 minutes to get everyone across to the other side.

To complicate matters, it is night and there is only one flashlight. A maximum of two people can cross at one time. Any party that crosses, either 1 or 2 people, <u>must</u> have the flashlight with them. The flashlight must be walked back and forth; it cannot be thrown.

Each student walks at a different speed. A pair must walk together at the rate of the slower student's pace.

> **Elizabeth:** 1 minute to cross
> **Brian:** 2 minutes to cross.
> **Dean:** 5 minutes to cross.
> **Leslie:** 10 minutes to cross.

For example, if Elizabeth and Leslie walk across first, 10 minutes have elapsed when they get to the other side of the bridge. If Leslie returns across the bridge with the flashlight, a total of 20 minutes has passed, and you have failed the mission.

**Your Task**:

- How can they get everyone across in 17 minutes?

- Do you think this is a good question for a computer firm to ask future employees? Explain.

## GM-14.    MAKE A GRAPH

Anyone can become an artist by following graphing directions. For example, graph the following design:

| | |
|---|---|
| $y = 2x + 8$ | $0 \le x \le 2$ |
| $y = 12$ | $2 \le x \le 4$ |
| $y = -x + 16$ | $4 \le x \le 6$ |
| $x = 6$ | $8 \le y \le 10$ |
| $y = \frac{4}{3}x$ | $0 \le x \le 6$ |
| $y = -\frac{4}{3}x$ | $-6 \le x \le 0$ |
| $x = -6$ | $8 \le y \le 10$ |
| $y = x + 16$ | $-6 \le x \le -4$ |
| $y = 12$ | $-4 \le x \le -2$ |
| $y = -2x + 8$ | $-2 \le x \le 0$ |

**Your Task**:    Make a design on graph paper which can be drawn by someone following your equation instructions.  Think about ways you can get curves in your design.  Be creative, but accurate.  Include your design on graph paper along with a listing of equations and domain (input) values like those shown above.

# The Amusement Park
### Factoring Quadratics

# Unit 8 Objectives
## The Amusement Park: FACTORING QUADRATICS

Previously, much of your work focused on different methods of solving linear equations and graphing lines. In Units 8 through 12, you will learn various methods for solving **quadratic equations** such as

$$x^2 + 5x + 6 = 0.$$

You have used subproblems to find the area of rectangles as both a product of its dimensions and as a sum of the area of smaller rectangles. You have multiplied binomials using the Algebra Tiles to write the sum of the areas of the small rectangles. In this unit you will be given the **sum of the parts of rectangles** and asked to find the dimensions, so you can write the area as a **product of factors**. Algebra Tiles have provided a handy device for modeling multiplication, and now will be used in factoring expressions. These factoring skills will provide you with yet another method to solve equations.

In this unit you will have the opportunity to:

- learn how to "undo" multiplying binomials by factoring trinomials.

- explore how to factor special products, such as differences of squares and perfect square trinomials.

- combine your factoring skills, including common terms, special binomial products, and trinomials.

- solve factorable quadratic equations algebraically using the Zero Product Property.

- study quadratic equations in relation to their graphs.

This unit builds on the development of sums and products of polynomials based on a geometric model. It continues to give you practice with solving various kinds of equations, writing equations from word problems, and finding x- an y-intercepts graphically and algebraically.

Read the following problem. **Do not try to solve it now.**

AP-0.     The figure at right shows the master plan for a proposed Amusement Park coming to our city. Park designers expect the Park size to change before it is built, so they made it square with a length of x. Rectangular rows of parking will be adjacent to two sides of the park, with a picnic area in a square corner. Based on data provided later in the unit, help the planners design the land space so that the three areas fit within the square design.

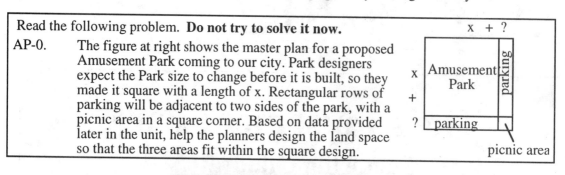

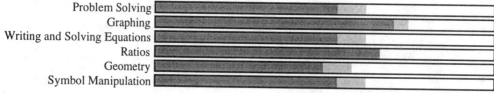

# Unit 8

*The Amusement Park:* **FACTORING QUADRATICS**

## MULTIPLYING BINOMIALS

AP-1.     Draw a rectangle to represent the product of $(x + 7)(x + 4)$.

    a)  What are the dimensions of this rectangle?

    b)  Write the area of this rectangle as a sum of the parts.

    c)  Write the area of this rectangle as an equation of the form (length)(width) = area.

AP-2.     Obtain a resource page from your teacher. Determine if a rectangle is possible for each set of tiles described in the chart below. If so, draw a sketch; if not, answer "No." Write the area of each tile in the center of each piece. Write the dimensions along the edges.

When recording your rectangles, be sure that the big squares are arranged in the upper left corner and the small squares are located in the lower right corner. The rectangles fill in the rest of the figure, below and to the right of the big square, to form a composite rectangle.

| Number of $x^2$'s | Number of x's | Number of 1's | Is it possible ? | Rectangle | Area as a sum and a product |
|---|---|---|---|---|---|
| 1 | 3 | 2 | Yes | | $x^2 + 2x + x + 2$<br>sum $= x^2 + 3x + 2$<br>product $= (x + 1)(x + 2)$ |
| 1 | 5 | 3 | No | | |
| 1 | 4 | 4 | | | |
| 1 | 6 | 5 | | | |
| 1 | 3 | 9 | | | |
| 1 | 4 | 3 | | | |
| 1 | 7 | 10 | | | |

AP-3.    Write an algebraic equation for the area of each of the following rectangles as shown in the example below.

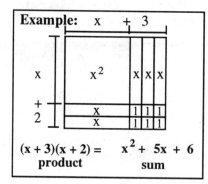

**Example:**  x  +  3

(x + 3)(x + 2) =    $x^2$ + 5x + 6
   **product**        **sum**

a)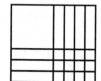

c)

e)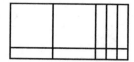

b)

d)

f)

AP-4.    Read the following information and add the vocabulary to your tool
         kit. Then identify the following polynomial expressions in parts (a)
         through (h) as either a sum or a product.

---

### POLYNOMIALS AS SUMS AND PRODUCTS

An expression of the form $3x^2$ or $5x$ or $7$ is called a **monomial**, from the
Greek words *monos* meaning *single,* and *nomos* meaning *part.*

The sum (or difference) of two monomials is called a **binomial**. For example,
$x + 2$, $x^2 - 4$, and $3 - 7x$ are binomials.

More generally, the sum of two or more monomials is called a **polynomial**
(from the Greek words *poly* for *many,* and *nomos* for *part*). Some
polynomials, such as the **trinomial** $x^2 + 5x + 6$, can be written as a product
of factors:

$$x^2 + 5x + 6 = (x + 2)(x + 3)$$

Here we have written the **SUM** $x^2 + 5x + 6$ as a **PRODUCT** of the two
**factors**, $(x + 2)$ and $(x + 3)$. We say we have **FACTORED** the polynomial
$x^2 + 5x + 6$ as "the quantity $x + 2$ times the quantity $x + 3$." The polynomials
that have $x^2$ and no higher exponents are called **QUADRATICS.**

---

a)    $2x + 1 = 3x$            e)    $(x + 5)(x + 2)$

b)    $x^2 + 7x + 12 =$        f)    $x(2x + 5)$

c)    $(x + 1)(x + 4)$         g)    $5x^3 + 8x^2 + 10x$

d)    $3x + 9$                 h)    $2x(x^2 - 3x + 5)$

i)    Which of the above expressions are quadratics? Hint: there are four.


AP-5.    Combine like terms.

   a)    $(-6w + 3q - w) + (8q - 4 - 2w)$      c)    $(f^2 + 3f - 5) - (f^2 - f - 2)$

   b)    $(3x + 4 + 2b) - (5b + 6x - 7)$       d)    $(p - 2r - 2c) + (5c + 9p - r)$

   e)    When combining like terms, which operations were used?

   f)    Explain how you identify like terms. When are you able to combine algebraic
         terms?

AP-6.     In the figure at right, points A, C, and E lie on
          the same line.

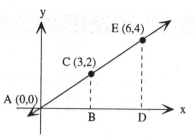

a)   Demonstrate that △ADE is an enlargement
     of △ABC. (Hint: what is the enlargement
     ratio for corresponding sides?)

b)   What is the ratio of the areas of △ADE and
     △ABC ?

c)   Describe how to move (slide) from point A to point C.

d)   Describe how to move (slide) from point A to point E.

e)   What is the slope of this line?

f)   What is the y-intercept?

g)   Write the equation of the line in the form y = mx + b.

AP-7.     Multiply or factor the following expressions. Hint: a sketch of a generic rectangle
          may help.

a)   3x(2x - 5)            c)   -6a(3a - 4)            e)   4x(5x + 4)

b)   $4x^2 - 8x$            d)   $14a^2 + 21b$            f)   $24c^2 + 16c$

AP-8.     Find the point of intersection for the following sets of lines.

a)   6 + 2x = y                    b)   4x - y = - 5
     2x - 4y = 12                        y = 9x + 1

AP-9.     Copy and solve each of the following Diamond Problems. Check for accuracy with
          your study team. You will need these for a later problem.

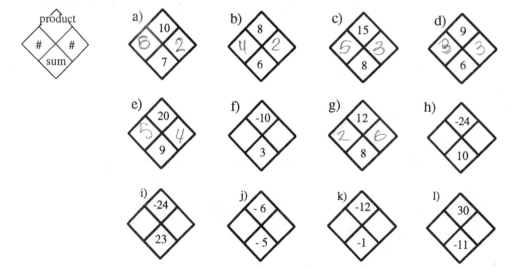

AP-10.  Summarize the following information in your tool kit. Then answer the questions that follow.

---

### FACTORING QUADRATICS

Yesterday, you solved problems in the form of (length)(width) = area. Today we will being working backwards from the area and find the dimensions. This is called **FACTORING QUADRATICS.**

Using this fact, you can show that $x^2 + 5x + 6 = (x + 3)(x + 2)$ because

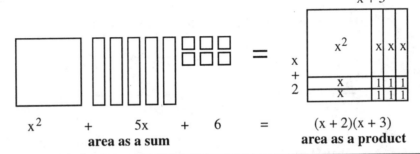

$$x^2 \quad + \quad 5x \quad + \quad 6 \quad = \quad (x + 2)(x + 3)$$

$$\text{\textbf{area as a sum}} \qquad\qquad \text{\textbf{area as a product}}$$

---

Use your tiles and arrange each of the areas below into a rectangle as shown in AP-2, AP-3, and the example above. Make a drawing to represent each equation. Label each part to show why the following equations are true. Write the area equation below each of your drawings.

a)   $x^2 + 7x + 6 = (x + 6)(x + 1)$      c)   $x^2 + 3x + 2 = (x + 2)(x + 1)$

b)   $x^2 + 4x + 4 = (x + 2)(x + 2)$      d)   $2x^2 + 5x + 3 = (2x + 3)(x + 1)$

AP-11. Find the dimensions of each of the following generic rectangles. The parts are not necessarily drawn to scale. Use Guess and Check to write the area of each as both a sum and a product as in the example.

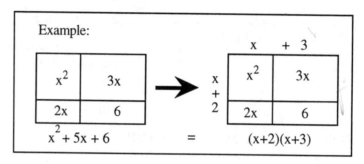

Example:

| $x^2$ | $3x$ |
| $2x$ | $6$ |

$x^2 + 5x + 6$  =  $(x+2)(x+3)$

a)

| $x^2$ | $5x$ |
| $3x$ | $15$ |

c)

| $x^2$ | $6x$ |
| $3x$ | $18$ |

e)

| $x^2$ | $5x$ |
| $2x$ | $10$ |

b)

| $x^2$ | $4x$ |
| $3x$ | $12$ |

d)

| $2x^2$ | $10x$ |

f)

| $x^2$ | $4xy$ |
| $4xy$ | $16y^2$ |

AP-12. Draw generic rectangles to multiply the pairs of binomials below. Label the dimensions and area parts using the example from AP-11. Apply what you know about multiplying positive and negative numbers.

a) $(2x + 6)(3x - 5)$

c) $(2x + y)(4x - 3y)$

b) $(2x + 1)(4x - 3)$

AP-13. Graph a line through the point (3, -5) with a slope of $-\frac{3}{2}$.

a) Estimate its y-intercept.

b) Find the equation of the line.

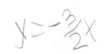

c) Find the equation of a parallel line through (2, 1).

AP-14. Use a generic rectangle to multiply these binomials. Label the dimensions and write the area as the sum of the parts.

a) $(x + 10)(x + 3)$

c) $(2x - 11)(3x - 5)$

b) $(x + 7)(x - 9)$

AP-15.     A damaged section of an apartment patio can be covered with 40 square tiles which are nine inches on a side. The owner decides to replace the section with square tiles which are three inches on a side. How many tiles will be needed? Drawing a picture may help you.

AP-16.     Solve for x. Leave answers as integers or fractions--not decimals or mixed fractions.

a)    $x + 3 = 0$          e)    $12x - 5 = 0$

b)    $x - 3 = 0$          f)    $12x + 5 = 0$

c)    $2x + 3 = 0$         g)    $ax + b = 0$

d)    $2x - 3 = 0$         h)    $ax - b = 0$

AP-17.     Recall from your previous classes that we have factored a number when it is written as the product of two or more integers. Since $6 \cdot 8 = 48$, 6 and 8 are factors of 48. All the factors of 48 are 1, 2, 3, 4, 6, 8, 12, 16, 24, 48. What is it called when an integer greater than zero has exactly two factors?

a)    List the factors of 36.

b)    What is the greatest common factor of 36 and 48 ?

c)    Find the greatest common factor of 64 and 72.

# FACTORING USING SUMS AND PRODUCTS

AP-18. USING ALGEBRA TILES TO FACTOR

What if we knew the area of a rectangle and we wanted to find the dimensions? We would have to work backwards. Start with the area represented by $x^2 + 6x + 8$. Normally, we would not be sure whether the expression represents the area of a rectangle. One way to find out is to use Algebra Tiles to try to form a rectangle.

You may find it easier to record the rectangle without drawing all the tiles. You may draw a generic rectangle instead. Write the dimensions along the edges and the area in each of the smaller parts as shown below.

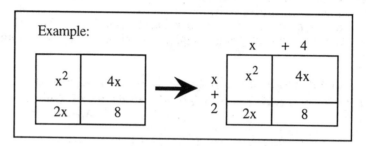

We can see that the rectangle with area $x^2 + 6x + 8$ has dimensions $(x + 2)$ and $(x + 4)$.

Use Algebra Tiles to build rectangles with each of the following areas. Draw the complete picture or a generic rectangle and write the dimensions algebraically as in the example above. Be sure you have written both the product and the sum.

a) $x^2 + 6x + 8$

b) $x^2 + 5x + 4$

c) $x^2 + 7x + 6$

d) $x^2 + 7x + 12$

e) $2x^2 + 8x$

f) $2x^2 + 5x + 3$

USING DIAMOND PROBLEMS TO FACTOR

Using Guess and Check is not the only way to find the dimensions of a rectangle when we know its area. Patterns will help us find another method. Start with $x^2 + 8x + 12$. Draw a generic rectangle and fill in the parts we know as shown at right.

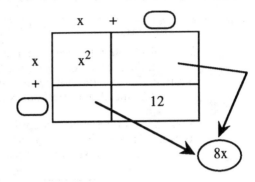

We know the sum of the areas of the two unlabeled parts must be 8x, but we do not know how to split the 8x between the two parts. The 8x could be split into **sums** of $7x + 1x$, or $6x + 2x$, or $3x + 5x$, or $4x + 4x$. However, we also know that the numbers that go in the two ovals must have a **product** of 12.

a)   Use the information above to write and solve a Diamond Problem to help us decide how the 8x should be split.

b)   Complete the generic rectangle and label the dimensions.

product

sum

AP-20.   Use either the Guess and Check method of problem AP-18 or the Diamonds in AP-19 to find the **factors** of each of the following quadratics. The factors are the binomials which represent the length and width of the rectangle.

Draw a picture for each problem and write an algebraic equation of the form:

area = (length)(width).

a)   $x^2 + 7x + 10$   (Hint:  it may be easier to think of the factors of 10 first and then find the pair whose sum is 7.)

b)   $x^2 + 6x + 8$          d)   $x^2 + 6x + 9$

c)   $x^2 + 8x + 15$        e)   $x^2 + 9x + 20$

AP-21.     SUMS AND PRODUCTS

a)    Use the worksheet your teacher provides you to record integer pairs whose sums and products are given below. Some of the pairs do not have integer solutions.

| Sum | Product | Integer Pair |
|---|---|---|
| 6 | 8 | 2, 4 |
| 7 | 10 | 2,5 |
| 13 | 12 | |
| 8 | 12 | 2,6 |
| 6 | 12 | |
| 6 | 9 | |
| 15 | 56 | |
| 8 | 15 | |
| 9 | 20 | |
| 2 | -35 | |
| 1 | -72 | |
| 3 | -10 | |
| 10 | -24 | |
| 0 | -16 | |
| 23 | -24 | |
| 0 | -32 | |

| Sum | Product | Integer Pair |
|---|---|---|
| -5 | 6 | |
| -7 | 6 | |
| -11 | 30 | |
| -8 | 16 | |
| -10 | 16 | |
| 0 | 16 | |
| -10 | 24 | |
| -9 | 18 | |
| -5 | -6 | |
| -2 | -35 | |
| -3 | -28 | |
| -1 | -12 | |
| -10 | -25 | |
| 0 | -25 | |
| -1 | -42 | |
| -12 | -13 | |

b)    Judy says the entries in the sum-product table in part (a) are just Diamond Problems in disguise. Explain what she means.

c)    We can use most lines in the sum and product table above to write a quadratic polynomial and its factors. For example, $x^2 - 10x + 24 = (x - 6)(x - 4)$. Write three more sum and product factoring examples from the table.

d)    Use the table to write a quadratic polynomial that has <u>no</u> integer factors.


AP-22.    Solve each system of equations for x and y. Check your solution.

a)      $y = 3x - 8$

        $y = 2x + 7$

b)      $y = 3x - 8$

        $2x + 3y = 12$

AP-23.    Graph points A (1, 1) and B (3, 4). Show your solution on graph paper.

a)    What is the slope of the line containing A and B?

b)    Point C is on the line which goes through points A and B. If the x-coordinate of C is 4, what is the y-coordinate? Draw two similar triangles to help you.

c)    Write the equation of the line from the graph.

d)    Verify that points A, B, and C make your equation from part (c) true. Revise if needed.

AP-24.    Make a table with at least six entries using $-3 \le x \le 5$. Draw a large graph of the equation $y = x^2 - 4x$. You will use this graph again for a later problem so label it clearly. Is it a line or a curve?

AP-25.    Draw a generic rectangle to factor these polynomials. Write an equation in the form: area = (length)(width).

a)    $x^2 + 15x + 56$              c)    $x^2 + 7x + 12$

b)    $x^2 + 13x + 12$

AP-26.    You have four cards: an ace of spades, an ace of hearts, a two of hearts, and a three of hearts.

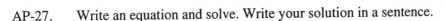

a)    List all possible combinations of two of the cards.

b)    You draw two cards. What is the probability that both are aces?

c)    You draw two cards. What is the probability they are both hearts?

d)    If you draw only one card, what is the probability it is an ace?

e)    If you draw two cards, what is the probability they are both spades?

AP-27.    Write an equation and solve. Write your solution in a sentence.

A stick 86 centimeters long is cut into five pieces. The three long pieces are all the same length and the two shorter pieces are both the same length. Each of the shorter pieces is two centimeters shorter than one of the longer pieces. Find the length of a longer piece.

The Amusement Park: Factoring Quadratics

AP-28.  Use your experience with sums and products of integers to help you factor each of the following quadratics.

a)  $x^2 + 9x + 8$          e)  $x^2 + 2x - 8$

b)  $x^2 + 6x + 8$          f)  $x^2 + x - 20$

c)  $x^2 - 6x + 8$          g)  $x^2 - x - 20$

d)  $x^2 - 2x - 8$


AP-29.  Use a Generic Rectangle to multiply.

a)  $3(x^2 - 3x + 2)$          c)  $-2(x^3 - 5x^2 + 6)$

b)  $4b(2b^2 + 3b - 1)$          d)  $3x(x^2 - 3x + 2)$


AP-30.  Sheila was asked to factor $2x^2 + 10x$ with her Algebra Tiles. By moving the tiles around she produced the following configurations with these tiles. With your study team, decide which of the configurations below represent a factored form of $2x^2 + 10x$.

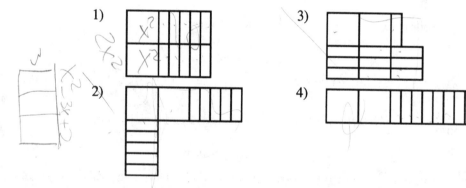

a)  On your paper, draw a copy of the tile configuration(s) that is (are) in correct factored form. How did your study team determine that these were correct?

b)  For each configuration in part (a), write the dimensions of the composite rectangle. Then express the area as a product and a sum.

c)  Of the composite rectangles, which one is closest to a square? This composite rectangles is considered **factored completely**. With your study team, decide which factored form in part (b) is factored completely.

AP-31.    We have seen cases in which only two types of tiles are given. Read
          the example below and add an example of the Greatest Common
          Factor to your tool kit. Then use a generic rectangle to find the factors
          of each of the polynomials below. In other words, find the dimensions
          of each rectangle with the given area.

**GREATEST COMMON FACTOR**

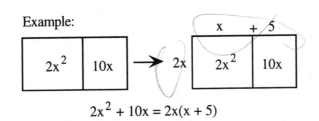

$$2x^2 + 10x = 2x(x + 5)$$

For $2x^2 + 10x$, "2x" is called the **GREATEST COMMON FACTOR.**
Although the diagram could have dimensions $2(x^2 + 5x)$, $x(2x + 10)$, or
$2x(x + 5)$, we usually choose $2x(x + 5)$ because the $2x$ is the largest factor
that is common to <u>both</u> $2x^2$ and $10x$. Unless directed otherwise, when told
to factor, you should always find the greatest common factor, then examine
the parentheses to see if any further factoring is possible.

a)    $x^2 + 7x$

b)    $3x^2 + 6x$

c)    $3x + 6$

d)    How does a generic rectangle with only two sections relate to the Distributive
      Property?

e)    Give an example of when you have used common factors before.


AP-32.    Factor by using the greatest common factor as in AP-31. Notice that this is an extension
          of the Distributive Property and the generic rectangles will need 3 sections.

a)    $8x^2 - 2x + 4$              c)    $25x^3 + 100x^2 + 50x$

b)    $9x^2 + 15x - 24$           d)    $10r^3 + 30r^2 - 20r$

AP-33.* From the twelve graphs below, choose one that best fits each of the situations described in parts (a) through (d). Copy the graph that fits each description and label the axes clearly with the labels shown in the parentheses. If you cannot find a graph you want, sketch your own and explain it fully.

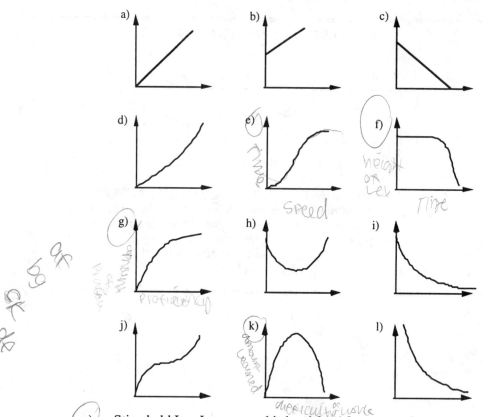

a) Sting held Lex Lugar over his head for a few unsteady moments, and then, with a violent crash, he dropped him. ( height of Lex / time )

b) When I started to swim competitively, I initially made very rapid progress, but I have found that the better you get, the more difficult it is to improve further. ( proficiency / amount of practice )

c) If schoolwork is too easy, you do not learn anything from doing it. On the other hand, if it is so difficult you cannot understand it, again you do not learn. That is why it is so important to plan work at the right level of difficulty. ( amount learned / difficulty of work )

d) When biking, I try to start off slowly, build up to a comfortable speed, and then gradually slow as I near the end of my training. ( speed / time )

e) Make up a story of your own to accompany one of the remaining graphs. In class you will give your story to a partner and see whether your partner chooses the same graph you wrote the story about.

* Adapted from *The Language of Functions and Graphs*, Joint Matriculation Board and the Shell Centre for Mathematical Education, University of Nottingham, England.

UNIT 8

AP-34. Recall what you know about square numbers to help you answer the questions below.

a) What <u>two</u> numbers can you square to get a result of 25?

b) Compare the question in part (a) with the equation at right. What do you notice?

$x^2 = 25$

c) Solve each of the following quadratic equations for x. Each equation has TWO solutions. Round decimal answers to the nearest 0.01.

1) $x^2 + 5 = 30$      3) $x^2 + 5 = 25$

2) $x^2 + 25 = 650$      4) $x^2 = 120$

AP-35. Find the equation of a line through the points (1, - 5) and (-2, 1) at right.

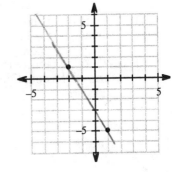

AP-36. Factor the following expressions. Be sure to look for the greatest common factor.

a) $x^2 + 10x + 16$      d) $2x^2 - 22x$

b) $x^2 + 15x + 56$      e) $5x^2 + 30x$

c) $x^2 + 11x + 30$      f) $3x^3 + 6x^2$

AP-37. The germination rate for zinnia seeds is 78%. This means that, on average, 78% of the seeds will sprout and grow. If Jim wants 60 plants for his yard, how many seeds should he plant?

AP-38. On the same set of axes, graph the lines $y = 3$, $x = -2$, $y = 0$, and $x = 2$. Find the area of the interior region defined by the four lines.

AP-39. Solve each of the following equations by Guess and Check.

a) $3x = 0$      d) $(x + 1)(x - 4) = 0$

b) $-\frac{1}{2}x = 0$      e) $(x - 2)(x + 5) = 0$

c) $x(x - 3) = 0$      f) $(x + 3)(2x - 3) = 0$

AP-40. We have been working with quadratic expressions such as $x^2 + 4x - 5$. We will now explore the graphs of quadratic expressions and see how factoring relates to the graph.

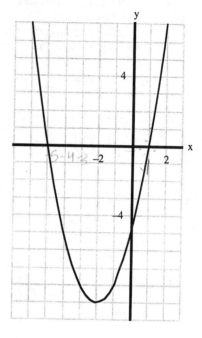

a) Highlight the line $y = 0$ on the resource page provided by your teacher. Where does the line $y = 0$ intersect the parabola $y = x^2 + 4x - 5$ ?

b) Factor $x^2 + 4x - 5$.

c) Use part (b) and Guess and Check to solve $0 = (x - 1)(x + 5)$.

d) What do you observe about the factored form of the equation and the solution in part (c)?

**ZERO PRODUCT PROPERTY**

You have factored quite a few quadratic
expressions similar to $x^2 + 2x - 3$. You have also
graphed several parabolas in "y-form" where a
quadratic expression appears on the right side of
the equation, such as $y = x^2 + 2x - 3$. The
following activities will help you to put these two
ideas together with the **Zero Product Property**.

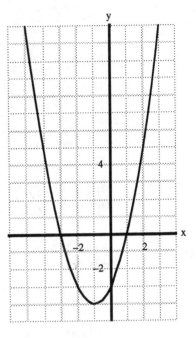

a)  Factor $x^2 + 2x - 3$ and compare the constant
in each binomial to the x-intercepts from the
graph on the resource page.

b)  Explore the following products carefully:

(1)  Find the value of the product
$(5)(8)(0)(4)$.

(2)  Find the value of $(5)(0)(8)(4)$. How
does this value compare to the value in
part (1) above?

(3)  Find the product of $(6)(x)(0)(7)$.

(4)  If $(6)(x)(4)(7) = 0$, what must be the value of x ?

(5)  If $(a)(b)(c) = 0$, what can you say about the possible values of a, b, and c ?

c)  In part (b)(5) above, you concluded that if $(a)(b)(c) = 0$, then either $a = 0$ OR
$b = 0$ OR $c = 0$. Now consider the equation $0 = (x - 1)(x + 3)$. Using this pattern,

if $0 = (x - 1)(x + 3)$, then $x - 1 = 0$ OR $x + 3 = 0$.

Solving each equation results in $x = 1$ OR $x = -3$.

d)  Compare these results to the x-intercepts you found from the graph in part (a)
above. Write a sentence or two about the relationship between the results of
solving $0 = x^2 + 2x - 3$ using algebra and finding where the graph of the equation
$y = x^2 + 2x - 3$ crosses the x-axis.

ROOTS OF A PARABOLA

Test your conjecture from the previous problem, AP-41, part (d), in the problems below.

a) Graph the parabola $y = x^2 - x - 2$ for $-2 \le x \le 3$ on the resource page. Mark the x-intercepts (also called **roots**) and label them with their coordinates.

b) Substitute $y = 0$ into the equation $y = x^2 - x - 2$ to obtain an equation with one variable. Then find two solutions to the new equation by first factoring the expression $x^2 - x - 2$.

c) Explain how solving the equation $0 = x^2 - x - 2$ gives you enough information to name the x-intercepts of the parabola $y = x^2 - x - 2$ without having to draw the graph.

d) Why do people call the method you followed in parts (b) and (c) the "Zero Product Property"?

e) In order to use the Zero Product Property, what must the product be?

f) Add this definition to your tool kit.

> The x-intercepts of a parabola are also referred to as the **ROOTS** of the quadratic equation.

AP-43. Without graphing, use the Zero Product Property developed in the previous problems to find where each graph crosses the x-axis. (Hint: what is the equation of the x-axis?)

a) $y = (x - 3)(x - 4)$

b) $y = x^2 + 5x - 24$

c) $y = x^2 + 10x + 16$

AP-44.     Add this information to your tool kit.

---

### ZERO PRODUCT PROPERTY

The **ZERO PRODUCT PROPERTY** states that when the product of two or more factors is zero, one of these factors must equal zero. We use this property to solve quadratic equations that are factorable using integers. The general statement of the property is:

**If $a \cdot b \cdot c = 0$, then $a = 0$ OR $b = 0$ OR $c = 0$.**

For example, given the equation:                                        $x^2 + 11x = -24$

1) Bring all the terms to one side so the equation            $x^2 + 11x + 24 = 0$
   is set equal to zero.

2) Factor the quadratic expression.                              $(x + 8)(x + 3) = 0$

3) Set each factor equal to zero and                    $(x + 8) = 0$ or $(x + 3) = 0$
   solve the equation.                                       $x = -8$ or $x = -3$

4) Check both solutions in the original equation:       $(-8)^2 + 11(-8) = -24$,
                                                   and   $(-3)^2 + 11(-3) = -24$

---

AP-45.     Use your experience with sums and products of integers to help you factor each of the following quadratics if possible.

a)   $x^2 + 3x - 10$                         c)   $x^2 + 3x + 10$

b)   $x^2 - 2x - 35$                         d)   $x^2 - 10x + 24$


AP-46.     Solve each of the following quadratic equations. Check each solution.

a)   $0 = (x + 3)(x - 6)$                    b)   $x^2 + 4x - 32 = 0$

c)   $0 = x^2 + 7x + 6$

d)   Find the coordinates of the x-intercepts of the parabola $y = x^2 + 4x - 32$ without graphing. (Hint: use what you found in part (b).)

AP-47. Solve each of the equations for the unknown variable. Use any method you choose.

a) $2x + 6 = 3x - 4$

b) $9s - 1 = 4$

c) $2(w + 4) - 6(w - 7) = 50$

d) $32 = \frac{1}{7}r + r$

e) $(x - 7)(2x + 6) = 0$

f) $3(9 - 2d) + 2(2d + 8) = 6 - 2d$

g) $\frac{5}{x + 2} = \frac{3}{x}$

AP-48. Marci correctly graphed an equation and got a vertical line.

a) If the line contained the point (-2, 3), hat equation did Marci graph?

b) On the same axes, Marci's team member graphed the line $y = 4x - 1$. At what point did this line hit Marci's line? (Be sure to explain how you arrived at your answer.)

AP-49. Add each pair of fractions below.

a) Add $\frac{4}{5} + \frac{1}{7}$. What did you do first? b) Add $\frac{9}{x} + \frac{3}{5}$. What did you do first?

# FACTORING DIFFERENCES OF SQUARES

AP-50. This investigation will tie together several concepts you have used and developed in this course: subproblems, area and factoring. We are going to look at a special factoring pattern known as the **difference of squares**.

a) Represent the difference of two numerical squares with graph paper by following these steps.

1) Cut a 20 by 20 square out of graph paper. Compute the area of the square and write its area using exponents.

2) Remove a 5 by 5 square by cutting it from the lower right corner of the 20 by 20 square. What is the area of this removed square? Write its area using exponents.

3) Write the measurements of the new shape along its edges. Find the remaining area. Is this expression a Difference of Squares?

4) We have been factoring quadratics by forming rectangles and finding their dimensions. Since this new shape is not a rectangle, we need to alter it by cutting off one of the extended pieces and attaching it in such a way that we form a new rectangle. What are the dimensions of this rectangle? Write its area as a product.

5) Describe in complete sentences how you can predict the dimensions of the new rectangle formed by any difference of squares.

>>**Problem continues on the next page.**>>

b)   We will now represent the difference of squares with Algebra Tiles using variables. Repeat the process with unknown lengths by following these steps.

   1)   Trace and cut out an $x^2$. Label the sides of your square with x. Write the area of the square on your paper as $x^2$.

   2)   Place a small square tile in the lower right corner of the $x^2$ square you cut out. Trace and cut out the small square from the lower right corner as shown in the diagram at right. Label the dimensions and area of this new shape. Write an expression for the remaining area.

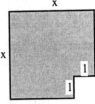

   3)   We have been factoring quadratics by forming rectangles and finding their dimensions. Form a rectangle with the remaining piece the same way as you did before. What are the dimensions of this new rectangle? Write its area as a product.

c)   Extend these ideas to other examples by answering these questions.

   1)   What would be the dimensions of the rectangle formed by the difference of $x^2 - 2^2$? Write this as both a product and a difference.

   2)   What would be the dimensions of the rectangle formed by the difference of $x^2 - 16$? Write this as both a product and a difference.

   3)   Factor $4x^2 - 9$. Refer to the diagram at right. Write the expression as both a product and a difference.

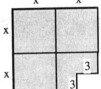

   4)   Factor $x^2 - y^2$. If you need to, cut a square as before to determine the dimensions. Write the expression as both a product and a difference.

d)   Add this information to your tool kit.

---

### DIFFERENCE OF SQUARES

We call this special case of factoring the **DIFFERENCE OF SQUARES**. The general pattern is written as

$$x^2 - y^2 = (x + y)(x - y).$$

Some students prefer to think of this special case as simply $x^2 + 0xy - y^2$

For example:   $x^2 + 0x - 16 = (x + 4)(x - 4)$

---

e)   We have shown geometrically that $x^2 - 1^2 = (x + 1)(x - 1)$.

   1)   Check that your factors or dimensions work by constructing a generic rectangle.

   2)   Graph the equation $y = x^2 - 1^2$. Find the x-intercepts. How does this relate to the factors?

The Amusement Park: Factoring Quadratics

AP-51. Factor each of the following quadratics. You may either use the pattern developed for the difference of squares in AP-50 or you can think of $x^2 - 49$ as $x^2 + 0x - 49$ and construct a generic rectangle.

a) $x^2 - 49$ 　　　　　 b) $x^2 - 16$ 　　　　 c) $x^2 - 144$

d) Write another quadratic which is the difference of squares, then factor it. Have a study team member verify that it works.

e) Extension: Factor $16x^2 - 9$.

f) Extension: Suppose we write $16x^2 - 9 = 0$. Use part (e) and the Zero Product Property to solve for the x-intercepts.

AP-52. Factor each of the following quadratics, if possible.

a) $x^2 - 6x + 5$ 　　　　　　　　 f) $6x^2 - 12x$

b) $x^2 - x - 6$ 　　　　　　　　 g) $x^2 + 9x + 7$

c) $x^2 - x - 42$ 　　　　　　　 h) $x^2 - 3x - 88$

d) $6x + x^2 - 16$ 　　　　　　 i) $x^2 - 25$

e) $x^2 - 100x + 2500$ 　　　　 j) $20x^2 - 100x$

AP-53. The following Zero Product Property problems were found but one of the problems was erased. Can you determine what problem (c) stated?

a) $(x - 3)(x + 2) = 0$
$x = 3$ or $x = -2$

c) $(\ \ )(\ \ ) = 0$
$x = -9$ or $x = 6$

b) $(2x - 5)(x + 4) = 0$
$x = \frac{5}{2}$ or $x = -4$

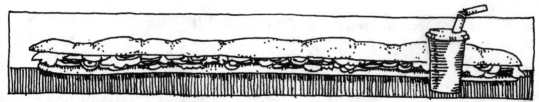

AP-54. Deli sandwiches can be bought at Giuseppi's in a variety of sizes. The smallest is the 6 inch long *Sub*, which weighs $\frac{3}{4}$ pounds and costs $2.35. The largest is a big version of the *Sub* called the *Party Giant*, which is 21 feet long.

a) How much does the *Party Giant* weigh?

b) Giuseppi charges by the weight of the sandwich. How much does the *Party Giant* cost?

AP-55.   Solve each of the following equations or system of equations.

a)   $3(x + 7) = 3x + 21$         c)   $2x(x - 5) = 0$

b)   $x^2 - 4x - 12 = 0$          d)   $y = 3x - 1$
                                       $x + 2y = 5$


AP-56.   Multiply. Describe any pattern you observe. Remember in part (a) that $3 = \frac{3}{1}$.

a)   $3 \cdot \frac{1}{3}$               d)   $6x \cdot \frac{1}{3}$

b)   $3x \cdot \frac{1}{3}$              e)   $12x \cdot \frac{3}{4x}$

c)   $3x \cdot \frac{1}{x}$              f)   $32x \cdot \frac{3}{8}$


# PERFECT SQUARE TRINOMIALS

AP-57.   From the pattern found in the previous lesson, factor the following
**difference of squares.**

a)   $x^2 - 9$                   c)   $9x^2 - 25$

b)   $x^2 - 25$                  d)   $x^2 - b^2$


AP-58.   The following quadratics contain a new pattern. With your study team, factor them
and discuss what special patterns appear .

a)   $x^2 + 6x + 9$             d)   $x^2 - 12x + 36$

b)   $x^2 + 10x + 25$           e)   $x^2 - 18x + 81$

c)   $x^2 + 20x + 100$          f)   $x^2 - 24x + 144$

g)   These are called "perfect square trinomials." Why?

h)   Each member of your study team should create a different example of a
perfect square trinomial that fits this pattern. Factor it. Check each other's
work by multiplying.

i)   The polynomial $9x^2 + 30x + 25$ is also a perfect square trinomial. Find its
factors. Sketch a generic rectangle to verify your factors.


AP-59.   With your study team, compare the various methods and patterns you have used to
factor polynomials. Write a brief summary of those methods, include an example
and your opinion of which you prefer.


The Amusement Park: Factoring Quadratics

**AP-60.** Pay close attention to the similarities and differences between the two equations below.

a) Solve the equation $x^2 + x - 6 = 0$ by factoring and the Zero Product Property.

b) Where does the graph of $y = x^2 + x - 6$ cross the x- axis?

c) Why are these two problems related?

**AP-61.** Solve each of the following equations. You may need to factor first.

a) $(x + 2)(x - 3) = 0$

b) $x^2 - 3x - 4 = 0$

c) $(x + 22)^2 = 0$

d) $x^2 + 3x - 10 = 0$

e) $x^2 - 16x + 64 = 0$

f) $(x + 3)(2x - 3) = 0$

**AP-62.** Graph $y = x^2 + 6x + 9$. Discuss with your study team how the factors from AP-58 part (a) tell you about a special property of this parabola.

**AP-63.** Factor the following.

a) $x^2 - 9$   $(x-3)(x-3)$

b) $x^2 - 6x + 9$

c) $x^2 + 9x + 20$

d) $x^2 + 26x + 169$

e) $9x^3 + 27x^2 + 108x$

f) $x^2 - 9x + 20$

g) $x^2 + 40x + 400$

h) $6x^2 - 9x$

**AP-64.** Solve for the variable in each of the following equations.

a) $0x = 5$

b) $7x = 7x$

c) $0c = 0$   What numbers could c be? Why?

**AP-65.** Show each subproblem in your solution. It may help to refer to your work from problem AP-49.

a) Add $\frac{3}{4} + \frac{1}{3}$.

b) Using part (a) as a model of subproblems, add $\frac{3}{x} + \frac{1}{3}$.

**AP-66.** Graph these equations using the slope and the y-intercept.

a) $y = 4x - 2$

b) $y = 3 - \frac{1}{5}x$

c) $2x + y = 7$

d) $2x + 3y = 7$

AP-67.    Find the x- and y-intercepts of the following lines.

   a)    $y = 3x - 6$                                       b)    $4x - y = 8$

AP-68.    Write a ratio and solve the following problems.

   a)    What is 12% of 210 ?

   b)    28 is what percent of 210 ?

   c)    Chelsea answered 54 problems correct on a test.
          Brandee informed her that her score was 45%.
          How many points were possible on the test?

AP-69.    A rectangular sign is twice as long as it is wide. Its
          area is 450 square centimeters. What are the
          dimensions of the sign?

AP-70.    Some expressions can be factored more than once. Add this example
          to your tool kit. Then factor the polynomials following the tool kit box.

---

### FACTORING COMPLETELY

Example: Factor $3x^3 - 6x^2 - 45x$ as completely as possible.

| $3x$ | $3x^3$ | $-6x^2$ | $-45x$ |

| | $x^2$ | $-2x$ | $-15$ |
|---|---|---|---|
| $3x$ | $3x^3$ | $-6x^2$ | $-45x$ |

We can factor $3x^3 - 6x^2 - 45x$ as $(3x)(x^2 - 2x - 15)$.

However, $x^2 - 2x - 15$ factors to $(x + 3)(x - 5)$.

Thus, the **complete factoring** of $3x^3 - 6x^2 - 45x$ is $3x(x + 3)(x - 5)$.

Notice that the greatest common factor, $3x$, is removed first.

Discuss this example with your study team and record how to determine if a
polynomial is **completely factored**.

---

Factor each of the following polynomials as completely as possible. Consider these
kinds of problems as another example of subproblems. Always look for the greatest
common factor first and write it as a product with the remaining polynomial. Then
continue factoring the polynomial, if possible.

   a)    $5x^2 + 15x - 20$                              c)    $2x^2 - 50$

   b)    $x^2y - 3xy - 10y$

The Amusement Park: Factoring Quadratics                                                    291

AP-71. So far this year you have been exposed to three basic groups of equations, each of which have methods of solution and different types of answers. Be sure that you can identify each type of problem, know the method to use to solve it, and the number and form of the answers.

Add examples of each to your tool kit.

---

## SUMMARY OF TYPES OF EQUATIONS

### ONE LINEAR EQUATION

### SYSTEMS OF LINEAR EQUATIONS

### QUADRATIC EQUATIONS

One variable, one answer.*

Two variables, two answers which make an ordered pair $(x, y)$.*

One variable squared, zero, one, or two answers.*

Remove any parenthesis, move all variables to one side, constants to another, and divide, if necessary.

Use substitution to combine the two equation into one, solve for the first variable, solve for the second variable.

Rearrange the equation so that it is set equal to zero, factor, and use the Zero Product Property.

Example:

$$2(2x-1)-6=-x+2$$
$$4x-2-6=-x+2$$
$$5x-8=2$$
$$5x=10$$
$$x=2$$

Example:

$$\begin{cases} x+2y=-8 \\ \quad y=2x+1 \end{cases}$$

$$x+2(2x+1)=-8$$
$$x+4x+2=-8$$
$$5x+2=-8$$
$$5x=-10$$
$$x=-2$$

$$y=2x+1$$
$$=2(-2)+1=-3$$
$$(-2,-3)$$

Example:

$$x^2+9x+10=-4$$
$$x^2+9x+14=0$$
$$(x+7)(x+2)=0$$

$$x+7=0 \text{ or } x+2=0$$
$$x=-7 \text{ or } x=-2$$

*Except for cases where there is no solution or the solution is all real numbers.

*Unless parallel or the same line.

*Zero answers (parabola above or below x-axis);

One answer (parabola vertex on x-axis); or,

Two answers (parabola intersects x-axis in two points).

AP-72.   Solve each of the following equations or systems by any method you choose. Show all your work. If you do not know where to begin, review the different types of equations in problem AP-71.

a)   $0 = 2x - 3$

b)   $0 = (2x - 3)(x + 5)$

c)   $2x - 5 = -x + 7$

d)   $x^2 + 5x + 6 = 0$

e)   $x^2 - 4x + 4 = 0$

f)   $y = 2x - 3$
     $x + y = 15$

g)   $x^2 + 5x + 9 = 3$

h)   $3(3x - 1) = -x + 1$

i)   $\frac{5 - 2x}{3} = \frac{x}{5}$

j)   $\frac{2x}{3} = 4$

k)   $x^2 - 6 = -2$

l)   $x^2 = y$
     $10 = y$

AP-73.   Find the x-intercepts for the graph of each of the following equations without graphing. Describe your method in complete sentences.

a)   $y = x^2 + 10x + 21$

b)   $y = 2x - 1$

c)   $y = 2x^2 - 5x + 2$

AP-74.   Combine like terms.

a)   $(5x^2 + x - 1) + (3x^2 - 4x - 8)$

b)   $(6x^2 - 8x + 7) - (2x^2 + 6x - 7)$

c)   $(8x^2 - 8x + 10) + (2x^2 + 8x - 6)$

d)   $(x^2 - x - 1) - (2x^2 + x - 1)$

AP-75.   Solve each of the following equations.

a)   $2(x - 3) + 2 = 4$

b)   $12 - 6x = 108$

c)   $2x + 5 = 0$

d)   $3x - 11 = 0$

e)   Solve the equation $Dx - C = 0$ for x.

AP-76.   Sonja notices that the lengths of the three sides on a right triangle are consecutive even numbers. The triangle's perimeter is 24. Write an equation and solve it to find the length of the longest side.

AP-77.   Factor each of the following quadratic polynomials as completely as possible. (It may help to look for a common factor first.)

a)   $2x^2 - 6x$

b)   $x2 - 12x + 35$

c)   $6x^2 - 30x + 18$

d)   $4x^2 - 16x + 12$

AP-78.    The area of the rectangle at right is 60 square units.

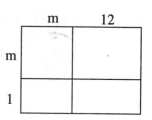

a)    Write the area as both a product and a sum.

b)    Use the area as a sum to write an equation where the area is 60 square units.

c)    Find the value of m.

d)    Can there be more than one value for m? Explain why or why not.


AP-79.    THE AMUSEMENT PARK PROBLEM

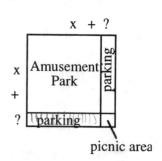

The city planning commission is reviewing the master plan of the proposed Amusement Park coming to our city. Your job is to help the Amusement Park planners design the land space.

Based on their projected daily attendance, the planning commission requires 15 rows of parking. The rectangular rows will be of the same length as the Amusement Park. Depending on funding, the Park size may change so planners are assuming the park will be square and have a length of x. The parking will be adjacent to two sides of the park as shown below.

Our city requires all development plans to include "green space" or planted area for sitting and picnicking. See the plan below.

a)    Your task is to list all the possible configurations of land use with the 15 rows of parking. Find the areas of the picnic space for each configuration. Use the techniques you have learned in this unit. There is more than one way to approach this problem, so show all your work.

b)    Record the configuration with the minimum and maximum picnic area. Write an equation for each that includes the dimensions and the total area for the project. Verify your solutions before moving to part (c).

c)    The Park is expected to be a success and the planners decide to expand the parking lot by adding 11 more rows. Assume that the new plan will add 11 additional rows of parking in such a way that the maximum original green space from part (b) will triple. Show all your work. Record your final solution as an equation describing the area of the total = product of the new dimensions.

d)    If the total area for the expanded Park, parking and picnic area is 2208 square units, find x. Use the dimensions from part (c) to write an equation and solve for the side of the Park.

AP-80. Factor each of the following quadratics. Write as both a product and a sum.

a) $x^2 + 4x + 3$

b) $x^2 - 7x + 12$

c) $x^2 + 10x + 16$

d) $x^2 + 5x - 24$

e) $x^2 - 3x - 18$

f) $3x^2 + 9x - 30$
$3x - 10$

AP-81. Start at point A (-1, 2). Move (slide) to point B (3, 5). Find the coordinates of a point C so that A, B, and C are on the same line.

a) What is the slope of the line?

b) Graph the line.

c) Write the equation of the line from the graph.

AP-82. Scott wants to enlarge the rectangle at right by making each side 3 times as long. Write algebraic expressions for the perimeter and the area of the new enlarged rectangle. Be sure to draw a picture of the enlarged rectangle and show its dimensions:

AP-83. Write an equation and solve the following problem. It costs $25 per day plus $0.06 per mile to rent a car. What is the greatest number of miles that you can drive if you only have $40?

AP-84. Find each of the following sums.

a) $\frac{2}{3} + \frac{1}{5}$

b) $\frac{1}{x} + \frac{1}{3}$

c) $\frac{2}{x} + \frac{3}{5}$

d) $\frac{3}{x} + \frac{5}{2x}$

# UNIT SUMMARY AND REVIEW

AP-85. UNIT 8 SUMMARY

Select 3 or 4 big ideas that you feel best represent Unit 8. Write a description of each main idea. For each topic, choose a problem that best demonstrates your understanding. Explain your solution as in the previous unit summaries. Show all your work.

AP-86.    Penny drew this diagram of a frame for
          an x by x + 1 rectangular picture.

          Write an algebraic expression to
          represent the total area of the frame.
          Show all subproblems.

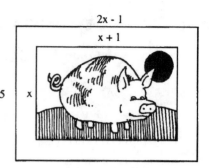

2x + 5    x

2x - 1
x + 1

AP-87.    Factor each of the following quadratics, if possible. Work together and treat this set
          as a puzzle. If the numbers you try do not work for one expression, they may work
          for another.

          a)   $x^2 - 2x - 24$                        e)   $x^2 - 10x - 24$

          b)   $x^2 + 11x + 24$                       f)   $x^2 + 8x + 24$

          c)   $x^2 - 10x + 24$  $-6 \& -4$           g)   $x^2 - 23x - 24$

          d)   $x^2 + 5x - 24$   No                   h)   $x^2 + 25x + 24$

AP-88.    Solve these equations:

          a)   $x^2 - 16 = 0$                         c)   $x^2 - 10x + 24 = 0$

          b)   $x^2 + 11x + 24 = 0$                   d)   $x^2 + 5x = -24$

AP-89.    We can use the idea of a generic rectangle to find more complicated kinds of products.
          For each of the following products, draw a generic rectangle and label the dimensions.
          Then find the given product by finding the area of the rectangle. The first answer is
          given so you can check your method.

          a)   $(x + 3)(x^2 + 4x + 7)$               c)   $(2x + 1)(x^2 - 3x + 4)$
               $x^3 + 7x^2 + 19x + 21$

          b)   $(3x - 2)(4x^2 + 2x + 1)$             d)   $(x - 2)(x^2 + 2x + 4)$

AP-90.    Solve for the missing area or side in each square. Do not use your calculator; use your
          number sense to estimate to a tenth.

          a)   11 by 11 square, A =

          b)   8 (square), A =

          c)   1.2 (square), A =

          d)   s (square), A = 0.81

          e)   s (square), A = 5

          f)   s (square), A = 10

296

AP-91.   Factor completely.

   a)   $x^2 - 17x + 42$

   b)   $2x^2 + 32x + 128$

   c)   $5x^3 - 5x^2 - 30x$

   d)   $3x^2 - 48$


AP-92.   Solve for x and y:

   a)   $3x + 5 = 2y$
        $y = 6 - x$

   b)   $2(x + 5) = y + 6$
        $y + 6 = 12x$
        $y = 12x - 6$


AP-93.   Graphs for equations (a) and (b) are drawn on your resource page. Graph part (c), then label each parabola clearly and identify the x- and y-intercepts for each one. If possible, use the factoring techniques you have learned to make your graphing easier.

   a)   $y = x^2 - 4$          b)   $y = x^2 + 4$          c)   $y = x^2 - 5x + 4$

   d)   Factor each of these equations, if possible.

   e)   What patterns do you notice relating the factors, equations and graphs of quadratics?


AP-94.   TOOL KIT CHECK-UP

   Your tool kit contains reference tools for algebra. Return to your tool kit entries. You may need to revise or add entries.

   Be sure that your tool kit contains entries for all of the items listed below. Add any topics that are missing to your tool kit NOW, as well as any other items that will help you in your study of algebra.

   - Sums and Products of Polynomials
   - Greatest Common Factor
   - Difference of Squares
   - Summary of Types of Equation
   - Roots of a Quadratic Equation

   - Factoring Quadratics
   - Zero Product Property
   - Factoring Completely
   - Factors

GM-15.    WEIGHING PUMPKINS

Every year at Half Moon Bay, there is a pumpkin contest to see who has grown the largest pumpkin for that year.

Last year, one pumpkin grower (who was also a mathematician) brought 5 pumpkins to the contest. Instead of weighing them one at a time, he informed the judges, "When I weighed them two at a time, I got the following weights: 110, 112, 113, 114, 115, 116, 117, 118, 120, and 121 pounds."

**Your Task:**    Find how much each pumpkin weighed.

## GM-16.    WITH OR WITHOUT FROSTING

Mr. Algebra baked a cake for the Midwest Mathematics Convention. He designed the cake in the shape of a big cube. As he was carrying the cake over to the frosting table, he slipped and sent the cake sailing into the vat of frosting.

Amazingly, the cake stayed in one piece, but all 6 sides were now frosted. He carefully got it out and put it on a platter.

The mathematicians were delighted when they saw the cube-cake with all sides frosted. One mathematician suggested the cake be cut into cube shaped pieces, all the same size. That way, some people could have a piece with no frosting, 1 side frosted, 2 sides frosted, or 3 sides frosted. Kawana, a very creative mathematician, said, "Cut the cake so that the number of pieces with no frosting is eight times more than the number of pieces with frosting on 3 sides. Then you will have the exact number of pieces of cake as there are mathematicians in this room."

**Your Task:**

- Using Kawana's clue, find out how many mathematicians were at the convention. Hint: build models of different size cakes.

- How many mathematicians would be at the convention if the number of pieces with 1 frosted side equaled the number of pieces with no frosting?

# Unit Nine
# The Birthday Party Piñata

## Using Diagrams to Solve Equations

# Unit 9 Objectives
## The Birthday Party Piñata: USING DIAGRAMS TO WRITE EQUATIONS

In this unit, you will be increasing your problem solving and algebraic skills as you investigate problems involving **right triangles**. You will work with square roots, graphs and algebraic fractions.

In this unit you will have the opportunity to:

- use diagrams and models as an aid to writing equations for two and three dimensional situations.

- apply the Pythagorean Theorem to calculate the distance between two points.

- solve equations that involve fractions.

- explore square roots in terms of their meaning as numbers.

- use patterns to discover the methods for doing arithmetic calculations with square roots.

- solve equations that include square roots.

- write the equation of a line given the coordinates of two points on the line.

The primary focus of this unit is solving problems by drawing diagrams and writing equations. You will learn how to use a diagram to help to solve a problem. Some of the situations that arise will involve square roots. You will have a chance to understand square root as well as work with square roots in equations and compare their graphs to others you have studied in this course.

---

BP-0.     THE BIRTHDAY PARTY PIÑATA

For Katja's party, her friends are going to hang a piñata half way between two poles with a rope over the top of each pole. Both poles are 20 feet high, and they are 30 feet apart. The piñata must hang four feet above the ground. How much rope is needed to hang the piñata? With your study team, model and sketch this situation.

---

| | |
|---|---|
| Problem Solving | |
| Graphing | |
| Writing and Solving Equations | |
| Ratios | |
| Geometry | |
| Symbol Manipulation | |

# Unit 9

## *The Birthday Party Piñata:* USING DIAGRAMS TO WRITE EQUATIONS

### DEVELOPING THE PYTHAGOREAN THEOREM

BP-1.    Copy the diagram and add the definitions to your tool kit.

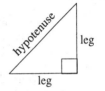

> In a **right triangle**, the longest side is called the
> **HYPOTENUSE** while the other two sides are called
> **LEGS**. Notice that the legs meet to form the right angle.

BP-2.    What is the relationship between the legs and hypotenuse of a right triangle? How
complicated is the relationship? To answer these questions, complete the table on the
resource page provided by your teacher for the five given triangles. Verify your
answers with your study team. Look for a relationship among the three columns on
the right.

a)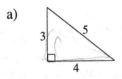

b)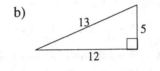

c)

d)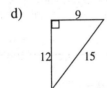

e)

| | length of leg #1 | length of leg #2 | length of hypotenuse | (length of leg #1)$^2$ | (length of leg #2)$^2$ | (length of hypotenuse)$^2$ |
|---|---|---|---|---|---|---|
| a) | | | | | | |
| b) | | | | | | |
| c) | | | | | | |
| d) | | | | | | |
| e) | | | | | | |

BP-3.    With your study team write an equation in words to describe the relationship you
found for the legs and the hypotenuse of a right triangle. Be prepared to present your
team's description to the class. The side lengths for the triangles in BP-2 were all
integers. Do you think the pattern you have developed works for every right triangle,
including those whose side lengths are fractional? Explain your answer.

**BP-4.** Solve for each unknown side using your "word equation" from BP-3.

a)

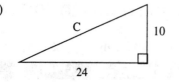

c)

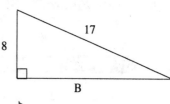

b)

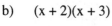

d)

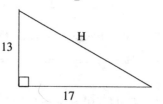

**BP-5.** Draw a diagram or generic rectangle to illustrate each of the following products. Write the products in simplest form by combining like terms.

a) x(2x + 1)

c) (x + 4)(x² + 5x + 3)

b) (x + 2)(x + 3)

**BP-6.** SQUARING A SQUARE ROOT

a) Pick a number between zero and twenty. Take the square root of your number, then square the result. What happens?

b) Pick a number from twenty to forty. Square your number, then take the square root of the result. What happens?

c) When picking a positive number, what do you notice about the process of squaring and square rooting, or square rooting and squaring?

d) Now try the process on any positive number you choose. Record your result.

e) Extension: This process does not always work. Can you find a number for which it does not appear to work? Explain why you think this happens.

**BP-7.** Use the Order of Operations to evaluate.

a) Does $3^2 + 4^2 = 7^2$ ?

b) Does $\sqrt{3^2 + 4^2} = 7$ ?

c) Using your observations from parts (a) and (b), does $\sqrt{a^2 + b^2} = a + b$ ?

BP-8. Solve each of the following equations for x. Remember there are two solutions. Round to the nearest hundredth.

a) $x^2 = 152 - 122$

b) $x^2 + (26.4)^2 = 29^2$

Solve each of the following equations for b. Remember there are two solutions.

c) $122 - 52 = b^2$

e) Extension: $a^2 + b^2 = c^2$

d) $25^2 + b^2 = 35^2$

BP-9. Multiply. Describe any patterns you observe.

a) $8\left(\frac{1}{8}\right)$

d) $18xy\left(\frac{3}{9x}\right)$

b) $x\left(\frac{6}{x}\right)$

e) $12\left(\frac{5x}{6} + \frac{y}{3}\right)$

c) $3x\left(\frac{5}{3x}\right)$

Hint: distribute first.

BP-10. a) Without a calculator, add: $\frac{3}{11} + \frac{2}{7}$.

b) Describe what you did in part (a) to find the sum of the two fractions.

c) Now find the sum of this pair of fractions: $\frac{3}{x} + \frac{1}{7}$.

## FINDING THE LENGTH OF A LINE SEGMENT

BP-11. Answer these questions to help you determine the hypotenuse in any right triangle.

a) Sketch a right triangle. Label the legs x and y and label the hypotenuse z.

b) Write a sentence or two to explain to a friend how to decide which side is the hypotenuse and which sides are the legs.

c) In your study team, discuss and write another way to tell the hypotenuse from the legs.

d) If a right triangle had the side lengths 6, 10, and 8, could the hypotenuse be the side with length 8? Explain why or why not.

BP-12. Add the following information and diagram to your tool kit:

The **PYTHAGOREAN THEOREM** states the relationship between the legs and hypotenuse of any right triangle:

$$(\text{leg \#1})^2 + (\text{leg \#2})^2 = (\text{hypotenuse})^2$$

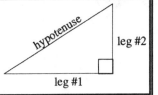

LENGTH OF A LINE SEGMENT

Copy each of the following graphs onto graph paper unless you have the resource page. For each graph, draw a right triangle and determine the length of the given line segment. Write the length as both a square root and its decimal approximation to the nearest hundredth.

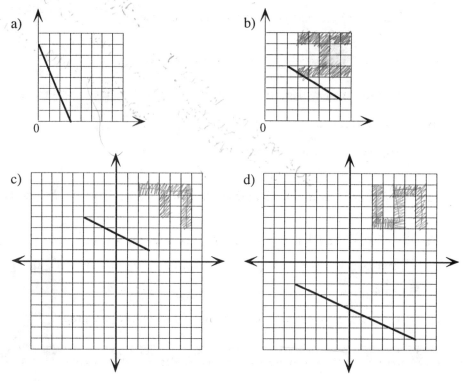

a)

b)

c)

d)

BP-14.     Draw a set of coordinate axes on a piece of graph paper. Plot the point (10, 6). Label it A. Move (slide) the point seven units down, then eight units to the left and stop.

a)     Write the coordinates of the stopping point. Label it B.

b)     Find the distance between A and B.

c)     How could we find the lengths of the legs of the right triangle without graphing?

**BP-15.** GRAPHING SQUARE ROOTS

Obtain the graph resource page from your teacher. (You need to keep track of this page because you will complete a portion of it each day for the next several days).

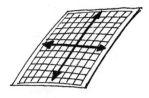

a) Graph $y = \sqrt{x}$. Record your points in the table on the resource page.

b) Try $x = -3$ in the rule. What is the result? Explain.

c) Describe the possible values for x that will yield solutions for the rule $y = \sqrt{x}$.

d) What y values are possible?

e) Describe your graph in words.

**BP-16.** Are 10, 24, and 26 the side lengths of a right triangle? Explain how you know.

**BP-17.** Use the substitution method to solve each pair of equations for x and y.

a) $y = 7 - 2x$
   $y = 6x - 1$

b) $y = 7 - 2x$
   $3x - y = 3$

c) What do the solutions to parts (a) and (b) represent on a graph?

**BP-18.** Evaluate each of the following expressions for $x = 3$, then $x = -2$.

a) $2x^2$

b) $-5x^2$

c) $(2x)^2$

d) $3x^3$

e) $(3x)^3$

f) $(-5x)^2$

**BP-19.** Find each of the following products. Generic rectangles may be helpful.

a) $(3x + 1)(x + 4)$

b) $(2x - 7)^2$

c) $(x - 2)(x^2 + 2x + 1)$

d) $(2x + 5)(7 - x)$

**BP-20.** Pat received 9 out of 10 on his quiz for the following work. He does not know what he did wrong. Study his work and find his mistake. Write Pat a note explaining to him his mistake and what his answer should have been.

Problem: Factor $x^2 - 8x + 12$

Pat's work: $x^2 - 8x + 12$
$(x - 6)(x - 2)$
$x = 6$ and $x = 2$

|   | x | - 6 |
|---|---|-----|
| x | $x^2$ | -6x |
| 2 | -2x | 12 |

The Birthday Party Piñata: Using Diagrams to Write Equations

**BP-21.** You <u>can</u> solve for x the equation: $x^2 - 8x + 12 = 0$

but <u>not</u> for the expression: $x^2 - 8x + 12$.

a) Explain why using a complete sentence.

For each of the following, decide if there is enough information to solve for the variable. If there is, then do so. If not, merely factor and move on to the next part.

b) $b^2 - 4b + 4$                    e) $b^2 - 6b + 5 = 0$

c) $b^2 - 5b + 4$                    f) $b^2 - 17b + 16$

d) $b^2 + 10b + 21 = 0$              g) Extension: $2x^2 - 3x + 1$

**BP-22.** Equations (d) and (e) in problem BP-21 each had two solutions. What do these solutions represent on the graph of the equation? What shape is each graph?

**BP-23.** Find the area of the triangles you drew in BP-13 parts (a) and (b).

## USING DIAGRAMS TO WRITE EQUATIONS

**BP-24.** The beautiful young princess of Polygonia is very distressed. Her father has chosen a husband for her: a very rich, but very old king from another land. However, the princess is in love with someone else. In order to ensure that the princess will not escape and elope with her prince charming, her father has locked her in the tower until the old king arrives for the marriage.

She could escape through the window, but it is 50 feet above the ground (rather a long distance to jump). An alligator-infested moat, which is 10 feet wide, surrounds the tower. Naturally her prince charming is planning to rescue her. His plan is to use an arrow to shoot a rope up to her window. She can then slide down the rope to the other side of the moat into his waiting arms, and off they will ride on his beautiful stallion.

However, even though the prince is charming, he is not too bright. Every night he has tried to rescue the princess with a rope that was too short. The old king arrives tomorrow and the prince needs your help. Remember: this is his last chance to rescue the princess!

With your study team, find the minimum amount of rope the prince needs. (Assume they need an extra 1.5 feet of rope at each end in order to tie the rope.) Write a complete explanation for the prince, including a diagram, that shows how to determine the minimum length of rope needed.

BP-25. On a baseball diamond, the bases are 90 feet apart. (Every baseball diamond is a square.) How far is it from home plate directly to second base? Sketch and label a diagram. Use it to write an equation, then solve the equation.

BP-26.

A 10 foot ladder is leaning against a tree. The foot of the ladder is 3.5 feet away from the base of the tree trunk.

a) Draw a diagram and label the ladder length and its distance from the tree.

b) How high on the tree does the ladder touch? Write an equation and solve it.

BP-27. Jehrico is studying the expression "2(x + 1)(2x + 3)" and is not sure where to start. He thought he should first multiply 2 and (x + 1), and then multiply the result by 2x + 3. But a teammate told him to first multiply (x + 1)(2x + 3) and then multiply that result by 2. He wants your team's help to decide which way is correct.

In your study team, choose some members to multiply the 2 and (x + 1) first, and then multiply the result by 2x + 3. The other members should first multiply (x + 1)(2x + 3), and then multiply that result by 2.

a) Write down both results. What do you notice?

Find each of the following products. Verify your answers with your study team.

b) 3(x - 1)(5x - 7)

c) 5(x + 3)(2x - 5)

BP-28. A careless construction worker drove a tractor into a telephone pole, cracking the pole. The top of the pole fell as if hinged at the crack. The tip of the pole hit the level ground 24 feet from its base. The stump of the pole stood seven feet above the ground. If an additional five feet of the pole extends into the ground to anchor it, how long should the replacement pole be? Draw a diagram. Write an equation. Show all subproblems as you solve.

BP-29.    Make a table and draw the graph of $y = x^2 - 4$.

    a)    Mark and label the points where the graph crosses the x-axis.

    b)    Factor the expression $x^2 - 4$.

    c)    Substitute $y = 0$ in the equation $y = x^2 - 4$ to get $0 = x^2 - 4$. Use the Zero Product Property to find the solutions of the equation $0 = x^2 - 4$ and explain how the solutions are related to the graph and the factors.

    d)    Solve $x^2 = 4$.

    e)    Solve $x^2 - 4 = 0$.

    f)    Did you get the same results in parts (c), (d), and (e)? What does this tell you about their graphs? Explain.

BP-30.    Write one polynomial to represent each of the following differences.

    a)    $(8x^2 + 5x + 7) - (3x^2 + 2x + 2)$          d)    $(16x^2 + 3x - 8) - (7x^2 + 8x - 10)$

    b)    $(8x^2 + 5x + 7) - (3x^2 - 2x + 2)$          e)    $(10x^2 - 13x + 1) - (3x^2 - 10x + 1)$

    c)    $(5x^2 + 14x + 3) - (2x^2 - 9x + 5)$

BP-31.    Factor each of the following polynomials.  Part (d) is an extension.

    a)    $y^2 - 3y - 10$                              c)    $x^2 + 27x + 50$

    b)    $x^2 - 15x + 50$                             d)    $5x^2 + 6xy + y^2$

BP-32.    Solve for x in each right triangle below.

    a)                              b)                              c)

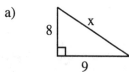
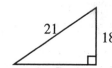
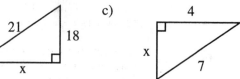

BP-33.    Graph the points (2, -6) and (-3, 5).

    a)    Find the distance between them.

    b)    Find the slope of the line through these two points.

    c)    Are the distance between the points and the slope of the line the same? Write a few sentences about what "distance" and "slope" means, and their relationship, if any.

BP-34.    Zal claims the y-intercept of the graph of $2x - y = 4$ is 4. Lida says that it is -4. Which claim is correct?  Explain how you know.

BP-35. Each of the following equations is in $y = mx + b$ form. For each equation, state the value of m and the value of b.

a) In an equation of the form **$y = mx + b$**, the **m** represents the _____ of the line and the **b** represents the_____ . This is why the form **$y = mx + b$** is called the **slope-intercept form** of a linear equation.

b) $y = 4x$

c) $y = -4x + 7$

d) $y = 4$

e) $y = x - \dfrac{3}{2}$

## MAKING A MODEL: THE FLAT FAMILY'S ROOF

BP-36. We have been studying right triangles from a two dimensional viewpoint. However, often triangles occur in three-dimensional settings.

The roof on the Flat Family's house is one large flat rectangle. It is parallel to the ground. Their TV antenna is mounted in the center of the roof. Guy wires are attached to the antenna five feet below its highest point, and are attached to the roof at each corner and at the midpoint of each edge. These wires support the antenna in the wind.

Each guy wire is the hypotenuse of a right triangle. How long does each wire need to be to keep the antenna upright?

a) Build a model of the Flat Family Roof. The model will serve as a reference while your study team is writing the subproblems necessary to find the lengths of the sides of the right triangles in a 3-dimensional setting.

1) For the roof, use a rectangular piece of cardboard. Draw the diagonals of the rectangle to locate the center.

2) Tape the string guy wires to the straw. Don't forget to leave a gap that represents the five feet between the strings and the top of the antenna. How many guy wires are there?

3) Attach the antenna (straw or stick) to the roof. Use tape, tie knots, or make slits to anchor your antenna and guy wires to the roof (cardboard).

b) Locate as many vertical right triangles as you can on your model. How many right triangles did you find?

c) Identify which right triangles are the same size and which are different sizes. How many different sized right triangles did you find?

d) Sketch each of the different sized right triangles on a different color of paper. Cut out the triangle. Tape the triangle in position on your model. Use this model to help you solve problem BP-37.

The Birthday Party Piñata: Using Diagrams to Write Equations

BP-37.   The Flat Family's roof is 60 feet long and 32 feet wide. The TV antenna is 30 feet tall. The wires are attached five feet below the top of the antenna.

How long must each guy wire be? Show all subproblems in your solution.

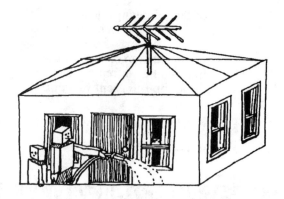

BP-38.   Bryce leaned his five foot rake against the shed. The base of the rake was 2 feet from the shed. How high up the shed did the tip of the rake reach?  Draw a right triangle diagram.  Write an equation and solve.

BP-39.   Find the distance between each pair of points.

a)   (5, -8) and (-3, 1)

b)   (0, -3) and (0, 5)

BP-40.   So far, in problems AP-49, AP-65, AP-84, and BP-10 we added fractions with variables using patterns we found in Unit Two. The problems below extend this notion of adding fractions to solving equations with fractions. Examine the work from those problems mentioned above and complete the following:

a)   Add $\frac{x}{3} + \frac{x}{5}$.

b)   Solve. $\frac{5x + 3x}{15} = 2$

BP-41.   Solve for x and y:       $5x - 2 = y$
$3x - y = -2$

BP-42.   Solve each equation by factoring:

a)   $x^2 - 13x + 40 = 0$

c)   $x^2 - 169 = 0$

b)   $x^2 + 15x + 56 = 0$

d)   $100 - x^2 = 0$

BP-43.   Find the slope and y-intercept of each line, using any method you prefer.

a)   $y = -\frac{2}{3}x - 1$

c)   $2x + 3y = 48$

b)   $y = 5 + \frac{8}{5}x$

**BP-44.**　GRAPHING SQUARE ROOTS

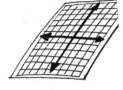

a)　On your resource page from problem BP-15, graph $y = \sqrt{x} + 2$.

b)　Try $x = -3$ in the rule. What is the result?  Explain.

c)　Describe the possible values for x that may be used for the rule $y = \sqrt{x} + 2$.

d)　What y values are possible?

e)　Compare your two square root graphs. How did adding 2 change the graph?

**BP-45.**　Multiply.

a)　$6x \cdot \dfrac{4}{x}$

b)　$6x \cdot \dfrac{11}{6}$

c)　$6x \cdot \dfrac{3}{2x}$

# SOLVING EQUATIONS WITH ALGEBRAIC FRACTIONS

**BP-46.**　Problems on preceding days of this unit have involved using diagrams to write equations you could solve. BP-46 will provide you with yet another equation-solving technique to rewrite more complicated equations into ones that you can more easily solve. Read the following example and add it to your tool kit:

---

### FRACTION BUSTERS
#### Solving Equations Containing Algebraic Fractions

Solve: $\dfrac{x}{3} + \dfrac{x}{5} = 2$

$$\dfrac{x}{3} + \dfrac{x}{5} = 2$$

The complicating issue in this problem is dealing with the fractions. We could add them by first writing them in terms of a common denominator, but there is an easier way.

*The lowest common denominator of $\frac{x}{3}$ and $\frac{x}{5}$ is 15.*

$$15 \cdot \left(\dfrac{x}{3} + \dfrac{x}{5}\right) = 15 \cdot 2$$

There is no need to use the often time consuming process of adding the fractions if we can "eliminate" the denominators. To do this, we will need to find a common denominator of all fractions, and then we will <u>multiply both sides of the equation</u> by that common denominator. In this case the lowest common denominator is 15, so we <u>multiply both sides</u> of the equation by 15.

$$15 \cdot \dfrac{x}{3} + 15 \cdot \dfrac{x}{5} = 15 \cdot 2$$

$$5x + 3x = 30$$

$$8x = 30$$

The result is an equivalent equation without fractions!

$$x = \dfrac{30}{8} = \dfrac{15}{4} = 3.75$$

The number we use to eliminate the denominators is called a **FRACTION BUSTER**. Now the equation looks like many we have seen before and we solve it in the usual way.

$$\dfrac{3.75}{3} + \dfrac{3.75}{5} = 2$$

Finally, remember to check your answer.

$$1.25 + 0.75 = 2$$

---

**>>Problem continues on the next page.>>**

The Birthday Party Piñata: Using Diagrams to Write Equations

Copy the following problem on your paper. Fill in each of the lines labeled (a) through (e) to explain how the equation to its right was obtained from the equation above it.

Solve the equation:

$$\frac{4}{x} + \frac{3}{2x} = \frac{11}{6}$$

a) _____

$$6x(\frac{4}{x} + \frac{3}{2x}) = 6x \cdot (\frac{11}{6})$$

b) _____

$$6x \cdot (\frac{4}{x}) + 6x \cdot (\frac{3}{2x}) = 6x \cdot (\frac{11}{6})$$

c) _____

$$24 + 9 = 11x$$

d) _____

$$33 = 11x$$

e) _____

$$3 = x$$

BP-47.   In each equation, find the lowest common denominator of all fractions first, as in problem BP-46, then use Fraction Busters, and solve.

a)   $\frac{x}{2} + \frac{x}{3} = \frac{1}{6}$

c)   $\frac{4}{x} - 1 = 7$

b)   $x + \frac{x}{2} + \frac{x}{3} = 22$

d)   $\frac{1}{x} + \frac{1}{2x} = 3$

BP-48.   THE BUCKLED RAILROAD TRACK

Railroad designers are always looking for ways to improve the safety and comfort of train travel.

Suppose technology made it possible to make and transport straight rails one mile long. If one winter two pairs of these rails were installed along a two mile portion of track in the desert, then each rail would expand approximately one foot in length in the summer heat. Suppose that instead of buckling, these rails keep their (straight) shape. In this case, the ends where they meet could jut upward to form a triangle. How high above the ground would the ends of the rails be?

Let H be the height (in feet) of the tracks above the ground where the two rails come together.

a)   How large do you think H is? Is it big enough for you to stick your arm between the ground and the tracks? Is it big enough walk through? Could you drive a car under the buckled tracks? Make a guess.

b)   Draw a picture and calculate H. (Note: a mile is 5280 feet long.)

c)   How does your calculated value for H compare with your guess in part (a)?

BP-49.   A child's shoe box measures 4" x 6" x 3". What is the longest pencil you could fit into this box? An empty box may help you visualize the varies ways you could fit the pencil in the box. If possible, draw a diagram to show the pencil's position. Show your subproblems.

314

**BP-50.** Solve for x. Use Fraction Busters from BP-46. Leave answers in **fraction** form.

a) $\frac{x}{2} + \frac{x}{6} = 7$

c) $\frac{x}{9} + \frac{2x}{5} = 3$

b) $\frac{x}{2} + \frac{x}{3} - \frac{x}{4} = 12$

d) $\frac{5}{2x} + \frac{1}{6} = 8$

**BP-51.** Solve each of the following systems for x and y.

a) $y = 4x$
$x + y = -1$

b) $-2x + y = 3$
$x = 3y$

**BP-52.** Find the distance between each set of points.

a) $(0, 5)$ and $(5, 0)$

b) $(-4, 7)$ and $(29, 76)$

**BP-53.** MONEY MONEY MONEY

Janelle has $20 and is saving at the rate of $6 per week. Jeanne has $150 and is saving at the rate of $4 per week. After how many weeks will each person have the same amount of money?

a) Make a graph to solve the problem.

b) Write equations to solve the problem algebraically.

c) If you were presenting your solution to students who did not know the problem, would the graph help them visualize the problem? Explain your graph to that student.

**BP-54.** Solve each of the following equations by factoring.

a) $g^2 + 5g + 6 = 0$

c) $e^2 - 10e + 21 = 0$

b) $m^2 + 5m - 6 = 0$

d) $h^2 - 16h - 36 = 0$

**BP-55.** Graph using the slope and y-intercept.

a) $y = \frac{3}{4}x - 2$

b) $y = 3x + 4$

**BP-56.** A jar has an even number of pennies, nickels, and dimes. When Juan puts 24 more pennies in the jar the probability of pulling out a penny becomes $\frac{1}{2}$. How many pennies, nickels and dimes were in the jar to begin with?

The Birthday Party Piñata: Using Diagrams to Write Equations

## SIMPLIFYING EXPRESSIONS WITH RADICALS

BP-57.    Use your calculator to determine which of the following statements containing unlike square roots are true and which are false.

a)    $\sqrt{2} + \sqrt{3} = \sqrt{5}$

b)    $\dfrac{\sqrt{12}}{\sqrt{4}} = \sqrt{3}$

c)    $(\sqrt{2})(\sqrt{3}) = \sqrt{6}$

d)    $\dfrac{\sqrt{7}}{\sqrt{2}} = \sqrt{3.5}$

e)    $\sqrt{5} - \sqrt{2} = \sqrt{3}$

f)    $\sqrt{16} + \sqrt{3} = \sqrt{19}$

g)    $\dfrac{\sqrt{6}}{\sqrt{3}} = \sqrt{2}$

h)    $(\sqrt{5})(\sqrt{7}) = \sqrt{35}$

BP-58.    Use your results from problem BP-57 above.

a)    Which kinds of square root operations in BP-57 were true?

b)    Which kinds of square root operations in BP-57 were false?

c)    With your study team, write conjectures about using the different operations (addition, subtraction, multiplication and division) with unlike square roots. Put these in your tool kit. For each conjecture give one or more examples that support it.

BP-59.    Use your conjectures to simplify these expressions as much as possible. Be sure not to leave perfect squares (such as 9 or 16) under a radical sign. Also, combine square root terms if possible. If the expression cannot be simplified, leave it as is. Check your answers with a calculator.

a)    $(\sqrt{3})(\sqrt{7})$

b)    $\dfrac{\sqrt{20}}{\sqrt{5}}$

c)    $\sqrt{3} + \sqrt{7}$

d)    $\sqrt{5} \cdot \sqrt{20}$

e)    $\sqrt{7} - \sqrt{3}$

f)    $\dfrac{\sqrt{21}}{\sqrt{3}}$

g)    $\sqrt{20} + \sqrt{5}$

h)    $\dfrac{\sqrt{144}}{\sqrt{3}\,\sqrt{4}}$

BP-60.    GRAPHING SQUARE ROOTS

a)    Graph $y = \sqrt{x - 2}$ on your resource page.

b)    What x values are possible in part (a) ?

c)    Compare this graph to BP-15 and BP-44.

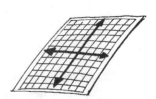

BP-61. A fly was sitting on the ground in the back left corner of your classroom. He flew to the ceiling in the opposite corner of the room. How far did he fly if he went in a straight line? Draw a diagram of your classroom, complete with the correct measurements. Write equations. Show your subproblems.

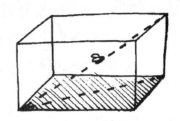

BP-62. Using graph paper, find the equation of the line through each pair of points below. Write your answer in $y = mx + b$ form.

a) (3, 4) and (4, 6)

b) (-5, -8) and the origin

c) (1, -5) and (-1, 1)

d) (1, -5) and (-2, 0)

BP-63. Use Fraction Busters to solve for x.

a) $\frac{2}{3} - \frac{x}{5} = 10$

b) $\frac{1}{x} - 5 = \frac{4}{3}$

BP-64. Since $x + x + x = 3x$, Hannah thinks that $3\sqrt{5}$ might be the simplified way to write $\sqrt{5} + \sqrt{5} + \sqrt{5}$.

a) Is Hannah correct? Use your calculator. Explain how you tested Hannah's conjecture.

b) Since $x + y + z$ cannot be simplified, can Mary simplify $\sqrt{5} + \sqrt{6} + \sqrt{7}$? Explain.

BP-65. GRAPHING SQUARE ROOTS

a) Graph $y = \sqrt{x + 5}$ on your resource page.

b) What happens if you use $x = -6$ in part (a)?

c) What values are possible for x?

d) Compare this graph to the graphs from BP-15, BP-44, and BP-60. Describe the effect of adding or subtracting a number from x under the square root symbol.

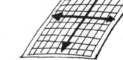

BP-66. Find the distance between this pair of points: (-2, -8) and (-2, 56).

BP-67.    In this problem, write two equations to describe the situation, and solve.

To fill Katja's piñata, her father used Choco-giggles and Fruity Scooters. Each Choco-giggle costs $0.25, and each Fruity Scooter costs $0.30. If he paid $73 for all 264 pieces of candy, how many of each type did he use?

BP-68.    Right triangles ABC and $\triangle$A'B'C' are similar, with right angles at B and B'. If AB = 12 cm, BC = 5 cm, and B'C' = 15 cm, draw a diagram and label it. Then find the length of A'C'.

## ADDITIONAL WORK WITH SIMPLIFYING RADICALS

BP-69.    Based on your conjectures about unlike square roots (the results of BP-58), quickly determine which of the following statements are true and which are false.

a)    $\sqrt{25} + \sqrt{9} = \sqrt{34}$

b)    $\sqrt{8} - \sqrt{3} = \sqrt{5}$

c)    $(\sqrt{1.5})(\sqrt{1.5}) = \sqrt{2.25}$

d)    $\sqrt{9} + \sqrt{8} = \sqrt{17}$

e)    $\sqrt{100} - \sqrt{36} = \sqrt{64}$

f)    $(\sqrt{5})(\sqrt{3}) = \sqrt{15}$

g)    $\sqrt{4^2 + 5^2} = \sqrt{9^2}$

h)    $\dfrac{\sqrt{90}}{\sqrt{3}} = \sqrt{30}$

i)    $(\sqrt{3704})^2 = 3704$

j)    $\sqrt{512^2} = 512$

k)    $\sqrt{5^2 \cdot 2} = 5\sqrt{2}$

l)    $\sqrt{3 \cdot 3 \cdot 7} = 3\sqrt{7}$

m)    Check your answers using a calculator. Be sure you follow the correct Order of Operations.

n)    For any of your answers that disagree with your check in part (m), review your work and compare it to your conjectures.

---

## SIMPLIFYING SQUARE ROOTS

Before calculators were universally available, people who wanted to use approximate decimal values for numbers like $\sqrt{45}$ had other techniques available to them:

1. Carry around long square root tables.

2. Use Guess and Check repeatedly to get desired accuracy.

3. "Simplify" the square roots. A square root is **SIMPLIFIED** when there are no more perfect square factors (square numbers such as 4, 25, and 81) under the radical sign.

Simplifying square roots was by far the fastest method. People factored the number as the product of integers hoping to find at least one perfect square number. They memorized approximations of the square roots of the integers from one to ten. Then they could figure out the decimal value by multiplying these memorized facts with the roots of the square numbers. Here is an example of this method.

Example: Simplify $\sqrt{45}$

Rewrite $\sqrt{45}$ in an equivalent factored form.
Factor 45 so that one of the factors is a perfect square.

$$\sqrt{45} = \sqrt{9 \cdot 5}$$
$$= \sqrt{9} \cdot \sqrt{5}$$

Simplify the square root of the perfect square.

$$= 3\sqrt{5}$$

On your calculator compute $3\sqrt{5}$ and $\sqrt{45}$. Show they are equal.

Here are two more examples:

$$\sqrt{27} \qquad\qquad \sqrt{72}$$
$$= \sqrt{9}\sqrt{3} \qquad\qquad = \sqrt{36}\sqrt{2}$$
$$= 3\sqrt{3} \qquad\qquad = 6\sqrt{2}$$

Note: We chose to write $\sqrt{72}$ as $\sqrt{36} \cdot \sqrt{2}$, rather than $\sqrt{9} \cdot \sqrt{8}$ or $\sqrt{4} \cdot \sqrt{18}$, because 36 is the largest perfect square factor of 72. However, since

$$\sqrt{4} \cdot \sqrt{18} = 2\sqrt{9 \cdot 2} = 2\sqrt{9} \cdot \sqrt{2} = 2 \cdot 3\sqrt{2} = 6\sqrt{2},$$

we can still get the same answer if we do it using different subproblems.

We live in the age of technology. When we want a decimal approximation of a square root we use a calculator. An exact answer uses the $\sqrt{\phantom{x}}$ symbol. We showed you the method of "simplifying" square roots because this simplified form may be useful in some situations.

---

BP-71.    Consider each factored choice below, then write the square root in simplified form.

   a)    To simplify $\sqrt{50}$, would you factor it into $\sqrt{5} \cdot \sqrt{10}$ or $\sqrt{25} \cdot \sqrt{2}$ ? Why?

   b)    To simplify $\sqrt{60}$ would you factor it into $\sqrt{6} \cdot \sqrt{10}$ or $\sqrt{4} \cdot \sqrt{15}$ ? Why?

   c)    To simplify $\sqrt{32}$ would you factor it into $\sqrt{4} \cdot \sqrt{8}$ or $\sqrt{16} \cdot \sqrt{2}$ ? Why?

BP-72.    Write each of the following square roots in simplest form.

   a)    $\sqrt{75}$                           d)    $\sqrt{24}$

   b)    $\sqrt{18}$                           e)    $\sqrt{250}$

   c)    $\sqrt{48}$                           f)    $\sqrt{1000}$

BP-73.    Match the number in the left-hand column with its equivalent in the right-hand column. Whenever possible do this without using a calculator.

   a)    $\sqrt{96}$                  $2\sqrt{15}$
   b)    $\sqrt{12}$                  $3\sqrt{2}$
   c)    $\sqrt{60}$                  $3\sqrt{5}$
   d)    $\sqrt{72}$                  $3\sqrt{6}$
   e)    $\sqrt{24}$                  $5\sqrt{2}$
   f)    $\sqrt{54}$                  $2\sqrt{3}$
   g)    $\sqrt{50}$                  $4\sqrt{6}$
   h)    $\sqrt{45}$                  $2\sqrt{5}$
   i)    $\sqrt{20}$                  $2\sqrt{6}$
   j)    $\sqrt{18}$                  $6\sqrt{2}$

BP-74.    Draw a sketch of two line segments which have the same slope but which are not part of the same line. What one word best describes the relationship of the two line segments?

BP-75.    Find the equation of the lines graphed below:

   a)                                          b)

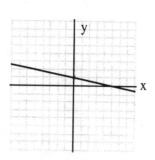       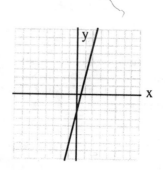

BP-76.    GRAPHING SQUARE ROOTS

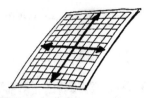

Use your calculator to graph $y = \sqrt{2x}$ on your resource
page from BP-15.

a)    What happens if you use $x = -3$ in the square root?

b)    What values are possible for x ?


BP-77.    Use your calculator to graph $y = \sqrt{x} + 2$ on your resource page.

a)    What happens if you use $x = -1$ in part (a) ?

b)    What values are possible for x ?

c)    Compare this graph to that from BP-15. What is the effect of adding a number
       to a $\sqrt{x}$ graph?

d)    How are the equation and the graph different from BP-44?


BP-78.    Factor each of the following expressions. (Hint:  Look for the greatest common factors.)

a)    $4x + 8$                          c)    $4x^2 + 20x + 24$

b)    $4x^2 + 8x$


BP-79.    Write the greatest common factor of the terms in each of the following polynomials,
          then factor.

a)    $2x^2 + 2x$            c)    $12x^3y - 3xy^3$

b)    $27x^2 - 3$                        d)    $5x^2y - 30xy + 45y$


BP-80.    Solve each of the following equations.

a)    $\frac{x}{3} = \frac{4}{5}$                    c)    $\frac{6}{15} = 2 - \frac{x}{5}$

b)    $\frac{x}{x+1} = \frac{5}{7}$                  d)    $\frac{2}{3} + \frac{x}{5} = 6$


BP-81.    Simplify the following:

a)    $\sqrt{24}$                        d)    $3\sqrt{18}$

b)    $\sqrt{120}$                       e)    $6\sqrt{40}$

c)    $\sqrt{300}$                       f)    $-3\sqrt{12}$


The Birthday Party Piñata: Using Diagrams to Write Equations

BP-82.    What is the longest stick that can be placed corner to corner inside a shoe box that has dimensions 24" by 30" by 18" ?

## FINDING THE EQUATION OF A LINE GIVEN TWO POINTS

BP-83.   Add this information to your tool kit.

> ### HOW TO FIND THE EQUATION OF A LINE WITHOUT GRAPHING
>
> We can find the equation of the line passing through (3, 4) and (4, 6) by drawing a graph, using the slope triangle, and estimating where the graph crosses they-axis. But what if the y-intercept were 396 or $1\frac{3}{7}$ ? In such cases it would be hard to use a graph to find an equation, so we will use the algebra we already know.
>
> Example: Find the equation of the line passing through (3, 4) and (4, 6).
>
> First, write the general equation of a line:
>
> $$y = mx + b$$
> where m is slope,
> and b is y-intercept
>
> Second, calculate slope by drawing a generic slope triangle, m = 2 so the equation must be y = 2x + b.
>
>
>
> $$m = \frac{2}{1} = 2$$
>
> $$y = 2x + b$$
>
> Third, find the y-intercept , "b," without a graph. Remember, we know that (3, 4) is on the line. This means that this point is a solution of the equation. Substitute (3, 4) for (x, y) and solve for b.
>
> $$4 = 2(3) + b$$
> $$4 = 6 + b$$
> $$-2 = b$$
>
> Finally, the equation of the line is:
>
> $$y = 2x - 2$$
>
> a)   In the third step we used (x, y) = (3, 4). See what happens if we use the other given point, (x, y) = (4, 6). Explain your results in a sentence.
>
> b)   Check your equation by drawing a line through the two points (3, 4) and (4, 6) and marking the y-intercept. Do the slope and intercept numbers in the equation actually fit the line?

BP-84.   Use the method described in BP-83 to find the equation of the line passing through each pair of points. In each case write the equation in the slope-intercept (y = mx + b) form. Show all your steps.

a)   (4, 6) and (6, 7)                     c)   (-3, 2) and (4, 5)

b)   (9, 8) and (3, 5)

BP-85.    A certain line with slope $\frac{1}{2}$ goes through the point $(6, 1)$.

a)    Find the equation of the line in the form of $y = mx + b$.

b)    Suppose the line $y = 2x + b$ goes through the point $(1, 4)$. Find the equation of the line.

BP-86.    Explain to a student who was absent how you would find an equation of the line through two given points.

BP-87.    Start with triangle ABC, where A is the point $(-1, 5)$, B is $(2, 7)$, and C is $(3, 4)$. Move (slide) $\triangle ABC$ five units down and six units to the left. (You can do this by sliding each of the vertices A, B, and C.) Call the new triangle $\triangle A'B'C'$. Find the coordinates of vertices A', B' and C', then determine the lengths of segments AA', BB', and CC'. What do you notice?

BP-88.    Solve each of the following equations for $x$.

a)    $\frac{x-3}{5} = 12(x-1)$      b)    $\frac{10}{x} + \frac{10}{2x} = 10$      c)    $x^2 - 12x + 35 = 0$

BP-89.    Solve for $x$. Show your work.

BP-90.    Add an example of F.O.I.L. to your tool kit.

---

**MULTIPLYING BINOMIALS:  A HISTORICAL PERSPECTIVE**

In multiplying binomials, such as  (3x - 2)(4x + 5),  you might use a generic rectangle.

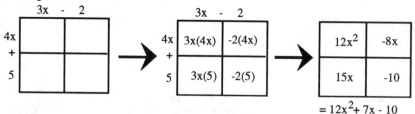

$$= 12x^2 + 7x - 10$$

You might view multiplying binomials with generic rectangles as a form of **double distribution**. The  4x  is distributed across the first row of the generic rectangle and then the  5  is distributed across the second row of the generic rectangle.

Another  approach to multiplying binomials is to use the mnemonic 'F.O.I.L.'
F.O.I.L. is an acronym for First, Outside, Inside, Last:

**F.**   multiply the FIRST terms of each binomial        $(3x)(4x) = 12x^2$
**O.**   multiply the OUTSIDE  terms                      $(3x)(5) = 15x$
**I.**   multiply the INSIDE terms                        $(-2)(4x) = -8x$
**L.**   multiply the LAST terms of each binomial         $(-2)(5) = -10$

Finally, we combine like terms:  $12x^2 + 15x - 8x - 10 = 12x^2 + 7x - 10.$

Notice how the generic rectangle relates to the F.O.I.L. method:

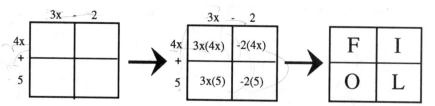

Use the approach to multiply binomials that makes the most sense to you.

---

BP-91.    Multiply these binomials. Check your work.

a)    $(7x - 4)(3x + 2)$                 d)    $(5x - 4)(3x - 2)$

b)    $(9x + 7)(4x - 3)$                 e)    $(x + 4)(x^2 + 5x + 7)$

c)    $(2x - 5)(3x - 10)$                f)    Will F.O.I.L. work in problem (e)?

BP-92. John Bluecloud builds four square pens (each with equal area) side by side in a row. He uses 83.2 feet of fencing material.

a) What are the dimensions of each pen?

b) Extension: John figures he can make each pen larger if he places the squares in a square pattern instead of in a row. Is he right? Justify your answer.

BP-93.

The top of Susan's telephone table is a semicircle (a half-circle) and is shown at left. Its diameter, against the wall, is 2.5 feet. Find the area of its top surface.

BP-94. Does $\frac{x-4}{x+8} = -\frac{1}{2}$? Substitute a value for x to support your answer.

BP-95. THE BIRTHDAY PARTY PIÑATA

For Katja's party, her friends are going to hang a piñata half way between two poles with a rope over the top of each pole. Both poles are 20 feet high, and they are 30 feet apart. The top of the piñata must hang four feet above the ground.

a) How much rope is needed to hang the piñata? Draw a diagram and write an equation to solve this problem. Show all your subproblems.

b) Katja's mom forgot to bring the rope. Bob found some rope in the trunk of his car. His rope is only 40 feet long, however the poles can be moved closer together. How far apart should the poles be placed so that the piñata remains four feet above the ground?

c) Scott is much taller than the other children so it was decided that the piñata should be raised to six feet above the ground during his turn. Using Bob's 40 foot rope, how far apart should the poles be for Scott's turn?

BP-96. In this unit, you have been working with numbers in square root form. It is time to consolidate what you know. Compare your tool kit entries from BP-58 and subsequent explorations to the general laws below. Revise them as necessary. Be sure that for each law you have recorded the law and a numerical example in your tool kit.

---

### LAWS FOR SQUARE ROOTS FOR POSITIVE NUMBERS

| | Numerical Example | In General |
|---|---|---|
| 1) | $\sqrt{3} \cdot \sqrt{7} = \sqrt{21}$ | $\sqrt{x} \cdot \sqrt{y} = \sqrt{x \cdot y}$ |
| 2) | $\sqrt{20} = \sqrt{4}\sqrt{5} = 2\sqrt{5}$ | $\sqrt{x \cdot y} = \sqrt{x} \cdot \sqrt{y}$ |
| 3) | $\dfrac{\sqrt{18}}{\sqrt{6}} = \sqrt{\dfrac{18}{6}} = \sqrt{3}$ | $\dfrac{\sqrt{x}}{\sqrt{y}} = \sqrt{\dfrac{x}{y}}$ |
| 4) | $\sqrt{3^2} = (\sqrt{3})^2 = 3$ | $\sqrt{x^2} = (\sqrt{x})^2 = x$ |
| 5) | $3\sqrt{7} + 8\sqrt{7} = 11\sqrt{7}$ | $a\sqrt{x} + b\sqrt{x} = (a+b)\sqrt{x}$ |
| | $9\sqrt{11} - 1\sqrt{11} = 8\sqrt{11}$ | |

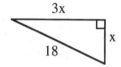

---

BP-97. Does $3x^2 = (3x)^2$ ? Think about what is being squared in each expression. Draw a picture to justify your answer.

BP-98. Solve for x.

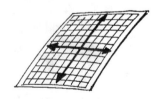

BP-99. Solve each system of equations for x and y:

a)  $y = 0$
   $y = x^2 + 5x + 4$

b)  $y = \dfrac{-2}{3}x + 4$
   $\dfrac{1}{3}x - y = 2$

BP-100. GRAPHING SQUARE ROOTS

For the graph $y = \sqrt{x - 4}$, what is its domain (the possible x-values)? Examine the other graphs on your resource page from problem BP-15. Predict its general shape and location. You do not need to graph it unless you want to verify your answer.

BP-101. Start with the generic point $(x, y)$. Imagine moving (sliding) the point 4.5 units up and 6 units to the left.

    a) What is the slope of the line through the two points?

    b) What are the coordinates of the point after the move?

    c) Draw a diagram. What is the length of the segment that joins the original point and its image after the move?

BP-102. A young redwood tree in Muir Woods casts a shadow 12 feet long. At the same time, a five-foot tall tourist casts a shadow two feet long. How tall is the tree? Draw a diagram, use ratios to write an equation, and then solve the equation.

BP-103. Solve each equation by factoring.

    a) $x^2 + 18x - 19 = 0$      b) $x^2 - 4x = 5$

BP-104. Suppose the line $y = \frac{1}{2}x + b$ goes through the point $(2, 3)$.

    a) Find the equation of the line.

    b) Another line with slope $\frac{2}{3}$ goes through the point $(-3, 5)$. Find the equation of the line.

BP-105. Solve each of the following equations for $x$.

    a) $x^2 - 140 = 4$      c) $1 - \frac{5}{6x} = \frac{x}{6}$

    b) $x(x + 1)(x + 2) = 0$      d) $2x + 3y = 5$

**BP-106.** UNIT 9 SUMMARY

Select 3 or 4 big ideas that you feel best represent Unit 9. Write a description of each main idea. For each topic, choose a problem that best demonstrates your understanding. Explain your solution as in the previous unit summaries. Show all your work.

**BP-107.** GRAPHING SQUARE ROOTS

Using your Square Root Graph Resource Page from problem BP-15, write several observations about square root graphs and their equations. On your own graph paper, sketch the curve $y = \sqrt{x} + 1$ using your observations.

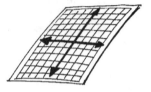

**BP-108.** Determine whether each of the following statements is true or false. Show why or why not.

a) $\sqrt{12} = \sqrt{4} \cdot \sqrt{3}$

b) $3\sqrt{3} = \sqrt{27}$

c) $\sqrt{48} = 4\sqrt{3}$

d) $\dfrac{\sqrt{10}}{2} = \sqrt{5}$

e) $\sqrt{2} + \sqrt{3} = \sqrt{5}$

f) $\sqrt{100} - \sqrt{64} = \sqrt{36}$

g) $\sqrt{3} \cdot \sqrt{3} = 3$

h) $\sqrt{7} \cdot \sqrt{7} = \sqrt{49}$

i) $\sqrt{5} \cdot \sqrt{5} = (\sqrt{5})^2$

**BP-109.** Find the length of the diagonal of a square whose sides have length 5 inches. Sketch a diagram and solve.

**BP-110.** Janis is going to fence off a rectangular garden. She will use an existing wall along the back, and she wants the length to be twice as long as the width. The total amount of fencing material she has is 84 meters long. What are the width and length of her garden? (Be sure to draw a diagram and write an equation.)

BP-111. The length of a certain rectangle is 6.3 feet longer than the width. The perimeter is 32.6 feet. Find the length and width.

BP-112. Find the equation of each line described below. Show all of your subproblems and find the equation of:

a) the line through points (-1, 4) and (2, 1).

b) the line through points (6, 3) and (5, 5).

c) the line with slope $\frac{1}{3}$ through the point (0, 5).

d) the line parallel to $y = 2x - 5$ through the point (1, 7).

BP-113. Solve each of the following equations for x.

a) $\frac{x}{2} + \frac{x}{3} = 5$

d) $\frac{5+x}{7} + \frac{2x}{3} = 5$

b) $\frac{5}{x} - 8 = 12$

e) $2x + y = 29$

c) $x^2 + 6x - 7 = 0$

BP-114. Solve each system for x and y:

a) $y = 9 - x$
   $y = 9 + x$

b) $3x - 2y = 20$
   $x = 5 - y$

BP-115. A circle has an area of 100 square inches.

a) What is its radius?

b) If another circle has a circumference of 100 inches, what is its radius?

BP-116. Factor.

a) $x^2 + 46x + 45$

c) $x^2 - 4x - 45$

b) $x^2 - 18x + 45$

d) $x^2 + 12x - 45$

BP-117. Put these lists of numbers in order from smallest to largest.

a) $3\sqrt{2}, 4, 7.5, 2\sqrt{3}$

b) $5\sqrt{2}, 2\sqrt{5}, 6.9, 6.12$

BP-118. Find at least ten points that are 10 units away from the origin and have integer coordinates. (Hint: the point (6, 8) works.)

The Birthday Party Piñata: Using Diagrams to Write Equations

BP-119.   Use a graph to find the coordinates of the midpoint of each pair of points.

   a)   (6, 2) and (10, 12)                  c)   (1, 7) and (-7, -5)

   b)   (-4, 3) and (5, -6)                   d)   (3, 9) and (7, -2)

   e)   Try this one without a graph:  (2, 24) and (-124, 135)

BP-120.   TOOL KIT CLEAN-UP

Tool kits often need to be reorganized to
continue to be useful.  Your tool kit spans
entries from three different units: 7, 8,
and 9, plus first semester.

   a)   Examine the list of tool kit entries
        from this unit.  Check to be sure you
        have all of these entries.  Add any
        you are missing.

   b)   Identify which concepts you feel you understand.

   c)   Which concepts are still not clear to you?

   d)   Choose entries to create a Unit 7 - 9 tool kit that is shorter, clear, and useful.
        You may want to consolidate or shorten some entries.

   e)   How have you used your tool kit in the last two weeks?

   - Hypotenuse and Legs of a Right
     Triangle
   - Pythagorean Theorem
   - Fraction Busters
   - Operations with Square Roots

   - Find Equation of a Line Using
     Two Points
   - Simplifying Square Roots
   - F.O.I.L.
   - Laws for Square Roots for
     Positive Integers

## GM-17.    HAPPY NUMBERS

Some numbers have special qualities that earn them a title, such as "Square Number" or "Prime Number." This problem will explore another type of number, called "Happy Numbers."

The number 23 is a Happy Number. To determine if a number is a Happy Number, square each of its digits and add.

$$2^2 + 3^2 = 13$$

Repeat this process.

$$1^2 + 3^2 = 10$$

When the final answer is 1, the original number is called a **"Happy Number."**

$$1^2 + 0^2 = 1$$

The number 34 is not Happy Number, as demonstrated below:

1)  $3^2 + 4^2 = 25$
2)  $2^2 + 5^2 = 29$
3)  $2^2 + 9^2 = 85$
4)  $8^2 + 5^2 = \mathbf{89}$
5)  $8^2 + 9^2 = 145$
6)  $1^2 + 4^2 + 5^2 = 42$
7)  $4^2 + 2^2 = 20$
8)  $2^2 + 0^2 = 4$
9)  $0^2 + 4^2 = 16$
10) $1^2 + 6^2 = 37$
11) $3^2 + 7^2 = 58$
12) $5^2 + 8^2 = \mathbf{89}$

*Since 89 is repeated in this series, the "Happy Number" process is in a never-ending loop and, consequently, will never equal 1. Therefore, 34 is **not** a Happy Number.*

**Your Task**:

- There are 17 two digit "Happy Numbers." Find as many as you can. Describe your technique for finding happy numbers.

- Remember to keep all your work and ideas so you can refer back to them when writing up what you discovered. It will save you time and help you look for patterns if you keep an organized record of what you try.

- Find five 3 digit happy numbers.

- Find five 4 digit happy numbers.

The Birthday Party Piñata: Using Diagrams to Write Equations

THE STREETS OF SAN FRANCISCO

Ms. Speedi lives at the corner of Chestnut and Mason and drives to school, which is located at the corner of Jackson and Grant, every morning. She usually drives down Mason, then turns left on Jackson. However, after going 12 blocks, she's late for school! See if you can find a shorter route.

The streets in downtown San Francisco are set up in a grid with Columbus Avenue running diagonally between them, as shown on the map at right. Columbus directly meets the intersection of Chestnut and Taylor, as well as the intersection of Washington and Montgomery.

One-way streets are shown with arrows. Kearny is unusual as it only allows traffic that heads toward Columbus.

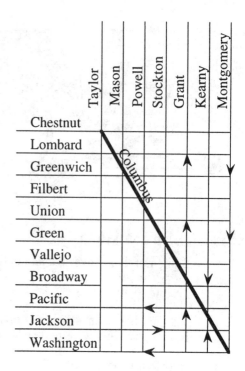

Columbus is a two-way street. You can turn on or off of Columbus from any street that intersects it.

**Your Task:**

- Help Ms. Speedi find the <u>shortest</u> route from home to school. Be sure to check out alternative routes!

- Find the shortest route for Ms. Speedi to take home after school. Is this route shorter or faster than her route to school?

# Unit 10
# Yearbook Sales
### Exponents and Quadratic Equations

# Unit 10 Objectives
## Yearbook Sales: EXPONENTS AND QUADRATICS

In this unit you will further develop your factoring skills to include work with more complicated expressions. These factoring skills will enable you to simplify algebraic fractions. You will also work with **exponents** and learn another technique for solving **quadratic equations**.

In this unit you will have the opportunity to:

- extend your ability to factor trinomials to cases where the coefficient of $x^2$ is not 1.

- explore exponents to develop basic procedures for working with positive, negative and zero exponents.

- simplify elementary rational expressions in preparation for more complicated cases in Units 11 and 12.

- learn how to solve quadratic equations using the Quadratic Formula.

This unit builds on several fundamental ideas to solve more complicated problems. Particular attention is given to quadratic equations. The patterns discovered when working with exponents are extended to simplifying rational expressions.

Read the following problem but **do not try to solve it now**. In this unit, you will learn the skills needed to solve it.

---

**YS-0.     YEARBOOK SALES**

Last year, the yearbook at Central High School cost $50 and only 500 books were sold. It cost so much because so few were sold and so few were sold because it cost so much! The student body officers want more people to be able to buy yearbooks this year. A student survey discovered that, on the average, for every $5 reduction in price, 100 more students will buy yearbooks. The yearbook company has also raised the minimum order per school to $27,500. What price should the school charge so that more students will buy the yearbook <u>and</u> the school can achieve the minimum sales amount?

---

|  |  |
|---|---|
| Problem Solving | |
| Graphing | |
| Writing and Solving Equations | |
| Ratios | |
| Geometry | |
| Symbol Manipulation | |

# Unit 10
## Yearbook Sales: EXPONENTS AND QUADRATICS

## FACTORING QUADRATICS: ADDITIONAL CASES

YS-1.    Add this information to your tool kit.

---

### EXTENDING FACTORING

In earlier units we used Diamond Problems to help factor sums like $x^2 + 6x + 8$.

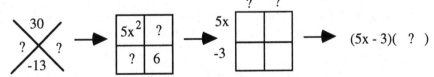

We can modify the diamond method slightly to factor problems that are a little different in that they no longer have a "1" in front of the $x^2$. For example, factor:

$2x^2 + 7x + 3$

multiply

$\text{?} \diagtimes \text{?} \begin{smallmatrix}6\\7\end{smallmatrix} \rightarrow 6 \diagtimes 1 \begin{smallmatrix}6\\7\end{smallmatrix} \rightarrow$
| $2x^2$ | $6x$ |
|---|---|
| $1x$ | $3$ |
$\rightarrow$
x + 3
| | $2x^2$ | $6x$ |
|---|---|---|
| | $1x$ | $3$ |
$\rightarrow (2x + 1)(x + 3)$

Try this problem: $5x^2 - 13x + 6$.

$\text{?} \diagtimes \text{?} \begin{smallmatrix}30\\-13\end{smallmatrix} \rightarrow$
| $5x^2$ | ? |
|---|---|
| ? | $6$ |
$\rightarrow$
5x ... -3
| ? | ? |
|---|---|
| | |
$\rightarrow (5x - 3)(\ ?\ )$

---

YS-2.    Factor each of the following quadratics using the modified diamond procedure.

a)   $3x^2 + 7x + 2$

b)   $3x^2 + x - 2$

c)   $2x^2 - 3x - 5$

d)   $x^2 - 4x - 45$

e)   $5x^2 + 13x + 6$

YS-3.   Remember that some quadratics have a common factor which requires that you factor twice. Factor each of the following quadratics completely.

EXAMPLE:   $2x^2 + 10x + 12 = 2(x^2 + 5x + 6) = 2(x + 2)(x + 3)$

a)   $3x^2 - 9x - 30$

c)   $4x^2 + 4$

b)   $5x^2 - 20$

d)   $3x^2 + 11x + 6$

YS-4.   Use the Zero Product Property to solve each quadratic equation.

a)   $(x + 2)(x - 7) = 0$

c)   $x^2 + 3x - 10 = 0$

b)   $(2x + 1)(x - 5) = 0$

d)   $y^2 - 7y + 10 = 0$

YS-5.   Factor each of these quadratics.

a)   $15x^2 - 37x + 18$

b)   $42x^2 + 17x - 15$

YS-6.   Examine the information provided in the graph at right. Find y. Show your work. Note: this graph is not to scale.

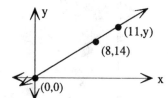

YS-7.   Look at the graph in the previous problem.

a)   What is the distance from (0, 0) to (8, 14)?

b)   What is the slope of the line?

c)   What is the equation of the line?

YS-8.   Rewrite $x^3$ and $\dfrac{x^3}{x^2}$ as repeated products of x (without exponents.)

YS-9.   For each triangle, solve for x. Write your answer in square root form, simplified square root form, and the decimal approximation.

a)

b)

YS-10. Mr. Nguyen is dividing $775 among his three daughters. If the oldest gets twice as much as the youngest, and the middle daughter gets $35 more than the youngest, how much does each girl get? Write an equation and solve.

YS-11. Multiply each of the following binomials. Use a generic rectangle, if necessary.

a) $(x + 1)(x + 1)$

b) $(x + 5)(x + 2)$

c) $2x(x + 5)$

d) $(2x + 1)(x + 5)$

e) $(x + y)(x + y)$

YS-12. Factor each of the following quadratics, if possible.

a) $x^2 + 3x - 10$

b) $y^2 - 7y + 10$

c) $x^2 + 3x + 10$

d) $2y^2 + 11y - 21$

YS-13. Look for and then apply the different types of factoring that you have encountered this year as you factor each of the following. Decide with your study team how to best check your answer.

a) $x^2 + 10x + 21$

b) $3x^2 + 7x + 2$

c) $2x^2 + 7x - 15$

d) $x^2 - 64$

e) $6y^2 - 2y - 48$

f) $m^2 - 14m + 49$

YS-14. Solve each of the following equations or systems by any method you choose. Show all your work.

a) $x^2 + 10x + 21 = 0$

b) $\frac{x+1}{3} = \frac{x}{2}$

c) $2x^2 + 7x - 15 = 0$

d) $\frac{x}{4} + \frac{5x}{3} = 1 + x$

e) $x = 2y - 1$
   $y - x = -5$

f) $x^2 + 5x = 24$

g) $2(x + 1) - 4(x - 2) = x + 3$

h) $y = -x - 2$
   $y = \frac{1}{2}x + 4$

YS-15.    Graph these two equations on the same set of axes and estimate where they intersect.
Use $-2 \le x \le 2$ in increments of 0.5 (e.g., -2, -1.5, ..., 1.5, 2).

$$y = x^3 - x + 2 \qquad \text{and} \qquad y = x + 2$$

YS-16.    The graph below shows 3 lines with their equations. Use subproblems and systems
of equations to answer the following questions.

a)    Where do the lines intersect?

b)    Find the area of the triangular
region formed by the three
equations.

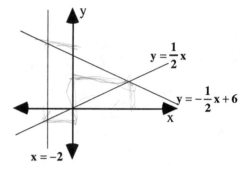

YS-17.    Factor each of the following quadratics by looking for common factors.

a)    $x(x + 2) + 3(x + 2)$

c)    $(x + 4)x^2 + 3(x + 4)$

b)    $2y(y - 3) + 5(y - 3)$

d)    $(y + 1)^2 + (y + 1)$

YS-18.    Use the slope and y-intercept to graph each of the following equations.

a)    $y = -2x + 4$

b)    $y = \frac{2}{3}x - 2$

YS-19.    Use the points $(2, -1)$ and $(1, 2)$.

a)    Draw a generic triangle to determine the slope. Is the slope negative
or positive?

b)    Find the equation of the line.

c)    Write the equation of a line that is parallel to the equation in part (b).

d)    Write the equation of a line that would intersect the line in part (b).

YS-20.    Use the diagram at right to find the lengths of the triangle's legs
and its area.

a)    Using x, write an expression for the area of the triangle.

b)    Find x to the nearest hundredth.

c)    Find the area of the triangle.

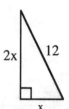

YS-21.  Simplify each of the following fractions:

a)  $\dfrac{5}{5}$

d)  $\dfrac{x^3}{x^3}$

b)  $\dfrac{-2.3}{-2.3}$

e)  $\dfrac{6}{18x}$

c)  $\dfrac{y}{y}$

f)  $\dfrac{24x}{100}$


YS-22.  Solve this system for $(x, y)$:   $y = 5x - 3$
$3y - 10x = -12$


YS-23.  Complete the following.

a)   Factor $3x^2 - 5x - 2$

b)   Solve $3x^2 - 5x - 2 = 0$

c)   What do your answers in part (b) tell you about the graph of $y = 3x^2 - 5x - 2$ ?


YS-24.  Divide. Write your answer in scientific and standard notation.

a)  $\dfrac{4.2 \cdot 10^5}{3.0 \cdot 10^2}$

b)  $\dfrac{3.0 \cdot 10^6}{1.5 \cdot 10^4}$


# PROPERTIES OF EXPONENTS

YS-25.  Write each of these expressions as simply as possible using the method shown below.

Knowing that $x^3 = x \cdot x \cdot x$ and $\dfrac{y}{y} = 1$ , then:

$$x(x^3) = x \cdot (x \cdot x \cdot x) = x^4 \quad \text{and}$$

$$y^3 \div y = \frac{y \cdot y \cdot y}{y} = y^2$$

a)  $x^2 \cdot x$

c)  $x^3 \cdot x^6$

b)  $y^2 \cdot y^5$

d)  $x^3 \div x^2$

YS-26. Most of the work you have done this semester has been with x or $x^2$. During the next few lessons you will use patterns of multiplication and division to work with other powers of x. Record the following definitions in your tool kit:

---

**BASE, EXPONENT, AND VALUE**

In the expression $2^5$, 2 is the **base**, 5 is the **exponent**, and the **value** is 32.

$$2^5 \text{ means } 2 \cdot 2 \cdot 2 \cdot 2 \cdot 2 = 32$$
$$x^3 \text{ means } x \cdot x \cdot x$$

---

YS-27. Use exponents to write each of the following expressions as simply as possible. Look for patterns as you do this with your study team. Write out the variables to show the meaning whenever necessary.

a) $(x^2)(x^5)$

b) $x^7 \cdot x^5$

c) $y^8 \cdot y^6$

d) $y^7 \div y^4$

e) $\dfrac{x^3}{x^1}$

f) $x^3 \cdot x^4$

g) $m^{13} \cdot m^{14}$

h) $x^{32} \cdot x^{59}$

i) $x^{31} \div x^{29}$

j) $\dfrac{x^3}{x^3}$

YS-28. Write out the meaning of each expression below and then simplify using exponents.

EXAMPLE: $(x^3)^2 = x^3 \cdot x^3 = (x \cdot x \cdot x)(x \cdot x \cdot x) = x^6$

a) $(x^4)^2$

b) $(y^2)^3$

c) $(x^5)^5$

d) $(x \cdot y)^2$

e) $(x^2 \cdot y^3)^3$

f) $(2x)^4$

YS-29. Using the patterns for exponents that you have found, write each expression below as simply as possible using exponents.

a) $x^3 \cdot x^4$

b) $(x^3)^4$

c) $x^4 \div x^3$

d) $(x\,y^2)^2$

e) $(2x^2)^3$

f) $(x^2 y^2)^4$

**YS-30.**   Use your calculator to write these exponential numbers as a decimal and as a fraction.

a)   $10^{-1}$          b)   $10^0$          c)   $5^{-1}$          d)   $5^{-2}$

e)   What effect does a negative sign have when it appears in an exponent? Was this what you expected?

f)   What effect does zero have when it appears as an exponent?


**YS-31.**   Use the modified Diamond method from YS-1 to factor.

a)   $6x^2 - 5x + 1$                    b)   $4x^2 + 4x + 1$


**YS-32.**   Factor each of the following

a)   $x^2 - 6x + 9$                    d)   $x^2 - 25$

b)   $5x^2 + 4x - 1$                    e)   $9x^2 - 25$

c)   $9x^2 - 18x$                    f)   $2x^2 - 7x + 3$


**YS-33.**   Look for a relationship between the two equations in parts (a) and (b).

a)   Solve the equation $3x^2 + 4x + 1 = 0$ by factoring.

b)   What are the x-intercepts for the quadratic equation $y = 3x^2 + 4x + 1$ ?

c)   How are (a) and (b) related?


**YS-34.**   Solve for x:  $\frac{4}{x} + \frac{3}{5} = \frac{7}{10}$. Look in your tool kit for Fraction Busters if you need help.


**YS-35.**   The two triangles in the diagram below are similar. Find x.

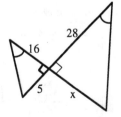


**YS-36.**   Find the missing side lengths in each triangle. Write each length in simplified square root and decimal forms.

a)             b)   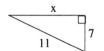          c)

YS-37.    Write each expression as simply as possible using exponents.

a)    $x^5 \cdot x^4$

c)    $\dfrac{x^4}{x^1}$

b)    $(x^2)^4$

d)    $(2x)^3$

## ZERO AND NEGATIVE EXPONENTS

YS-38.    With your study team, summarize the patterns that you found in yesterday's exponent problems. Describe how to write the examples below as simply as possible.

a)    $(x^2)(x^3)$    What patterns did you find?  Use the words <u>base</u> and <u>exponent</u>.

b)    $\dfrac{x^6}{x^3}$    What patterns did you find?  Use the words <u>base</u> and <u>exponent</u>.

c)    $(x^3)^4$    What patterns did you find?  Use the words <u>base</u> and <u>exponent</u>.

YS-39.    Use the patterns that you described in the previous problems to write each expression as simply as possible.

a)    $x^7 \cdot x^4$

e)    $(2x^2)^3$

b)    $(x^3)^3$

f)    $(x^2y^2)^4$

c)    $x^6 \div x^3$

g)    $\dfrac{x^2y^{11}}{x^5y^3}$

d)    $8^6 \div 8^3$

h)    $\dfrac{2x^{12}}{3x^2}$

YS-40.    Add this information to your tool kit.

---

### LAWS OF EXPONENTS

The patterns that you have been working with are called the **LAWS OF EXPONENTS**.  Here are the basic patterns with examples:

1)  $x^a \cdot x^b = x^{a+b}$    examples:  $x^3 \cdot x^4 = x^{3+4} = x^7; \; 2^7 \cdot 2^4 = 2^{11}$

2)  $\dfrac{x^a}{x^b} = x^{a-b}$    examples:  $x^{10} \div x^4 = x^{10-4} = x^6; \; \dfrac{2^4}{2^7} = 2^{-3}$

3)  $(x^a)^b = x^{ab}$    examples:  $(x^4)^3 = x^{4 \cdot 3} = x^{12}; \; (2x^3)^4 = 2^4 \cdot x^{12} = 16x^{12}$

---

**YS-41.** How should we simplify $x^0$ ?

a) What does your calculator display for $2^0$ ? $17^0$ ? $1000^0$ ?

b) The following should help convince you why it is reasonable that $x^0 = 1$. From the patterns we found when dividing with exponents, what is "t" in $\frac{x^3}{x^3} = x^t$ ?

c) From arithmetic we know that $\frac{\text{anything}}{\text{itself}} = ?$ Therefore, $x^0 = \_\_$ ?

**YS-42.** How can we write $x^{-2}$ without negative exponents?

a) From the patterns we found when dividing with exponents, what is "t" in $\frac{x^3}{x^5} = x^t$ ?

b) Remembering that $\frac{x}{x} = 1$, write out $\frac{x^3}{x^5}$ without exponents and then simplify the fraction by finding as many "ones" $\left(\frac{x}{x}\right)$ as you can. What is left?

c) Therefore, since $x^{-2} = \frac{1}{x^2}$, what should $x^{-3} = ?$ What should $3^{-4} = ?$

YS-43. Add this information to your tool kit.

---

### ZERO EXPONENTS AND NEGATIVE EXPONENTS

$x^0 = 1$. Examples: $2^0 = 1$, $\qquad (-3)^0 = 1$, $\qquad (\frac{1}{4})^0 = 1$.

$x^{-n} = \frac{1}{x^n}$. Examples: $x^{-3} = \frac{1}{x^3}$, $\qquad y^{-4} = \frac{1}{y^4}$, $\qquad 4^{-2} = \frac{1}{4^2} = \frac{1}{16}$.

$\frac{1}{x^{-n}} = x^n$. Examples: $\frac{1}{x^{-5}} = x^5$, $\qquad \frac{1}{x^{-2}} = x^2$, $\qquad \frac{1}{3^{-2}} = 3^2 = 9$

Rewrite each expression without negative or zero exponents.

a) $x^{-5}$  c) $m^0$  e) $4^{-1}$

b) $y^{-3}$  d) $5^{-2}$  f) $5^0$

---

**YS-44.** You know that when your calculator displays $\boxed{2.3 \quad ^{03}}$ it means $2.3 \cdot 10^3$ or 2,300. Recall that $2.3 \times 10^3$ is called **scientific notation** and 2,300 is called **standard form**. (Refer to problem KF-96.) Notice that the positive exponent of 3 moved the decimal 3 places to the right when the number was written in standard form. If your calculator displays $\boxed{1.5 \quad ^{-03}}$, write the equivalent expression in scientific notation and standard form.

**YS-45.** Use your scientific calculator and type in $1.5 \cdot 10^{-3}$. How did multiplying by $10^{-3}$ move the decimal point? How does that compare with multiplying by $10^3$?

**YS-46.** Convert the following scientific notation numbers to standard form.

a) $2.75 \cdot 10^{-4}$

b) $4.5 \cdot 10^{-5}$

c) $1.56 \cdot 10^{-4}$

d) $2.5 \cdot 10^6$

**YS-47.** Write each of the following expressions in simpler exponential form (<u>not</u> the value).

a) $10^3 \cdot 10^4$

b) $10^5 \div 10^3$

c) $(10^3)^4$

d) $x^2y \cdot x^3y^2$

e) $3^2 \cdot 3^5$

f) $3^7 \div 3^3$

g) $(2^3)^{-2}$

h) $(x^2y)^3$

i) $x^3 \cdot x^5$

j) $x^7 \div x^2$

k) $(x^3)^4$

l) $x^2 \cdot (x^3)^2$

**YS-48.** Write the equation of:

a) the line with slope $\frac{3}{4}$ and passes through (6, 20).

b) the line passes through (-3, 8) and (-1, 5).

**YS-49.** Factor the following expressions:

a) $x^2 + 17x + 42$

b) $2x^2 - x - 15$

c) $9x^2 - 6x + 1$

d) $9x^2 - 25$

YS-50.    The perimeter of the triangle at right is 86 units.

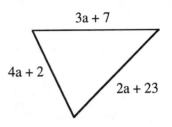

a)    Write an equation and find a.

b)    Find the lengths of the sides of the triangle.

c)    Could this be a right triangle? Justify your answer.


YS-51.    Simplify the following expressions.

a)    $\dfrac{7659}{7659}$

d)    $\dfrac{12x}{3x}$

b)    $\dfrac{x}{x}$

e)    Does $\dfrac{2+3}{2} = 3$ ?

c)    $\dfrac{x+3}{x+3}$

f)    Does $\dfrac{x+3}{x} = 3$ ?


# INTRODUCTION TO RATIONAL EXPRESSIONS

YS-52.    Since, for example, $m^3 = m \cdot m \cdot m$, how would you write:

a)    $x^5$ ?

b)    $(x+1)^3$ ?

c)    $(x+1)^0$ ?


YS-53.    With your study team, write each of the following expressions in simplest fraction form by looking for factors in fraction form that are equivalent to one.

Example: $\dfrac{15}{6} = \dfrac{5 \cdot 3}{2 \cdot 3} = \dfrac{5}{2} \cdot \dfrac{3}{3} = \dfrac{5}{2} \cdot 1 = \dfrac{5}{2}$

a)    $\dfrac{5 \cdot 5 \cdot 5}{5 \cdot 5 \cdot 6}$

e)    $\dfrac{(x-1)}{(x-1)^2}$

b)    $\dfrac{10}{10^3}$

f)    $\dfrac{12(x-2)^2}{3(x-2)}$

c)    $\dfrac{8x^3y^4}{4x^2y}$

g)    $\dfrac{6(m+1)^8}{6(m+1)}$

d)    $\dfrac{5(x+2)}{2(x+2)}$

h)    In the next several days you will solve problems that will require your factoring, fraction and exponent skills. As you approach these problems, look for the subproblems you need to solve to make these complicated problems easier. Explain in one or two sentences how your team found its solution to part (g).

**YS-54.** Write each of the following expressions in simplest form.

a) $\dfrac{(x+3)^2}{(x+3)(x-2)}$

c) $\dfrac{12(x+1)^2(x-2)^3}{6(x+1)^3(x-2)^5}$

b) $\dfrac{8(2x-5)^3}{4(2x-5)^2(x+4)}$

d) $\dfrac{x^2+4x-12}{x^2+12x+36}$

(Hint: you must factor first!)

**YS-55.** Decide whether each of the following statements is correct or not.

a) Does $\dfrac{34}{32} = \dfrac{30+4}{30+2} = 2$ ?

c) Does $\dfrac{x^2}{x}$ always equal 2 ?

b) Does $\dfrac{x+7}{x+14} = \dfrac{1}{2}$ ?

**YS-56.** Factor each of the following expressions. Be sure to look for any common factors.

a) $4x^2 - 12x$

c) $3y^2 + 6y + 3$

b) $2m^2 + 7m + 3$

d) $3x^2 + 4x - 4$

**YS-57.** For the rectangle at right:

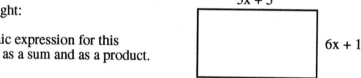

a) write an algebraic expression for this rectangle's area as a sum and as a product.

b) find the area of the rectangle when $x = 1$ and again when $x = 3$.

**YS-58.** Graph the two points $(-2, 3)$ and $(2, 1)$.

a) Determine the slope of the line.

b) Determine the equation of the line.

c) Is the point $(30, -17)$ on the same line? Show how you determined your answer.

d) Find the distance between the two original points.

**YS-59.** Factor and solve each of the following quadratic equations.

a) $y^2 + 6y - 16 = 0$

c) $5z^2 - 13z = 0$

(Hint: look for a common factor.)

b) $2x^2 + 11x - 6 = 0$

YS-60.    Explain your methods in parts (a) and (b) below.

a)    Solve this system for x and y.

b)    Describe another way to solve this problem.

$$3x + y = 9$$
$$2x + y = 1$$

YS-61.    Solve for x.

a)    $\sqrt{144} = x$

c)    How are these problems different?

b)    $x^2 = 144$

d)    Compare the graphs of $y = \sqrt{x}$ and then $y = x^2$. You do not need to graph, just describe the comparison in words.

YS-62.    A rectangular sign is three times as tall as it is wide. Its area is 588 square centimeters. What are the dimensions of the sign? Write an equation and solve.

## SIMPLIFYING RATIONAL EXPRESSIONS

YS-63.    Investigate the following problems.

a)    Is $\frac{2+3}{2} = 3$ ?

b)    Is $\frac{9-3}{3} = 9$ ?

c)    Is $\frac{2 \cdot 3}{2} = 3$ ?

d)    Is $\frac{9 \cdot 3}{3} = 9$ ?

e)    What was the only mathematical operation that allowed us to write the same factor in the numerator and denominator as ONE (i.e. $\frac{1}{1} = 1$)?

f)    Therefore, which of the following is true?

1)    $\frac{x^2 + x + 3}{x + 3} = x^2$

2)    $\frac{(x + 2)(x + 3)}{(x + 3)} = x + 2$

YS-64. Add this information to your tool kit about simplifying rational expressions.

---

### SIMPLIFYING RATIONAL EXPRESSIONS

To simplify rational expressions, both the numerator and denominator must be factored. Then look for factors that make ONE (1).

$$\text{Example: } \frac{x^2 + 5x + 4}{x^2 + x - 12} = \frac{(x+4)(x+1)}{(x+4)(x-3)} = 1 \cdot \frac{(x+1)}{(x-3)} = \frac{x+1}{x-3}$$

Simplify each rational expression. Show all subproblems.

a) $\dfrac{(x+2)(x+2)}{(x-3)(x+2)}$

d) $\dfrac{x^2 + 6x + 9}{x^2 - 9}$

b) $\dfrac{x^2 + 5x + 6}{x^2 + x - 6}$

e) $\dfrac{2x^2 + x - 3}{x^2 + 4x - 5}$

c) $\dfrac{x^2 + 4x}{2x + 8}$

f) $\dfrac{2x^2 - x - 10}{3x^2 + 7x + 2}$

---

YS-65. Use what you know about slope and intercepts to graph each line.

a) $y = \frac{2}{3}x - 1$

b) $2x + 3y = 6$

c) Describe your process to part (b) above.

YS-66. For the line $2x + 3y = 6$, show how to calculate the coordinates of the x-intercept and the y-intercept. Does the graph in part (b) of the previous problem pass through the points you found?

YS-67. Graph the equation $y = x^2 - 4$ for $-5 \leq x \leq 5$.

a) Estimate where the graph crosses the x-axis.

b) Solve the equation $x^2 - 4 = 0$ for x by factoring.

c) Write a sentence comparing your solutions to parts (a) and (b). Be sure to note differences, if any, as well as similarities.

YS-68. Solve this system for x and y. Then state precisely where the two lines intersect.

$$x = 3y - 7$$
$$3x - y = 3$$

YS-69. Explain whether each of the following equations is true and how you know.

a)  $3^4 + 3^3 = 3^7$

b)  $x^4 + x^3 = x^7$

c)  $\dfrac{(x+1)(x+3)}{x+1} = x + 3$

d)  $\dfrac{(x+1)+(x+3)}{x+1} = x + 3$

YS-70. Use what you know about exponents to write each of the following expressions in a simpler form.

a)  $3x^2 \cdot x$

b)  $(-2x^2)(-2x)$

c)  $\dfrac{n^{12}}{n^3}$

d)  $\dfrac{-8x^6 y^2}{-4xy}$

e)  $(x^3)^2$

f)  $(2x^3)^3$

YS-71. Copy and complete the table for $(x, y)$, then write the rule.

| x | -3 | -2 | -1 | 5 | | 1 | $\frac{1}{3}$ | 6 |
|---|----|----|----|----|---|---|---|---|
| y | -10 | -7 | | 14 | -1 | | | 17 |

$\dfrac{-7+10}{-2+3} = 3$

YS-72. Maxine paid $2,379.29 for a computer that was originally priced at $2,500.00. What percent of the original price did Maxine pay? What was the discount percent? Write an equation and solve.

YS-73. Fill in the missing expressions.

a)  $\dfrac{2^3(x^2 yw)^2}{(2wx)^4} \cdot \left(\dfrac{?}{?}\right) = x$

b)  $\dfrac{5^4(xy^2)^3}{(3^2+4^2)y^2} \cdot \left(\dfrac{?}{?}\right) = x$

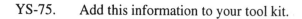

**YS-74.** Explore the following quadratic equation.

a) Graph the equation $y = x^2 + 6x + 2$ and estimate the x-intercepts.

b) Substitute the values you found for x in part (a) into the equation $y = x^2 + 6x + 2$ and compute the value.

c) How close to correct were your estimates from part (a)?

d) Is the expression $x^2 + 6x + 2$ factorable? Explain your answer.

e) Are there solutions to the equation $0 = x^2 + 6x + 2$? Explain your answer.

**YS-75.** Add this information to your tool kit.

---

### STANDARD FORM OF A QUADRATIC EQUATION

Problems such as YS-74 suggest that another method besides the Zero Product Property is needed to solve quadratic equations. There is a formula that accomplishes this task. To use the formula, a quadratic equation must be in what is called **STANDARD FORM,** that is, written as $ax^2 + bx + c$. Then the coefficients **a, b,** and **c** are easily recognized.

> EXAMPLE: The quadratic equation $2x^2 - 13x + 21 = 0$
> is in **standard form**.
>
> What does $a = ? \ b = ? \ c = ?$ .

When a quadratic equation is not in standard form, you first need to convert it to standard form <u>before</u> you can identify a, b, and c.

> EXAMPLE: The quadratic equation $3x^2 = 14x - 8$
> is <u>not</u> in standard form.

By adding the opposites of 14x and -8, to both sides of our equation, we get:

$$3x^2 - 14x + 8 = 0$$

which <u>is</u> in standard form. The coefficients are a = 3, b = -14, and c = 8.

---

YS-76. Identify the values of **a, b,** and **c** in each of the following quadratic equations. Some of the equations will need to be written in standard form first.

a) $3x^2 - 5x + 4 = 0$

b) $x^2 + 9x - 1 = 0$

c) $-2x^2 + 9x = 0$

d) $0.017x^2 - 0.4x + 20 = 0$

e) $-6x + 5x^2 = 8$

f) $x(2x + 4) = 7x - 5$

YS-77. a) Find an approximate value of

$$\frac{-2 + \sqrt{(-3)^2 - 4(2)(-3)}}{-3}$$

on your calculator. It will help to list the sub-problems before you use the calculator. Verify your answer before going to part (b).

b) Use a calculator to find the value of each of the following expressions to the nearest hundredth. In parts (c) and (d) the "±" means there are two solutions. One is with addition and one is with subtraction. Find both. Verify your answers with your study team.

1) $8 + \sqrt{8^2 - (4)(5)(3)}$

2) $\frac{-2 + \sqrt{2^2 - 4(3)(-7)}}{2(3)}$

3) $\frac{-2 \pm \sqrt{16}}{2}$

4) $\frac{1 \pm \sqrt{5}}{2}$

YS-78. Solve each equation.

a) $x^2 + 19x + 90 = 0$

b) $2(3x + 1)(x - 7) = 0$

c) $3x^2 + 7x + 2 = 0$

YS-79. Sketch each pair of points and find the distance between them. You may use graph paper or draw generic triangles. Give answers in square root form and the decimal approximation.

a) (3, -6) and (-2, 5)

b) (5, -8) and (-3, 1)

c) (0, 5) and (5, 0)

d) Write the distance you found in part (c) in simplified square root form.

YS-80. Find the area of the shaded region.

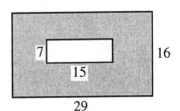

YS-81.   Use the Laws of Exponents to rewrite the following expressions, if possible.

a)   $\dfrac{m^{16}y^{31}}{m^{12}y^{17}}$

d)   $x^2 + y^2$

b)   $\left(6x^3z\right)^3$

e)   $\left(3x^2\right)^2 \div \left(6x^4\right)$

c)   $(5x)^2(3y)^3$

f)   $(2x - 5)^2$

YS-82.   Find where the graphs of the lines $y = 2x - 7$ and $y = -x + 5$ intersect. Describe your process and find another way to solve this problem.

YS-83.   A right triangle has an area of 40 square centimeters and its shortest side has length 8 centimeters. Draw a diagram and find the length of the hypotenuse.

YS-84.   Simplify.

a)   $\dfrac{2(x+4)(x-2)}{8(x-1)(x+4)}$

c)   $\dfrac{3x^2 - 2x - 8}{x^2 - 4}$

b)   $\dfrac{x^2 - 2x - 3}{x^2 - x - 6}$

# THE QUADRATIC FORMULA

YS-85.   Solve $2x^2 - 9x - 35 = 0$ by factoring and applying the Zero Product Property. How many solutions are there?

YS-86.    Problems that do not factor quickly and problems such as YS-74 that
          do not factor at all create the need for another method of solving
          quadratic equations. Read the information in the box below. Enter
          the formula and the example in your tool kit.

---

## USING THE QUADRATIC FORMULA

Once a quadratic equation is in the form $ax^2 + bx + c = 0$, you can use the values for a, b and
c to calculate the solutions for the equation; that is, you can find those values of x that make
the equation true by using the **QUADRATIC FORMULA**:

$$\text{If } ax^2 + bx + c = 0, \text{ then } x = \frac{-b \pm \sqrt{b^2 - 4ac}}{2a}$$

In words this says:

"The values of x which make the quadratic equation $ax^2 + bx + c = 0$ true are equal to
the opposite of **b**, plus or minus the square root of the quantity **b** squared minus the
product **4ac**, all divided by the product **2a**."

Remember the $\pm$ is an efficient, shorthand way to write the <u>two</u> solutions to the equation. The
formula actually says:

$$x = \frac{-b + \sqrt{b^2 - 4ac}}{2a} \quad \text{or} \quad x = \frac{-b - \sqrt{b^2 - 4ac}}{2a}$$

Unless the quantity $b^2$ - 4ac is negative or zero, the graph of $ax^2 + bx + c = 0$ crosses the
x-axis at <u>two points.</u>

For example, the quadratic equation $x^2 + 5x + 3 = 0$ is in standard form with a = 1, b = 5,
and c = 3. When we substitute these values into the Quadratic Formula we get :

$$x = \frac{-5 \pm \sqrt{5^2 - 4(1)(3)}}{2(1)} = \frac{-5 \pm \sqrt{25 - 12}}{2} = \frac{-5 \pm \sqrt{13}}{2} ,$$

$$\text{which means } x = \frac{-5 + \sqrt{13}}{2} \quad \text{or} \quad x = \frac{-5 - \sqrt{13}}{2} .$$

These square root values of x are the EXACT solutions to the equation $x^2 + 5x + 3 = 0$.

We can use our calculators to find approximate values:

$$x = \frac{-5 + \sqrt{13}}{2} \approx -0.70 \quad \text{OR} \quad x = \frac{-5 - \sqrt{13}}{2} \approx -4.30$$

Here is a summary of the procedure for using the **Quadratic Formula**:

Step 1   Put the equation in standard form (zero on one side of the equation).

Step 2   List the numerical values of the coefficients a, b, and c.

Step 3   Write the Quadratic Formula, <u>even if it is given</u>.

Step 4   Substitute the numerical values for a, b, and c in the Quadratic Formula.

Step 5   Simplify to get the exact solutions.

Step 6   Use a calculator, if necessary, to get approximate solutions

---

YS-87. Copy and complete the following example in your notebook. Verify the accuracy of each step with your study team.

Use the Quadratic Formula to solve the equation $x^2 - 2x = 4$.

Step 1   $x^2 - 2x - 4 = 0$

Step 2   $a = ?\ \ b = ?\ \ c = ?$

Step 3   If $ax^2 + bx + c = 0$, then $x = \dfrac{-b \pm \sqrt{b^2 - 4ac}}{2a}$.

Step 4   $x = \dfrac{-(-2) \pm \sqrt{(-2)^2 - 4(1)(-4)}}{2(1)}$

Step 5   $x = \dfrac{2 \pm \sqrt{4 + 16}}{2} = \dfrac{2 \pm \sqrt{20}}{2}$

Step 6   $x \approx ?$ or $x \approx -1.24$

YS-88. Solve each of the following equations using the six step Quadratic Formula procedure demonstrated in YS-87. Write your answers first in square root form, similar to that in Step 5 of the example, and then in decimal form.

a)   $2x^2 - 9x - 35 = 0$ (Compare your answers with YS-85. Did both methods give the same answer?)

b)   $3x^2 + 7x = -2$          d)   $8x^2 + 10x + 3 = 0$

c)   $x^2 - 5x - 2 = 0$          e)   Extension:   $(x - 3)(x + 4) = 7x$

YS-89. Use the figure at right to answer the questions below.

a)   Find the equation of line $t$.

b)   Find the equation of another line parallel to line $t$.

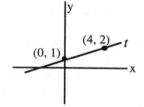

YS-90. The two points $(30, -25)$ and $(50, 65)$ determine a line.

a)   Find the slope of the line.

b)   Find an equation of the line.

YS-91. Find the length of the diagonal of a square with side lengths of 15 inches.

YS-92. Solve the system of equations: $2x + 3y = 5$ and $x - y = 5$. There are two methods that can be used to solve the system: algebraic or graphic. Which method did you choose and why?

YS-93. Use what you know about exponents to write each of the following expressions in a simpler form:

a) $(x + 3)^2$

b) $(6x^3y^{-1})^2$

c) $\dfrac{(x+5)(2x-7)^3}{(x+5)^5(2x-7)^2}$

YS-94. Solve each equation for the variable.

a) $9x - 5.4 = -2.7x + 42$

c) $x^2 + 1 = 26$

b) $8(3x - 5) + 2 = 6$

d) $\sqrt{x} = 11$

YS-95. Use the Quadratic Formula to solve each of the following equations. Be sure to use all six steps of the procedure. Remember to copy the formula each time you use it. Verify your solutions with your study team.

a) $-4x^2 + 8x + 3 = 0$

d) $0.09x^2 - 0.86x + 2 = 0$

b) $-3x = -x^2 + 14$

e) $3x^2 + 4x = 0$

c) $-5 + 11x = 2x^2$

f) $25x^2 - 49 = 0$

g) Which of these equations could you have solved by factoring?

YS-96. Look again at the equations in YS-95 and your solutions to them.

a) List the values of $\sqrt{b^2 - 4ac}$ for each part of problem YS-95.

b) Find the equations that had rational numbers (integers or fractions) for their solutions. Compare the values of $\sqrt{b^2 - 4ac}$ for these equations to the values of $\sqrt{b^2 - 4ac}$ for the equations whose solutions were not integers or fractions. What do you notice?

c) Can $3x^2 + 8x + 5 = 0$ be solved by factoring? Factor if possible and solve.

d) Calculate the value of $\sqrt{b^2 - 4ac}$ for the equation $3x^2 + 8x + 5 = 0$. What kind of number do you get? Write one or two sentences that explains the relation of this result to your conclusion in part (b).

e) Explain what the value of $\sqrt{b^2 - 4ac}$ tells you about the solutions of the quadratic equation $ax^2 + bx + c = 0$. What does it tell you about the factorability of the polynomial $ax^2 + bx + c$?

YS-97.    A right triangle has one leg two centimeters longer than the other. The hypotenuse
          is 17 centimeters long.

    a)    Draw a diagram of this right triangle and label the length of each side.

    b)    Write an equation to find the lengths of the legs.

    c)    Find the length of each leg of the triangle.


YS-98.    Use the slope and y-intercept to graph each of the following equations.

    a)    $y = 2x - 4$                      c)    Find the point of intersection for
                                                  the lines in parts (a) and (b).

    b)    $y = -0.5x + 2$


YS-99.    Find an equation of the line:

    a)    with slope $\frac{2}{3}$ passing through the point $(-6, -1)$.

    b)    passing through the points $(60, 400)$ and $(50, 500)$.


YS-100.   Test to see if each of the following quadratic equations can be solved by factoring
          by applying your conclusion from problem YS-96. Remember to put each equation
          in standard form first!

    a)    $x^2 + 4x - 5 = 0$                 c)    $x^2 + 7x + 5 = 0$

    b)    $5x = -x^2 + 6$                    d)    $5x^2 = 6 + 14x$
          $x^2 5x -6$


YS-101.   Use the Laws of Exponents to rewrite each of the following expressions.

    a)    $\left(3x^{11}z^5\right)^2$         c)    $x^{13} \cdot x^{-16} \cdot x^9$

    b)    $(2b)^5\left(3k^2\right)^2$         d)    $(3x - 4)^2$


YS-102.   Simplify the following rational expressions.

    a)    $\dfrac{(x-3)(x+5)}{(x-2)(x-3)}$    c)    $\dfrac{3x^2 + x - 2}{2x^2 + 7x + 5}$

    b)    $\left(\dfrac{3x^2}{6x^5}\right)^3$  d)    $(6x)^2 \div \left(24x^3\right)$

YS-103.   UNIT 10 SUMMARY

Select 3 or 4 big ideas that you feel best represent Unit
10. Write a description of each main idea. For each topic,
choose a problem that best demonstrates your
understanding. Explain your solution as in the previous
unit summaries. Show all your work.

YS-104.   YEARBOOK SALES

Last year, the yearbook at Central High School
cost $50 and only 500 books were sold. It cost so
much because so few were sold and so few were
sold because it cost so much! The student body
officers want more people to be able to buy
yearbooks this year. A student survey discovered
that, on the average, for every $5 reduction in
price, 100 more students will buy yearbooks. The
yearbook company has also raised the minimum
order for any school to $27,500. What price
should the school charge this year so that more
students will buy the yearbook and the school can
achieve the minimum sales amount?

a)   Graph this situation. Let x represent the cost of the book and let y represent the
     number of books sold.

b)   Use the points on your line to find an equation relating the number of books
     sold to cost.

c)   The total sales revenue is (cost of one book)(number of books sold). Write this
     expression in terms of x.

d)   Since the minimum school order is $27,500, take your answer to part (c) and make
     it equal to $27,500 and solve the quadratic equation.

e)   What do these answers represent? What is the cost and expected number sales
     associated with each answer?

f)   What price should the school charge and why?

g)   Extension: What price should the student body charge to have the greatest
     amount of revenue under the same conditions?

YS-105. Solve each of the following equations either by factoring or by using the Quadratic Formula, whichever method you prefer.

a) $x^2 + 8x + 5 = 0$

c) $x^2 + 7x + 5 = 0$

b) $2x^2 + 5x + 3 = 0$

d) $x^2 = 10 - 3x$

YS-106. Karen Camero drives straight south on Interstate 405 from the Santa Monica Freeway interchange going 10 miles per hour faster than Melinda Mustang, who leaves the same interchange at the same time going straight east on Interstate 10. After one hour they are 108 miles apart, measured by a straight line drawn between them.. If the highways were actually straight, how fast would each driver be going? (Hint: use a solution procedure similar to what you did the day before in problem YS-97.)

YS-107. A certain rectangle has an area of 50 square meters and its length is five more than twice its width. Find the lengths of the sides of the rectangle.

a) Draw a diagram and label the length of each side. Think about whether you want to use "x" for the length or for the width.

b) Write an equation for the area in terms of the width and length.

c) Find the lengths of each side of the rectangle.

YS-108. Write each of the expressions below in a simpler exponential form.

a) $x^2y^3 \cdot x^3y^4$

c) $(x^3)^4$

e) $\dfrac{6x^2y^3}{2xy}$

b) $-3x^2 \cdot 4x^3$

d) $(2x^2)^3$

f) $(x^3y)^2(2x)^3$

YS-109. Simplify.

a) $\dfrac{x^2 + 7x + 10}{2x^2 + 11x + 5}$

c) $\dfrac{2x + 1}{4x^2 + x - 1}$

b) $\dfrac{x^2 + 3x - 10}{x^2 - 7x + 10}$

d) $\dfrac{3x^2 + 21x + 30}{3x^2 + 3x - 6}$

## YS-110. TOOL KIT CHECK-UP

Your tool kit contains reference tools for algebra. Return to your tool kit entries. You may need to revise or add entries.

Be sure that your tool kit contains entries for all of the items listed below. Add any topics that are missing to your tool kit NOW, as well as any other items that will help you in your study of algebra.

- Definition of Base, Exponent, and Value

- Laws of Exponents

- Zero Exponents and Negative Exponents

- Extended Factoring of $ax^2 + bx + c$ when $a \neq 1$

- Standard Form of Quadratic Equations

- Using the Quadratic Formula

- Simplifying Rational Expressions

## GM-19. PYTHAGOREAN TRIPLES

### 3, 4, 5          7, 24, 25

Above are two examples of a Pythagorean Triple. Pythagorean Triples are made up of whole numbers. These two examples are special because in both cases the hypotenuse is 1 greater than the longer leg.

**Your Task:**

- How many Pythagorean Triples can you find where the hypotenuse is one more than the longer leg? How many do you think there are? Explain your answer.

- Find one where one of the legs is 37 and the hypotenuse is one more than the longer leg. Explain how you got your answer.

## GM-20.    COOKIES FOR DESSERT

a)   Three algebra students were doing their homework together. As a treat, one mom offered to bake some cookies. While waiting for them to cool, all three students fell asleep. After a while, Latisha woke up, ate her equal share of cookies and went back to sleep. A little while later, Susan woke up, ate what she  thought was her equal share and fell asleep again. Then Hieu woke up, ate what she thought was her equal share, and went back to sleep. Later, all three kids woke up and discovered 8 cookies left. How many cookies were baked originally?

b)   The next day, four students got together to study. Another mom baked cookies. Again the four students fell asleep. As before, they woke up one at a time and each ate her equal share. When they all awakened, they discovered 81 cookies remained.

How many cookies were baked originally?

**Your Task:**

- Solve both problems.

- Compare the original cookie numbers to the final numbers of cookies left. What is their relationship?

- **What would happen if there were 5 students?  As before, each student ate her equal share of what was left.  When they all awakened, how many cookies remained?  How many cookies were baked originally?**

- Explain how this problem would work for any number of students.

# Unit 11
# The Cola Machine

# Functions and Equality

# Unit 11 Objectives
### *The Cola Machine:* **FUNCTIONS AND EQUALITY**

This unit is intended to help you focus and formalize your study of equations. You will study two more types of equations, learn another way to solve linear systems, and tie work you have done with equations to the laws and properties that govern the real numbers.

You will study some formal structures of algebra, namely, relations and functions and the properties of real numbers that are the basis for the work you did this year with variables.

In this unit you will have the opportunity to:

- explore the nature of relations and functions.

- add the Elimination (addition) Method to your list of strategies to solve systems of linear equations.

- work with absolute value in the context of distance from a reference point.

- solve equations with absolute value and square roots.

- extend your work with rational expressions to include multiplying and dividing them.

- explore the properties of real numbers and identify them in the context of algebraic expressions.

Look for patterns in the investigations of the new ideas you encounter in this unit. Also look for ideas that help you see the "big picture" for all the work you have done with equations this year.

Read the following problem carefully. **Do not try to solve it now**. During this unit, you will gain more proficiency and skills to solve this problem.

---

CM-0.    The cola machine at your school offers several types of soda. Your favorite drink, *Blast!*, has two buttons dedicated to it, while the other drinks (*Slurp, Lemon Twister,* and *Diet Slurp)* each have one button.

Your task is to determine whether the machine models the mathematical idea known as a "function." You must determine whether the machine can be depended upon to deliver the same kind of soda each time a specific button is pushed.

Think about this model for a few days, especially when you are buying a soda from a vending machine. We will return to it later.

---

| | |
|---|---|
| Problem Solving | |
| Graphing | |
| Writing and Solving Equations | |
| Ratios | |
| Geometry | |
| Symbol Manipulation | |

# Unit 11
## The Cola Machine: **FUNCTIONS AND EQUALITY**

# RELATIONS

CM-1. Examine the table of input (x) and output (y) values below. Is there a relationship between the input and output values? If so, state the relationship.

| x | -3 | -2 | -1 | 0 | 1 | 2 | 3 |
|---|----|----|----|----|----|----|----|
| y | 8 | 3 | 0 | -1 | 0 | 3 | 8 |

CM-2. Use the table from problem CM-1 to graph $y = x^2 - 1$. Using the table and graph, answer the questions below:

a) Each equation that relates inputs to outputs is called a **RELATION**. This is easy to remember because the equation helps us know how all the y-values (outputs) on our graph are related to their corresponding x-values (inputs).

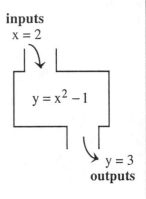

   A relation works like a machine, as shown in the diagram at right. Numbers are put into a relation (in this case, $y = x^2 - 1$), the relation performs operations on each input, and determines an output. For example, for the relation $y = x^2 - 1$, when $x = 2$ is put into the relation, the output is $y = 3$. Find the output when the input is $x = 4$.

b) The set of all possible inputs of a relation is called the **DOMAIN** of the relation. If <u>any</u> number can go into the equation for x, we called the domain "all real numbers," meaning that all real numbers can be put into our relation. Explain why the domain for the relation $y = x^2 - 1$ is the set of all real numbers.

c) Likewise, the set of all possible outputs of a relation is called the **RANGE** of the relation. Examine your table and graph and decide which outputs are possible for the relation $y = x^2 - 1$.

d) If the output of the relation is 24, what was the input? Is there more than one possible input?

CM-3.    Find the outputs for the following relations and the given inputs.  If there is no possible output for the given input, explain why not.

a)    x = -3

$y = -2x + 4$

y = ?

c)    x = 11

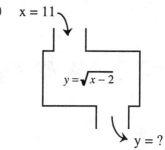

$y = \sqrt{x - 2}$

y = ?

b)    x = 5

$y = 3 - x^2$

y = ?

d)    x = 2

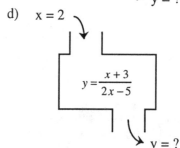

$y = \dfrac{x + 3}{2x - 5}$

y = ?

CM-4.    In problem CM-14, we will focus on solving system of equations. Review what you know now by completing parts (a) through (c) to solve the system of equations at right.

$$2x + y = 11$$
$$x - y = 4$$

a)    Change each equation into y-form.

b)    Solve the system by graphing. (Where do the lines cross?)

c)    Solve the system using substitution.

CM-5.    The incidence of rabies in skunks was recently reported to be three of every 10 skunks in a particular county. Sampling studies (just like fish sampling) revealed that there are about 22,400 skunks in the county. About how many carry rabies?

CM-6.    Start at the point (- 4, 5). Move (slide) ten units down and six units to the right.

a)    Write the coordinates of the resulting point and find the distance between the two points.

b)    What is the slope of the line containing these two points?

c)    Compare your answers to parts (a) and (b). Are the length and slope of the segment connecting the two points the same?

CM-7. Simplify by factoring and looking for fractions that are equivalent to one.

a) $\dfrac{(x+4)^2}{(x+4)(x-2)}$

c) $\dfrac{8(x+2)^2\,(x-3)^3}{4(x+2)^3\,(x-3)^5}$

b) $\dfrac{6(3x-1)^3}{3(3x-1)^2(x+4)}$

d) $\dfrac{x^2+3x}{x^2+6x+9}$

CM-8. Write each expression without negative or zero exponents. Use your tool kit to verify your answers.

a) $4^{-1}$

c) $7^0$

b) $5^{-2}$

d) $x^{-2}$

CM-9. Arturo has earned 134 points so far this quarter in algebra. To get an A, he needs to earn 90% of the total possible points. One more test, worth 45 points, is scheduled. It will bring the total number of points to 195. How many points does Arturo need to get on this test in order to get an A for the quarter? Write an equation and solve the problem.

CM-10. Factor each polynomial completely.

a) $2x^2 - 5x + 3$

b) $36x^2 - 25$

CM-11. Find the distance between each pair of points by drawing a generic right triangle. Write the distances you calculate in parts (a) and (b) in square root form, simplified square root form, and decimal form rounded to the nearest 0.01. Write the distances you calculate in parts (c) and (d) only in decimal form to the nearest 0.01.

a) (0, 0) and (4, 4)

c) (12, 18) and (-16, -19)

b) (-2, 4) and (4, 7)

d) (0, 0) and (25, 25)

## SOLVING LINEAR SYSTEMS BY ELIMINATION

CM-12. With your study team, examine the balanced scales in figures 1 and 2. Determine what could be placed on the right side of the scale in figure 3 to balance with the left side. Draw a picture on your paper to represent this balance and justify your solution in complete sentences.

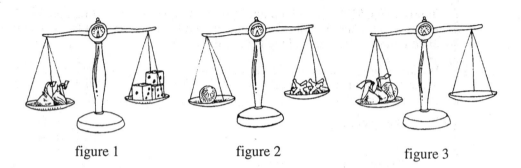

figure 1             figure 2             figure 3

CM-13. Rianna thinks that if

$$a = b$$

and if $\qquad c = d$

then $\qquad a + c = b + d$

Is she correct? Explain why or why not.

**CM-14.** We will use the same concept as in problems CM-12 and CM-13 to solve systems of equations. Read the following information and summarize it in your tool kit. Then complete parts (a) through (c) on your paper.

---

### THE ELIMINATION METHOD
### Part One

In problem CM-4, you solved one system of equations by both graphing and substitution. There is a third algebraic method that can be used to solve systems of equations. This method uses subproblems.

We know how to solve single-variable equations. When we have a pair of two-variable equations, we can often **ELIMINATE** one of the variables to obtain one single variable equation. We can do this by adding, as shown below.

Solve the system:
$$2x + y = 11$$
$$x - y = 4$$

To eliminate the y terms,
**ADD** the two equations together,

$$\begin{array}{r} 2x + y = 11 \\ \underline{x - y = 4} \\ 3x \quad = 15 \end{array}$$

then solve for x.

$$3x = 15$$
$$x = 5$$

Once we know the x-value we can substitute it into <u>either</u> of the original equations to find the corresponding value of y.

Using the first equation:
$$2x + y = 11$$
$$2(5) + y = 11$$
$$10 + y = 11$$
$$y = 1$$

We can check our solution by substituting both the x-value and y-value into the other original equation, $x - y = 4$, and $5 - 1 = 4$ checks!

a) What happens if you first substitute the x-value into the second original equation? Try it and check your answer.

b) Now write the solution to the system as an ordered pair and compare this answer to the one you got in problem CM-4.

c) Which of the three methods for solving the given system of equations (graphing, substitution, or elimination) was easiest for you? Write one or two sentences to explain your response.

---

**CM-15.** Solve the following pairs of equations by eliminating one of the variables. Check your solutions as shown in the tool kit example above.

a) $4x + 2y = 14$
   $x - 2y = 1$

b) $5x + 3y = 25$
   $7x - 3y = -1$

c) $x + 3y = 13$
   $-x + 2y = 2$

d) $5x + y = 20$
   $2x + y = 8$

CM-16. Find the outputs for the following relations using the given inputs. If there is no possible output for the given input, explain why not.

a) x = 4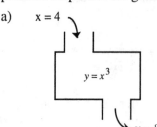

$y = x^3$

y = ?

b) x = 1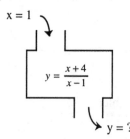

$y = \dfrac{x+4}{x-1}$

y = ?

CM-17. Examine the table of input (x) and output (y) values below. Is there a relationship between the input and output values? If so, state the relationship.

| x | -3 | -2 | -1 | 0 | 1 | 2 | 3 |
|---|----|----|----|---|---|---|---|
| y | -11 | -7 | -3 | 1 | 5 | 9 | 13 |

CM-18. The points (-23, 345) and (127, 311) are on a line. Find the coordinates of a third point.

CM-19. Factor each polynomial completely. (Hint: Look for a common factor first.)

a) $3x^2 - 6x + 3$

b) $2xy - 4y^2$

CM-20. Simplify each expression using the Laws of Exponents.

a) $(x^2)(x^2y^3)$

b) $(2x^2)(-3x^4)$

c) $\dfrac{x^3y^4}{x^2y^3}$

d) $(2x)^3$

CM-21. Joe and Jahi are cutting a deck of cards to see who will mow the lawn this week. Joe cuts the deck and shows Jahi his card, a ten. He then replaces it and reshuffles the deck. What is the probability that Jahi will cut to a higher card? (A Jack, Queen, King, and Ace beat a 10.)

CM-22. Simplify by factoring and looking for fractions that are equivalent to one.

a) $\dfrac{(x-9)(x-5)^4}{(x-5)(x-9)^2}$

b) $\dfrac{6(x-2)^3(3x-2)^4}{2(x-2)(3x-2)^5}$

CM-23. Complete the following problem on the same set of axes. Label each graph with its equation.

a) Graph $y = \frac{1}{2}x - 3$.

c) How are the equations the same? How are they different?

b) Find the equation of the line parallel to part (a) that passes through the point (4, 4).

CM-24. Use the Elimination Method to find x and y.

a) $3x + 2y = 11$
$4x - 2y = 3$

b) $3x + 2y = 11$
$4x + 2y = 3$

c) Discuss the difference between parts (a) and (b) with your teammates. What must be done to systems like the one in part (b)?

CM-25. Consider what happens when you multiply an entire equation by some number.

a) If $2x - 5y = 13$, then does $4x - 10y = 13$ or does $4x - 10y = 26$? Why or why not?

b) Jovan thinks that if $a = b$, then $a \cdot c = b \cdot c$. Is he correct? Explain why or why not.

CM-26. Samantha used Elimination in the problem below but got stuck with an equation she did not know how to solve. Examine her work below:

$$3x + 4y = 1$$
$$\underline{4x + y = 10}$$
$$7x + 5y = 11 \ ??$$

a) With your study team, describe what went wrong.

b) Compare Samantha's problem and part (a) of problem CM-24. In order to eliminate a variable, what must be true about the equations? Explain using complete sentences.

c) Use Jovan's observation (problem CM-25 (b)) to alter the second equation so that the y-values will meet the requirement you stated in part (b) above. Then use Elimination to solve for the point of intersection.

**CM-27.** Here is another example of solving a system of equations by first eliminating one of the variables. Continue your tool kit entry for The Elimination Method with the following example. Then use the Elimination Method to solve parts (a) through (c).

---

### SOLVING SYSTEMS BY ELIMINATION
### Part Two

Suppose we want to solve this system of equations:  $\quad\quad$ $3x + 2y = 11$
$$4x + 3y = 14$$

Again, one subproblem is to <u>eliminate</u> either  x  or  y  when we add the equations together.  In this case we need to do something to BOTH equations before we add them.  To eliminate  y  we can multiply the first equation by  3 and multiply the second equation by  -2  to get:

$$9x + 6y = 33$$
$$-8x - 6y = -28$$

We can eliminate the y terms by adding $\quad\quad$ $9x + 6y = 33$
the two new equations: $\quad\quad\quad\quad\quad\quad\quad\quad$ $\underline{-8x - 6y = -28}$
$$x = 5$$

Now we know  x = 5  and can substitute to find that  y = -2. Therefore, the solution to the system of equations is (5, -2).

a) Discuss the example in your study team. Could you solve the system by multiplying the first equation by  4  and the second equation by  -3?  Try this and show your subproblems.

---

Solve each of the following systems of equations. There may be more than one way to do them, so expect a variety of <u>methods</u> in your study team, but the <u>same solutions</u>, (x, y). Remember to check your solution.

b) $\quad$ $2x + 3y = -1$
$\quad\quad$ $5x - 2y = -12$

c) $\quad$ $2x + 3y = 17$
$\quad\quad$ $x + 3y = 16$

**CM-28.** SOLVING ANY SYSTEM OF EQUATIONS

In this course we have solved systems of equations with a variety of methods.  We started with graphing, moved to the Substitution Method, and have now learned the Elimination Method.  Each method works best with certain forms of equations.

For each system below, determine which method would be best (easiest) to use. Then solve the system to find the point of intersection.

a) $\quad$ $x = 4y - 7$
$\quad\quad$ $3x - 2y = 1$

c) $\quad$ $y = \frac{3}{4}x - 1$
$\quad\quad$ $y = -\frac{1}{3}x - 1$

b) $\quad$ $x + 2y = 16$
$\quad\quad$ $x - y = 2$

d) $\quad$ $x + 3y = 4$
$\quad\quad$ $3x - y = 2$

**CM-29.** Examine the graph at right for the relation $y = \sqrt{x} - 2$. Then answer the following questions.

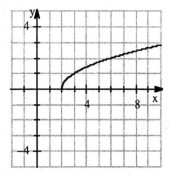

a) Find the outputs for the inputs $x = 2, 3$, and $6$.

b) What happens when the input is $x = 0$?

c) What do all the outputs of this relation have in common?

d) Find the domain and range of $y = \sqrt{x} - 2$.

e) Use the graph to find x when $y = 1$ and when $y = 2$.

**CM-30.** Find the inputs for the following relations with the given outputs. If there is no possible input for the given output, explain why not.

a)  x = ?

$y = 3x - 7$

y = -1

b)  x = ?

$y = \sqrt{2x + 6}$

y = 10

**CM-31.** Simplify by factoring and looking for fractions that are equivalent to one.

a) $\dfrac{x^2 + 2x}{x + 2}$

b) $\dfrac{x^2 + 2x + 1}{x^2 + x}$

**CM-32.** On the same set of axes, use the slope and y-intercept to sketch a graph of the following lines.

a) $y = 2x + 3$

b) $y = \dfrac{1}{2}x + 3$

c) $y = -\dfrac{1}{2}x + 3$

**CM-33.** Felice works as a sales clerk at Stacy's Department Store. She is paid $5.00 per hour plus a $7.50 meal allowance when she works evenings.

a) How much does she make for a typical eight hour day that ends at 9:00 p.m.? Write an expression to represent how much money she would be paid on this day if she worked $n$ hours.

b) Felice's hours last week included just one evening shift. If she made $190 last week, how many hours did Felice work? Write an equation and solve it.

CM-34.   Use the Laws of Exponents to rewrite the following expressions.

a)   $(2x^2)(3x^2y^3)$

d)   $x^{-2}x^4$

b)   $(-3x^4)^3$

e)   $(x-2)^2$

c)   $\dfrac{20x^3y^4}{5xy^4}$

f)   $(2x+1)^2$

## MULTIPLYING AND DIVIDING RATIONAL EXPRESSIONS

CM-35.   Without your calculator, complete each part below. Pay particular attention to explaining how you do each problem.

a)   Multiply $\dfrac{2}{3} \cdot \dfrac{9}{14}$ and reduce your result. Using complete sentences, describe your method for multiplying fractions.

b)   Divide $\dfrac{3}{5} \div \dfrac{12}{25}$ and reduce your result. Using complete sentences, describe your method for dividing fractions.

CM-36.   Use your method for multiplying and dividing fractions to simplify these expressions.

a)   $\dfrac{x+2}{x-1} \cdot \dfrac{x-1}{x-6}$

d)   $\dfrac{(x-6)^2}{(2x+1)(x-6)} \cdot \dfrac{x(2x+1)(x+7)}{(x-1)(x+7)}$

b)   $\dfrac{(4x-3)(x+2)}{(x-5)(x-3)} \cdot \dfrac{(x-1)(x-3)}{(x-1)(x+2)}$

e)   $\dfrac{(x+3)(2x-5)}{(3x-4)(x-7)} \div \dfrac{(2x-5)}{(3x-4)}$

c)   $\dfrac{3x-1}{x+4} \div \dfrac{x-5}{x+4}$

f)   $\dfrac{x-3}{x+4} \cdot \dfrac{3x-10}{x+11} \cdot \dfrac{x+4}{3x-10}$

CM-37.   Find the output for the following relation with the given input. If there is no possible output for the given input, explain why not.

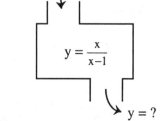

CM-38.   What input number(s) would cause the same problem for these machines as the one illustrated in the previous problem?

a)

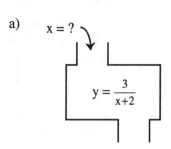

b)

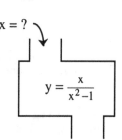

Read the following information and summarize it in your tool kit.
Then complete the problems below it on your paper.

---

### MULTIPLYING AND DIVIDING RATIONAL EXPRESSIONS

Just as we can multiply and divide fractions, we can multiply and divide rational expressions. Study the following examples and answer the summary questions below.

**Problem A:** Multiply $\dfrac{x^2+6x}{(x+6)^2} \cdot \dfrac{x^2+7x+6}{x^2-1}$ and simplify your result.

After factoring, our expression becomes: $\dfrac{x(x+6)}{(x+6)(x+6)} \cdot \dfrac{(x+6)(x+1)}{(x+1)(x-1)}$

After multiplying, reorder the factors: $\dfrac{(x+6)}{(x+6)} \cdot \dfrac{(x+6)}{(x+6)} \cdot \dfrac{x}{(x-1)} \cdot \dfrac{(x+1)}{(x+1)}$

Since $\dfrac{(x+6)}{(x+6)}=1$ and $\dfrac{(x+1)}{(x+1)}=1$, simplify: $1 \cdot 1 \cdot \dfrac{x}{x-1} \cdot 1 => \dfrac{x}{x-1}$.

**Problem B:** Divide $\dfrac{x^2-4x-5}{x^2-4x+4} \div \dfrac{x^2-2x-15}{x^2+4x-12}$ and simplify your result.

First, change to a multiplication expression: $\dfrac{x^2-4x-5}{x^2-4x+4} \cdot \dfrac{x^2+4x-12}{x^2-2x-15}$

After factoring, we get: $\dfrac{(x-5)(x+1)}{(x-2)(x-2)} \cdot \dfrac{(x+6)(x-2)}{(x-5)(x+3)}$

After multiplying, reorder the factors: $\dfrac{(x-5)}{(x-5)} \cdot \dfrac{(x-2)}{(x-2)} \cdot \dfrac{(x+1)}{(x-2)} \cdot \dfrac{(x+6)}{(x+3)}$

Since $\dfrac{(x-5)}{(x-5)}=1$ and $\dfrac{(x-2)}{(x-2)}=1$, simplify: $\dfrac{(x+1)(x+6)}{(x-2)(x+3)}$

Thus, $\dfrac{x^2-4x-5}{x^2-4x+4} \div \dfrac{x^2-2x-15}{x^2+4x-12} = \dfrac{(x+1)(x+6)}{(x-2)(x+3)}$ or $\dfrac{x^2+7x+6}{x^2+x-6}$

---

a) Verify that $\dfrac{x^2+6x}{(x+6)^2} \cdot \dfrac{x^2+7x+6}{x^2-1} = \dfrac{x}{x-1}$ by substituting two different values for x.

b) There are three values of x that cannot be used when verifying our equality. What are these restrictions? Why can x not assume these values?

CM-40. For each system below, decide to use graphing, Substitution or Elimination. Then solve the system to find the point of intersection.

a) $y = -3x + 5$
   $y = x - 11$

c) $2x + y = -2$
   $2x + 3y = 14$

b) $7x - 2y = 2$
   $y = x + 4$

d) $9x - 5y = 4$
   $3x + 2y = 5$

CM-41. Find the outputs for the following relations with the given inputs. If there is no possible output for the given input, explain why not.

a) $x = -3$

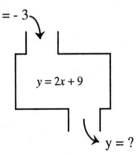

b) $x = 13$

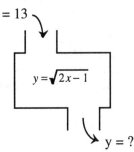

CM-42. Solve the following equations for x.

a) $2x^2 + x - 6 = 0$

c) $3x^2 - 11 = 5x$

b) $5 - 2(3x - 4) = 17$

d) $x(x - 7)(3x - 1) = 0$

CM-43. Use your knowledge of exponents to rewrite the following expressions:

a) $\dfrac{5}{x^{-1}}$

c) $\dfrac{32x^3y^7}{18x^5y^2}$

b) $\left(3x^5\right)^2\left(2x^{-2}\right)^3$

d) $\left(x^4\right)\left(x^{-1}\right)\left(x^{-3}\right)$

CM-44. Find the product: $(3x - 1)(2x^2 + 6x + 1)$

CM-45. An isosceles right triangle has two legs of equal length. If the length of each leg is increased by two, the length of the hypotenuse becomes $5\sqrt{2}$. Find the dimensions of the original triangle.

# INTRODUCTION TO FUNCTIONS

**CM-46.** THE COLA MACHINE

The cola machine at your school offers several types of
soda. Your favorite drink, *Blast!*, has two buttons
dedicated to it, while the other drinks (*Slurp, Lemon
Twister,* and *Diet Slurp*) each have one button.

a) Explain how the soda machine is a relation.

b) Describe the **domain** and **range** of this soda
machine.

c) While buying a soda, Mr. Hagen pushed the button for *Lemon Twister* and got a
can of *Lemon Twister*. Later he went back to the same machine but this time
pushing the *Lemon Twister* button got him a can of *Blast!* Is the machine
functioning consistently? Why or why not?

d) When Karen pushed the top button for *Blast!* she received a can of *Blast!* Her
friend, Miguel, decided to be different and pushed the second button for *Blast!*
He, too, received a can of *Blast!* Is the machine functioning consistently? Why or
why not?

e) When Loufti pushed a button for *Slurp*, he received a can of *Lemon Twister*!
Later, Tayeisha also pushed the *Slurp* button and received a can of *Lemon Twister*.
Still later, Tayeisha noticed that everyone else who pushed the *Slurp* button
received a *Lemon Twister*. Is the machine functioning consistently? Explain why
or why not.

f) When a relation is functioning consistently, we call that relation a **function**. What
is the main difference between a relation that is a function and a relation that is not
a function?

**CM-47.** Using your own words, write a definition of a function.

**CM-48.** Examine each of the relations below. Compare the inputs and outputs of each relation
and decide if the relation is a function. Explain why or why not. Use your definition of
a function (from problem CM-47) to help you justify your conclusion.

a)

| x | 7 | -2 | 0 | 4 | 9~ | -3 | 6 |
|---|---|----|---|---|----|----|---|
| y | 6 | -3 | 4 | 2 | 10 | -3 | 0 |

b)

| x | 1 | -5 | 3 | 8 | 1 | -4 | 5 |
|---|---|----|---|---|---|----|---|
| y | 3 | -7 | 2 | 3 | 3 | 10 | 5 |

c)

| x | 3 | -1 | 2 | 2 | 1 | 0  | 9 |
|---|---|----|---|---|---|----|---|
| y | 4 | -5 | 9 | 7 | 4 | -8 | 2 |

CM-49. Examine the graph of lines *a* and *b* at right.

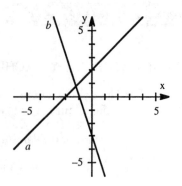

a) Find the equation for each line.

b) Are lines *a* and *b* functions? Explain how you know.

c) Are all lines functions? If not, draw an example of a line that is not a function.

CM-50. Solve each of the following systems of equations for x and y.

a) $x + 2y = 5$
$x + y = 5$

b) $2x + 3y = 5$
$x + 3y = 4$

c) $2x + y = 7$
$x + 5y = 12$

d) $3x + 2y = 11$
$2x - y = 1$

CM-51. Simplify the expressions below.

a) $\dfrac{(x+5)(2x-3)}{x+4} \cdot \dfrac{(x+1)(x+4)}{(x+5)(x-3)}$

b) $\dfrac{(3x+4)(x+5)}{(3x+15)(x+4)} \div \dfrac{(3x-4)}{(x+4)}$

CM-52. Use the given information to find the equation of the line that:

a) has slope $-\dfrac{2}{3}$ and passes through (0, -6).

b) passes through (-1, 7) and (3, 7).

CM-53. Find the x-intercepts of the parabola $y = 3x^2 - x - 11$.

CM-54. Write a shorter expression for each of the following polynomials.

a) $(3x^2 + 0.8) - (7x^2 - 5x)$

b) $(12x^2 - 3x) + (2x^2 - 4x + 3)$

c) $(7x^2 + 5) - (3x^2 + 2x - 4)$

d) $(x^2 + 3x + 4) + (3x^2 - 4x - 7)$

e) $(x^3 + 2x^2 + 4) - (5x^2 - 4)$

CM-55. Solve each quadratic equation by the method of your choice.

a) $x^2 + 3x - 5 = 0$

c) What do your answers to (a) and (b) tell you about whether the problems can be factored?

b) $4x^2 + 19x - 63 = 0$

# FUNCTION NOTATION

CM-56. Using complete sentences, explain the meaning of **relation** and **function**. Be sure to offer examples to demonstrate your understanding.

CM-57. Examine the graph of the relation at right. Then find the output(s) of the relation when:

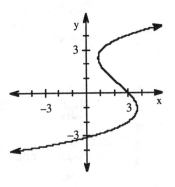

a) the input is 3.

b) the input is 1.

c) the input is - 4.

d) Is this relation a function? Why or why not?

CM-58. The graphs of several relations are shown below. Decide if each is a function. If the relation is not a function, explain why not.

a)

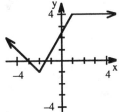

c)

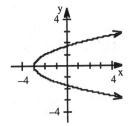

e)

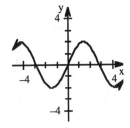

b)

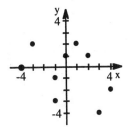

d)

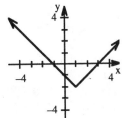

f)

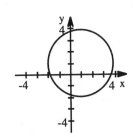

CM-59.    Review the definition of domain and range in your tool kit. The domain and range of a relation can be determined by carefully examining its graph. For example, the relation graphed in problem CM-58 part (a) above has a domain of all reals and a range of all numbers $y \geq -1$.

Find the domain and range for the relations in parts (b) through (f) in problem CM-58.

CM-60.    Carefully read the following definitions regarding relations and functions and add them to your tool kit.

---

### RELATIONS AND FUNCTIONS

#### Definitions and Vocabulary

A **RELATION** is an equation which establishes the relationship between two variables and helps determine one variable when given the other. Some examples of relations are:

$$y = x^2, \quad y = \frac{x}{x+3}, \quad y = -2x + 5$$

Since y depends on the value assigned to x, y is often referred to as the **DEPENDENT VARIABLE**, while x is called the **INDEPENDENT VARIABLE**.

The set of possible inputs of a relation is called the **DOMAIN**, while the set of all possible outputs of a relation is called the **RANGE**.

A **relation** is called a **FUNCTION** if there exists <u>no more than one</u> output for each input. If a relation has two or more outputs for a single input value, it is not a function. For example, problem CM-58 part (c) is not a function because there are two outputs for each input value greater than -3.

Functions are often given names, most commonly "f," "g" or "h". The notation **f(x)** represents the output of a function, named f, when x is the input. It is pronounced "f of x." The notation g(2), pronounced "g of 2," represents the output of function g when x = 2.

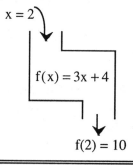

Similarly, the function y = 3x + 4 and f(x) = 3x + 4 represent the <u>same function</u>. Notice that this notation is interchangeable, that is, y = f(x). In some textbooks, 3x + 4 is called the **RULE** of the function.

---

CM-61.    If $f(x) = x^2$, then $f(4) = 4^2 = 16$. Find f(1), f(-3), and f(t).

CM-62.    If $g(x) = \sqrt{x - 7}$, find g(8), g(32) and g(80).

CM-63.    Before class, Jethro and Janice were chatting on the stairs.  Jethro was two steps from the bottom, while Janice was five steps from the bottom.

   a)    How many steps was Janice from Jethro?

   b)    How did you determine your answer to part (a)?

   c)    How many steps from Jethro was Janice?

   d)    Your answer to parts (a) and (c) represent a <u>distance</u>.  Can distance be negative?  Why or why not?

CM-64.    Solve each system for x and y:

   a)    $y = 3x - 4$
         $y = \frac{1}{2}x + 7$

   b)    $2x - 5y = 5$
         $2x + 5y = -25$

   c)    $2x + y = 6$
         $y = 12 - 3x$

   d)    $y = 0$
         $y = x^2 - 2x + 1$

CM-65.    If $f(x) = -x^2$, find $f(1)$, $f(-1)$ and $f(4)$.

CM-66.    Solve each of the following quadratic equations by factoring or by using the Quadratic Formula.

   a)    $2x^2 + 6x = 8$

   b)    $x^2 - 7x + 10 = 0$

   c)    $3x(x - 5) = 17 - x$

   d)    $(x - 1)(x - 5) + 4 = 0$

CM-67.    Simplify the expressions below.

   a)    $\dfrac{x^2+5x+6}{x+2} \div \dfrac{x+3}{4x-1}$

   b)    $\dfrac{2x^2+7x-30}{3x^2-20x-7} \cdot \dfrac{x-7}{2x-5}$

CM-68.    In Unit Four, you used a Guess and Check table to solve the following problem and write an equation in one variable. Now that you know how to solve equations with two variables, write two equations with two different variables, and solve the problem.

   A stick 152 centimeters long is cut up into six pieces: four short pieces, all the same length, and two longer pieces (both the same length). A long piece is 10 centimeters longer than a short piece. What are the lengths of the pieces? (Hint: let S represent the length of a short piece and let L represent the length of a long piece.)

CM-69.   WHAT'S THE DIFFERENCE?

Examine the following situations in which we need to find the difference between two amounts.

a)   Rocio has $298 saved in the bank, while Thomas has $314. What is the difference between their bank balances? How did you get your answer?

b)   Herneisha is 24 years old, while her brother, Jason, is 17. What is the difference of their ages? How did you get your answer?

c)   Urban High School has 1850 students while Saint Ignatius has 1490 students. What is the difference of their student populations?

d)   Explain why these differences are all positive.


CM-70.   ARE YOU POSITIVE?

Problems CM-63 and CM-69 offer examples of situations in which we want to calculate a positive difference. This difference helps us compare two quantities, regardless of which is larger. To find these differences, we subtract the smaller amount from the larger. However, what if we want to compare two amounts we do not know?

For example, what if Herneisha is $x$ years old and Jason is $y$ years old?

a)   If Herneisha is older, what is the difference of their ages?

b)   If Jason is older, what is the difference of their ages?

**CM-71.**   Read the following information and summarize it in your tool kit.

---

### ABSOLUTE VALUE DEFINITION AND NOTATION

An **ABSOLUTE VALUE**, represented by two vertical bars, "| |", determines the positive value of a number. Numerically, it represents a distance between the number and zero. Since a distance is always positive, the absolute value always returns a positive value or zero.

For example, the number -3 is a distance of 3 units from 0, as shown on the number line at right. The absolute value of -3 is 3. This is written

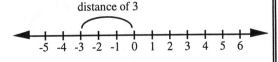

$$|-3| = 3$$

Likewise, the number 5 is a distance of 5 units from 0. The absolute value of 5 is 5, written:

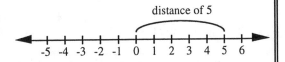

$$|5| = 5$$

In the case of Herneisha and Jason in problem CM-70, we wanted to find a positive difference between their ages. The absolute value offers us another way to write this difference:

$$|x - y|$$

In this notation, the vertical bars indicate that we want the result to be positive. It does not matter if x or y is larger. Once we subtract, the absolute value (which is always positive) will be given.

---

**CM-72.**   Find the following absolute values.

a)   $|-7|$       b)   $|4|$       c)   $|0|$       d)   $|3-8|$

**CM-73.**   Explain why there are two solutions to the equation $|x| = 10$.

CM-74. The absolute value can be used in relations as well. Find the corresponding inputs or outputs for the following relations. If there is no solution, explain why not. Be careful: in some cases, there is more than one solution.

a) $x = -3$

$y = |x|$

$y = ?$

c) $x = ?$

$y = |x|$

$y = 2$

b) $x = 9$

$y = |x|$

$y = ?$

d) $x = ?$

$y = |x|$

$y = -2$

CM-75. Complete this table to graph the function $f(x) = |x + 2| - 4$. Then answer the questions below.

| x | - 4 | - 3 | - 2 | - 1 | 0 | 1 | 2 |
|---|-----|-----|-----|-----|---|---|---|
| y |     |     |     |     |   |   |   |

a) Find f(6), f(-10), f(-5) and f($\frac{1}{2}$).

b) Determine the domain and range of f(x).

c) Find the x-value(s) at which the y-value, or f(x), is 3.

CM-76. Make a table and graph $y = |x|$ for $-5 \le x \le 5$. Use your graph to answer the following questions.

a) Describe the shape of the graph.

b) Find the **domain** and **range** of the relation.

c) Is this relation a function? Explain.

d) Find all x-values for which y = 2.

CM-77. Make a table and graph $f(x) = |x - 2|$ on the same set of axes as problem CM-76. Use your graph to answer the following questions.

a) Compare this graph with the graph from CM-76. Write down any observations.

b) On your graph, label the x- and y-intercepts.

c) Find all x-values for which $y = 1$.

d) Find $f(2)$, $f(-6)$ and $f(10)$.

CM-78. Solve each of the following equations.

a) $\frac{x}{4} = x - 1$

b) $\frac{2x}{3} = x - 4$

c) $\frac{x}{4} = \frac{x - 2}{3}$

d) $\frac{x}{2} + \frac{x}{5} = 7$

CM-79. Solve for x in the triangle:

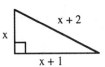

CM-80. Solve each system for x and y.

a) $5x - y = 3$
   $3x + y = 5$

b) $2x + y = 6$
   $y = 12 - 3x$

CM-81. Simplify using only positive exponents

a) $(3x^2y)(5x)^2$

b) $(x^2y^3)(x^{-2}y^{-2})$

c) $\frac{x^3}{x^{-2}}$

d) $(2x^{-1})^3$

# SOLVING ABSOLUTE VALUE EQUATIONS

CM-82. Find the following absolute values.

a) $|0.75|$
b) $|-99|$
c) $|4 - 2 \cdot 3|$
d) $|\pi|$

CM-83. Solve for x. Be sure to find all possible solutions. Check your solutions by substituting them back into the original equation. If there is no solution, explain why not.

a) $|x| = 2$

b) $|x| = 5$

c) $|x| - 3 = 8$

d) $|x| + 6 = 7$

e) $|x - 4| = 1$

f) $|x + 8| = 2$

**CM-84.**

Since absolute value is defined as the distance from zero, Sherry wondered if the solutions to the equation $|x| = 5$ are related to distance. She plotted her solutions (5 and -5) on a number line and noticed that both points were 5 units away from zero.

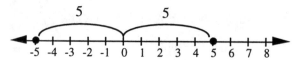

This result interested her! She decided to try the same thing with her solutions to $|x - 2| = 3$. Her solutions, -1 and 5, are plotted below.

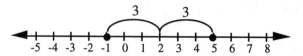

a)  Examine her number line carefully. Using complete sentences, explain how the solutions x = -1 and x = 5 are related to the equation $|x - 2| = 3$.

b)  For part (a), the central number 2 is called a **REFERENCE POINT**, since the solutions - 1 and 5 are an equal distance away from it. On a number line, locate the reference point for the equation $|x - 10| = 2$. Then use the idea of distance to find the solutions to $|x - 10| = 2$.

c)  Translate the equation $|x - 4| = 3$ into a sentence describing distance. Then find the solutions to the equation.

d)  Using complete sentences, describe how to find the solutions of any absolute value equation of the form $|x - a| = b$.

**CM-85.**  Use Sherry's method to find the solutions to $|x - 1| = 5$. Compare with your answer to problem CM-83 part (e). Did it work?

**CM-86.**  When solving $|x + 3| = 1$, Sherry noticed that there was no longer a difference in the absolute value. In order to find her reference point, she needed to first rewrite her expression as $|x - (^-3)| = 1$. Using this expression:

a)  What is the reference point for the equation $|x + 3| = 1$?

b)  Use the reference point and a number line to solve for x.

**CM-87.**  Draw a number line on your paper. Then use Sherry's method to find the solutions to the following equations. You may need to re-write the problem first. Check your solutions by substituting them into your original equation.

a)  $|x| = 3$

b)  $|x - 4| = 2$

c)  $|x - 5| + 2 = 3$

d)  $|x + 1| = 6$

CM-88. Make a table and graph $f(x) = |x + 3|$ for $-4 \le x \le 4$. Compare this graph with your graph from CM-76. Write down any observations.

CM-89. Find the corresponding inputs for the following relations. If there is no solution, explain why not. Be careful: in both cases, there is more than one solution. Find both.

a)   x = ?

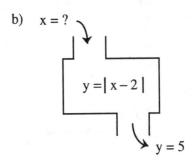

b)   x = ?

CM-90. Use the Elimination Method to solve for x and y:

a)   $x + y = 3$
     $2x - y = -9$

b)   $2x + 3y = 13$
     $x - 2y = -11$

CM-91. For the equation $|x| = 4$,

a)   what is the reference point?

b)   find the solutions for x.

CM-92. Solve each of the following equations.

a)   $x^2 - 1 = 15$

c)   $2x^2 = -x + 7$

b)   $x^2 - 2x - 8 = 0$

CM-93. For the equation: $4x + 2y = 8$:

a)   Write the coordinates of the x-intercept and the y-intercept.

b)   Draw a graph of the equation.

c)   Solve the equation for y.

d)   Is the point (23, -42) on the graph? Explain how you know.

CM-94. For the parabola $y = 2x^2 - 7x + 3$,

    a) give the coordinates of the y-intercept.

    b) give the coordinates of the two x-intercepts. Explain how you found your solution.


CM-95. Explain why $|-2| = |2|$.


CM-96. Draw a number line on your paper. Then use Sherry's method to find the solutions to the following equations. Check your solutions by substituting them into each original equation.

    a)    $|x - 9| = 2$                     b)    $|x + 5| = 4$


CM-97. Let's re-examine the equation $|x - 9| = 2$ from problem CM-96 part (a).

    a) Explain why the quantity inside the absolute value (x - 9) must equal 2 or - 2.

    b) We can use the reasoning from part (a) above to write two new equalities, as shown below.

$$|x - 9| = 2$$

$$x - 9 = 2 \quad \text{or} \quad x - 9 = -2$$

Solve each of these new equalities to find solutions for x. Check these solutions by substituting them into the original equation $|x - 9| = 2$. Do your solutions match those found in problem CM-96 part (a)?

    c) Use similar reasoning to solve the equation $|x + 5| = 4$. Check your solutions with those you found in problem CM-96 part (b).


CM-98. Explain why $|x + 5| = -4$ has no solution.

**CM-99.** Read the following information, then summarize it in your tool kit.

## SOLVING ABSOLUTE VALUE EQUATIONS ALGEBRAICALLY

To solve an equation with an absolute value algebraically, first determine the possible values of the quantity inside the absolute value.

For example, if $|2x + 3| = 7$, then the quantity $(2x + 3)$ must equal 7 or -7.

With these two values, set up new equations and solve as shown below.

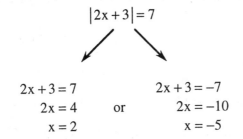

$$|2x + 3| = 7$$

$$\begin{array}{ccc} 2x + 3 = 7 & & 2x + 3 = -7 \\ 2x = 4 & \text{or} & 2x = -10 \\ x = 2 & & x = -5 \end{array}$$

Always check your solutions by substituting them into the original equation:

Test x = 2:  $|2(2) + 3| = 7$  True        Test x = - 5:  $|2(-5) + 3| = 7$  True

**CM-100.** Solve for x. Use any method. Check your solution(s) by testing them in the original equation.

a)  $|x - 3| = 5$

b)  $|x + 1| = 2$

c)  $5|x| = 35$

d)  $|x + 3| - 6 = -4$

**CM-101.** Plot the points  A(5, 2),  B(0, -1), C(3, -6) on graph paper.

a)  Find the slope of line AB.

b)  Draw a line through point C that is parallel to the line through points A and B. What is the slope of this parallel line?

c)  Draw the line through points B and C.  Line BC is **perpendicular** to the lines from parts (a) and (b) above because the lines meet at right angles.  What is the slope of line BC?

d)  Compare the slopes of the perpendicular lines AB and BC. Record your observation in your tool kit.

CM-102. Solve for x. Use any method. Check your solution(s) by testing them in the original equation.

a) $8 = |x - 4|$

c) $|x - 1.5| = 2$

b) $|x| + 7 = 8$

d) $|x + 7| + 1 = -1$

CM-103. Solve each of the following systems for x and y. Use any method you choose.

a) $y = 3x - 5$
$y = 5x - 9$

c) $y = 2x + 5$
$3x + 2y = 31$

b) $x + 2y = 1$
$3x - 2y = -5$

d) If $y = 3x - 5$ and $y = 5x - 9$ were graphed on the same set of axes, at what point would the lines intersect?

CM-104. Solve each of the following equations.

a) $\dfrac{3x}{5} = \dfrac{x - 2}{4}$

c) $\dfrac{4x - 1}{x} = 3x$

b) $\dfrac{2x}{5} - \dfrac{1}{3} = \dfrac{137}{3}$

d) $\dfrac{4x - 1}{x + 1} = x - 1$

CM-105. Find each of the values below if $g(x) = 2x^2 - 3$.

a) $g(0)$

b) $g(-1)$

c) $g(14)$

CM-106. THRIFTY PEOPLE

Janet has $290 and saves $5 a week. David has $200 and saves $8 a week. In how many weeks will they both have the same amount of money?

a) Let x represent the number of weeks Janet saves her money. Write an equation which describes how much money Janet will save, using y to represent her total savings. Label the equation "Janet's savings."

b) Use the same variables to write and label a similar equation for David.

c) Use your two equations to determine the number of weeks needed for Janet and David to save the same amount of money.

d) If you had graphed the lines, where would they intersect?

CM-107. Compute each of the following products.

a) $(\sqrt{36})^2$

d) $\left(\sqrt{x^2+4}\right)^2$

b) $(\sqrt{5})^2$

e) $(x+3)^2$

c) $\left(\sqrt{x+2}\right)^2$

f) Based on your answers to (a) through (d), what is the effect of "squaring a square root?"

CM-108. Using the patterns from the previous problem, discuss in your team how to rewrite this equation without square roots: $\sqrt{x+1} = 4$. Solve the equation and check your answer.

CM-109. Bradford was given the equation $\sqrt{x^2+6} = x+2$ and did not know what to do. His teacher suggested that eliminating the square root symbol was a subproblem.

a) Describe how you can eliminate the square root.

b) Solve for x.

CM-110. Sean was given this problem: Solve the equation $\sqrt{5x+3} + 7 = 10$.

a) Compare Sean's equation with Bradford's in the previous problem. To solve Sean's equation, what is the first subproblem?

b) What would be the next subproblem? Show how to do this.

c) Find x.

CM-111. Use the graph at right for $y = -|x-2|+3$ to explain why the equation below has no solution for x.

$$4 = -|x-2|+3$$

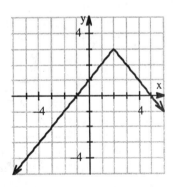

CM-112. Solve for x. Use any method. Check your solution(s) by testing them in the original equation.

a) $|2x+1| = 5$

b) $|x-1|-2 = -3$

CM-113. Solve each of the following systems of equations.

a)    $2x - y = 16$
        $x + y = 14$

c)    $x^2 - y = 9$
        $3x + y = 19$

b)    $2x - y = 16$
        $3x + 4y = 24$

CM-114. Simplify each expression using the Laws of Exponents, if possible.

a)    $(x^5)(y^2x^3)$

c)    $\dfrac{x^6y^8}{x^{11}y^{-4}}$

b)    $(-6x^2)^2(-x^5)$

d)    $x^2 - x^3$

CM-115. Make a table and graph $f(x) = |2x| - 3$ for $-4 \le x \le 4$. Compare this graph with your graph from problem CM-76. Write down any observations.

CM-116. For each part below:

a)    Solve for x:  $\sqrt{x^2 + 5} = 5$

c)    Solve for m:  $m(m - 7) = 3$

b)    Solve for (x, y):  $\frac{1}{2}x + \frac{1}{3}y = 6$
                        $-\frac{1}{2}x + y = 2$

d)    Solve for (x, y):  $x + y = 16$
        and  $2y = x - 4$

CM-117. Determine the corresponding input(s) or output(s) for the given function. If there is no possible input or output, explain why not.

a)    $x = 5$

b)    $x = ?$

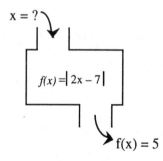

$f(x) = 3 + \sqrt{x}$      $f(x) = |2x - 7|$

$f(5) = ?$      $f(x) = 5$

CM-118. Find the slope of the line $4x + 2y = 9$. Then find the slope of a line perpendicular to it. (Hint: you may want to review problem CM-101.)

**CM-119.  ALGEBRAIC PROPERTIES**

Throughout this course we have focused on the meaning of equality and have studied how to solve equations.  During this process, several important algebraic properties have naturally emerged.  Although most have not been formally introduced and labeled, they should all be familiar from your experiences once we state them.

Two of these properties, the Distributive and the Substitution Properties, were stated explicitly in Unit Two.  These properties are summarized below.   Notice that along with a generalization of the property, a description and several examples are given.

Your task today is to similarly describe another property in a presentation to the class. Once your team has been assigned a property, design a presentation that demonstrates the multiple uses of the property.  Be sure to include a numerical example and a generalization of the property and be prepared to answer questions about it.

During the team presentations, take careful notes about the properties presented by other study teams.  Your notes should include a numerical example for each property. Your notes from these presentations will become a tool kit entry entitled, "Algebraic Properties of Real Numbers."

---

### THE DISTRIBUTIVE PROPERTY

**Generalization:**    $a(b + c) = ab + ac$

The Distributive Property basically states that if you multiply a quantity with two or more terms, such as $(b + c)$, by a number "a," then <u>each</u> term in the quantity is multiplied by "a."

For example, simplify:

$$2(5x^2 - 4x + 11) = 2 \cdot 5x^2 - 2 \cdot 4x + 2 \cdot 11$$
$$= 10x^2 - 8x + 22$$

Even multiplying binomials can be viewed as a form of the Distributive Property:

Multiply and simplify:

$$(4x + 5)(2x - 7) = 4x(2x - 7) + 5(2x - 7)$$
$$= 8x^2 - 28x + 10x - 35$$
$$= 8x^2 - 18x - 35$$

---

# THE SUBSTITUTION PROPERTY

**Generalization:**   If  $a = b$, then either a or b can be replaced by the other.

The Substitution Property allows us to replace one expression with another that is equal to it. Substitution is used most often to rewrite an equation in a form that can be solved or simplified. For example, values can be substituted for variables as shown this example:

Evaluate $\frac{1}{2}x^2 - 7$, if $x = 8$.

   Since $x = 8$, then  $\frac{1}{2}x^2 - 7 = \frac{1}{2}(8)^2 - 7 = \frac{1}{2}(64) - 7 = 32 - 7 = 25$

Substitution also provides us with a method for solving systems of equations. For example, variable expressions can be substituted as follows:

Find the point of intersection for the system:
$$x = 3y - 2$$
$$5x + y = 22$$

Since $x = 3y - 2$,
x can be <u>replaced</u> with 3y - 2 in the second equation.
Therefore, $5x + y = 22$  becomes:

$$5(3y - 2) + y = 22$$
$$15y - 10 + y = 22$$
$$16y - 10 = 22$$
$$16y = 32$$
$$y = 2$$

Substituting $y = 2$ back into the first equation:

Therefore, the point of intersection is (4, 2).

$$x = 3y - 2$$
$$x = 3(2) - 2$$
$$x = 4$$

# ALGEBRAIC PROPERTIES OF REAL NUMBERS

## Commutative Property

The Commutative Property states that if two terms are added or multiplied, the order is reversible.

$$a + b = b + a$$
$$ab = ba$$

## Multiplicative and Additive Identity

The Multiplicative Identity Property states that any term multiplied by one (1) remains unchanged, while the Additive Identity Property states that any term added to zero (0) remains unchanged.

$$a \cdot 1 = a$$
$$a + 0 = a$$

## Substitution Property

The Substitution Property allows us to replace one expression with another that is equal to it.

If $a = b$, then $a$ can be replaced by $b$.

## Multiplicative Inverse

The Multiplicative Inverse Property states that when multiplying a term by its reciprocal, the result is always one.

$$\frac{a}{b} \cdot \frac{b}{a} = 1$$

## Symmetric Property

The Symmetric Property states that if two terms are equal, it does not matter which is stated first.

If $a = b$, then $b = a$

## Additive Inverse

The Additive Inverse Property states that when opposites are added, the result is always zero.

$$a + (-a) = 0$$

## Reflexive Property

The Reflexive Property states that a term is always equal to itself.

$$a = a$$

## Transitive Property of Equality

The Transitive Property of Equality states that if two terms (a and c) are both equal to a third term (b), then they must also be equal to each other.

If $a = b$ and $b = c$, then $a = c$

## Distributive Property

The Distributive Property states that if you multiply a quantity (b + c) by a number "a," then each term in the quantity is multiplied by "a."

$$a(b + c) = ab + ac$$

## Associative Property

The Associative Property states that if a sum or product contains terms that are grouped, then the sum or product can be grouped differently with no affect on the sum or product.

$$a + (b + c) = (a + b) + c$$
$$a \cdot (b \cdot c) = (a \cdot b) \cdot c$$

## Additive Property of Equality

The Additive Property of Equality states that equality is maintained if you add the same amount to both sides of an equation.

If $a = b$, then $a + c = b + c$

## Multiplicative Property of Equality

The Multiplicative Property of Equality states that equality is maintained if you multiply both sides of an equation by the same amount.

If $a = b$, then $a \cdot c = b \cdot c$

CM-120. Solve each of the following equations for x.

a) $x^2 - 4 = 16$

c) $\sqrt{x - 4} + 2 = 16$

b) $\sqrt{x^2 - 4} = 16$

d) $x^2 - 4x + 2 = 0$

CM-121. Solve each of the following systems of equations.

a) $3x - 2y = 4$
$4x + 2y = 10$

c) $y = x + 2$
$x + y = -4$

b) $p + q = 4$
$-p + q = 7$

d) $2x - 5y = 16$
$3x + y = 11$

CM-122. Find each of the values below if $h(x) = 2x + 3$.

a) $h(0)$

b) $h(0.5)$

c) $h(-11)$

CM-123. Determine the corresponding input(s) or output(s) for the given function. If there is no possible input or output, explain why not.

a) $x = -7$

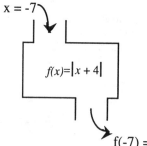

$f(x)=|x + 4|$

$f(-7) = ?$

b) $x = ?$

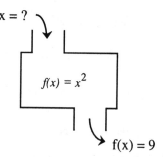

$f(x) = x^2$

$f(x) = 9$

CM-124. Find the area of a right triangle with a hypotenuse of length 13 centimeters and one leg of length 5 centimeters. What subproblem did you need to solve?

CM-125. A rectangle has one side of length 7 centimeters and a **diagonal** 10 centimeters long. Draw a diagram and find its area.

CM-126. Simplify the expressions below.

a) $\dfrac{3x^2 + 8x + 5}{x^2 - 5x - 6} \cdot \dfrac{2x - 5}{3x + 5}$

b) $\dfrac{x^2 + x - 12}{x^2 - x - 6} \div \dfrac{x - 5}{x^2 - 3x - 10}$

**CM-127.** UNIT 11 SUMMARY

With your study team, list 3 or 4 big ideas that you feel best represent Unit 11. Write a description of each main idea. For each topic, choose a problem that best demonstrates your understanding. Explain your solution as in previous unit summaries. Show all your work.

**CM-128.** Review the Algebraic Properties in your tool kit. Then identify which property is being used below.

a) $\dfrac{(x+4)^2}{(x+4)(x-2)} = \dfrac{x+4}{x-2}$

b) $16 + 2x = 2x + 16$

c) If $x + y = 16$ and $16 = m^2$, then $x + y = m^2$.

d) $4 + (-4) = 0$

e) $3 + (6 + 2x) = (3 + 6) + 2x$

f) $18x^2y^3 + 0 = 18x^2y^3$

g) $-4x(3x - 16x^2) = -12x^2 + 64x^3$

h) If $\dfrac{3}{4}x = 21$, then $x = 21 \cdot \dfrac{4}{3}$.

**CM-129.** Solve for x using any method. Check your solution(s) by testing them in the original equation.

a) $|2 - x| = 4$

b) $|x - 2| = 4$

c) Explain why the equations in parts (a) and (b) above had to have the same solution.

**CM-130.** Find the equation of the line perpendicular to $y = \dfrac{4}{3}x + 7$ and which passes through the point (-4, 5).

**CM-131.** Simplify the expressions below.

a) $\dfrac{2x^2 - x - 15}{x + 4} \cdot \dfrac{x^2 + 4x}{2x + 5}$

b) $\dfrac{2x-3}{x^2+2x-35} \div \dfrac{x-6}{x^2-11x+30}$

CM-132. Solve for x. Use any method. Check your solution(s) by testing them in the original equation.

a) $|x - 2| = 3$

b) $|x - 2| + 3 = 6$

c) Explain why the equations in parts (a) and (b) above had to have the same solution.

CM-133. Solve each of the following equations.

a) $\frac{x}{3} = x + 4$

b) $\frac{x + 6}{3} = x$

c) $\sqrt{3x - 1} = 18$

d) $\frac{2x + 3}{6} + \frac{1}{2} = \frac{x}{2}$

CM-134. Find the area of each triangle described below:

a) The triangle enclosed by the line $y = 2x + 6$, the x-axis and the y-axis.

b) The triangle enclosed by the line $y = 7x - 56$, the x-axis and the y-axis.

CM-135. Solve each system for x and y:

a) $3x + 3y = 15$
$x - y = 6$

b) $x = 6 - 2y$
$3 - 2x = -5y$

c) $y = 2x + 4$
$y = 4x - 3$

d) Extension: $2x^2 - y = 5$
$x + 2y = -5$

CM-136. TOOL KIT CHECK-UP

Your tool kit contains reference tools for algebra. Return to your tool kit entries. You may need to revise or add entries.

Be sure that your tool kit contains entries for all of the items listed below. Add any topics that are missing to your tool kit NOW, as well as any other items that will help you in your study of algebra.

- Algebraic Properties
- The Elimination Method, Parts One and Two
- Solving Equations with Absolute Value Algebraically

- Relations and Functions
- Definition of Absolute Value
- Using a Reference Point to Solve Equations with Absolute Value

GM-21.  HOW IS THAT POSSIBLE?

Ms. Speedi needs your help! She wrote a test question (without making a key) and does not know the answer. To her surprise, her class arrived at two different solutions and Ms. Speedi does not know which answer is correct. The question was:

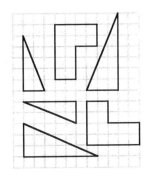

"Using scissors, cut out the shapes at right, form a large triangle, and find the total area of all the pieces. Be sure to sketch your large triangle and justify your solution."

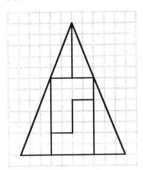

Figure 1

Half of the class put the pieces together as shown in figure 1 at left.

By using the triangle formula, the total area of the pieces in Figure 1 is 60 un$^2$.

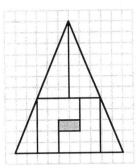

Figure 2

However, the other half of her class put the pieces together as shown in Figure 2. This triangle had the same overall area, but there was a gap of 2 square units inside!

Subtracting the missing area, the total area of the pieces in Figure 2 is 58 un$^2$.

Ms. Speedi is not sure which answer is correct and needs to know so she can grade these tests. She's provided you with a Resource Page so you can cut out the pieces for yourself and test these two solutions.

**<< problem continues on next page >>**

**Your Task:**

- Cut out the pieces on the Resource Page and arrange them as shown in both figures.

- Calculate the areas of both configurations and check the solutions given above.

- Write a letter to Ms. Speedi explaining to her what happened. Give her advice on how to grade these tests.

GM-22.   STAIRCASES

Study the following staircases.

The first staircase is made of one cube (its volume is one cubic unit) and its surface is composed of six squares.

  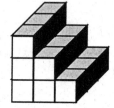

The second staircase has a volume of 6 cubic units and a surface area of 22 square units.

**Your Task:**

- Find the volume and surface area of the third staircase shown above.

- Describe what the 50th staircase will look like.  Use geometric patterns, tables, and sketches to find its volume and the surface area.

- In your explanation, describe as many **patterns** as you can and explain how you arrived at your answers and why you think they are correct.

# Unit 12
## The Grazing Goat
## Problem Solving and Inequality

# Unit 12 Objectives
## The Grazing Goat:  PROBLEM SOLVING AND INEQUALITY

Throughout the year you have learned to solve various kinds of equations. This unit will use those skills as the basis for learning how to solve inequalities. In addition, this unit will give you more practice with your problem solving strategies for problems that involve distance, rate, and time as well as rate of work, mixture, and area problems.

You will use the **subproblem** approach to "uncomplicate" many of the problems in this unit. The Grazing Goat problems (GG-0 and GG-127) are examples of a complicated situation that can be most easily approached by looking for subproblems (smaller, more manageable problems).

In this unit you will have the opportunity to:

- review and extend the various problem solving strategies that have been introduced during the year.

- extend your study of solving equations to solving inequalities.

- extend your study of linear systems to linear inequalities.

- solve more challenging problems that involve area and subproblems.

- add and subtract rational expressions.

You will review solving equations and systems of equations while extending them to inequalities. Your work with rational expressions will help you practice factoring. The entire unit will challenge you to apply the problem solving strategies you have learned this year.

Read the following problem carefully. **Do not try to solve it now**. During this unit, you will gain more proficiency and skills to solve this problem.

---

GG-0.    THE GRAZING GOAT

A barn  15  meters by  25  meters stands in the middle of a large grassy field. Zoe the goat, who is always hungry, is tied by a rope to one corner of the barn. Over what area of the field can Zoe graze if the rope is  x  meters long?

---

# Unit 12
## *The Grazing Goat:* PROBLEM SOLVING AND INEQUALITY

## PROBLEM SOLVING WITH DISTANCE, RATE AND TIME

GG-1. Carol and Jan leave from the same place and travel on the same road. Carol walks at a rate of two miles per hour. Carol left five hours earlier than Jan, but Jan bikes at a rate of six miles per hour. When will Jan catch up? To solve this problem, answer the questions below:

a) We know that they left from the same place, are traveling in the same direction, and that Jan catches up with Carol, so draw a diagram like the one at right on your paper.

b) Carol has a head start. How many miles has Carol traveled before Jan leaves? Place that distance in the proper place on the diagram.

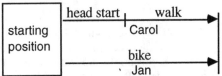

c) Let x represent the time Carol travels <u>after</u> her head start. On your diagram, write an expression using x to represent the distance Carol travels <u>after</u> her head start. Then write an expression that represents Carol's <u>total</u> distance. On your paper, write "Carol's total distance = _____ " so that you know what the expression represents.

d) On your diagram, write an expression using x to represent the distance Jan travels. Be sure to label your expression with "Jan's distance = _____ ."

e) Use your diagram to write an equation that says Carol and Jan travel the <u>same</u> distance, and then solve the equation.

f) How long does it take Jan to catch up with Carol?

GG-2. Matilda and Nancy are 60 miles apart, bicycling <u>toward</u> each other on the same road. Matilda rides 12 miles per hour and Nancy rides eight miles per hour. In how many hours will they meet?

GG-3. Two trucks leave a rest stop at the same time. One heads due east; the other heads due north and travels twice as fast as the first truck. The trucks lose radio contact when they are 47 miles apart. (They are obviously using an illegal power amplifier since FCC regulations limit CB's to five watts, a normal range of about five miles.) How far has each truck traveled when they lose contact?

**GG-4.** Two cars start together and travel in the <u>same</u> direction. One car goes twice as fast as the other. After five hours, they are 275 kilometers apart. How fast is each car traveling?

**GG-5.** Two cars leave a parking lot at the same time. One goes south and one goes west. One car is traveling at 55 miles per hour and the other at 45 miles per hour. How long will it take before the cars are 150 miles apart?

**GG-6.** A cheetah spots a gazelle 132 meters away. The cheetah starts towards the gazelle at a speed of 18 meters per second. At the same instant, the gazelle starts moving away at 11 meters per second. How long will it take the cheetah to get dinner?

**GG-7.** Two trucks leave the same rest stop at the same time traveling at the same speed. One heads south, and the other travels west. When the two trucks lose CB contact, they are 53 miles apart. How far has each traveled?

**GG-8.** Without a calculator, add $\frac{5}{12} + \frac{1}{12}$. Simplify your solution. Describe your method.

**GG-9.** Simplify the expressions below.

a) $\dfrac{x+3}{x^2+6x+9}$

b) $\dfrac{2x-10}{x^2-x-12} \cdot \dfrac{x-4}{x-5}$

**GG-10.** Solve each of the following systems of equations for x and y.

a) $4x + y = -4$
$2x - 3y = 19$

b) $2x - 5y = 7$
$x + 3y = 5$

**GG-11.** Solve for x. Use any method. Check your solution(s) by testing them in the original equation.

a) $|x+4| = 2$

b) $|x-5| = -5$

c) $|x-0.5| = 0.5$

d) $\frac{1}{2}|x-2| = 6$

GG-12.  Solve for r in parts (a) and (b).

   a)   $A = \pi r^2$

   b)   $C = 2\pi r$

   c)   What part of the circle is associated
        with the length 2r ?

GG-13.  Write an absolute value equation that represents the solutions shown on the number
        line below.

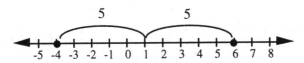

GG-14.  Review the Algebraic Properties in your tool kit. Then identify which property is being
        used below.

   a)   $x + (-x) = 0$

   b)   $5x(2y - 3x) = 10xy - 15x^2$

   c)   If $y = 4x$ and $y = 2x - 1$,
        then $4x = 2x - 1$.

   d)   $-7 + 0 = -7$

# ADDING AND SUBTRACTING RATIONAL EXPRESSIONS

GG-15.  Without your calculator, complete each part below. Pay particular attention to
        explaining how you do each problem.

   a)   Add $\frac{3}{8} + \frac{1}{8}$ and reduce your result, if possible. Using complete sentences,
        describe your method for adding fractions with a common denominator.

   b)   Subtract $\frac{1}{3} - \frac{3}{4}$ and reduce your result if possible. Using complete sentences,
        describe your method for subtracting fractions with unlike denominators.

GG-16.  Add the following fractions. Simplify your solution, if possible.

   a)   $\frac{2}{x+3} + \frac{x}{x+3}$

   b)   $\frac{x}{(x+2)(x+3)} + \frac{2}{(x+2)(x+3)}$

GG-17.    Subtract $(3x + 4) - (x - 5)$.

     a)    What did you have to do to the second polynomial?

     b)    Subtract and simplify, if possible: $\dfrac{3x + 4}{x + 3} - \dfrac{x - 5}{x + 3}$.

     c)    Subtract and simplify, if possible: $\dfrac{8x + 3}{2x + 3} - \dfrac{2x - 6}{2x + 3}$.

GG-18.    Add or subtract, then simplify if possible.

     a)    $\dfrac{x^2}{x - 5} - \dfrac{25}{x - 5}$            c)    $\dfrac{a^2}{a + 5} + \dfrac{10a + 25}{a + 5}$

     b)    $\dfrac{x^2}{x - y} - \dfrac{2xy - y^2}{x - y}$         d)    $\dfrac{x}{x + 1} - \dfrac{1}{x + 1}$

GG-19.    Add $\dfrac{3}{4} + \dfrac{1}{6}$. Reduce your answer.

     a)    What did you do to add these fractions? Describe each subproblem thoroughly.

     b)    What would be the least common multiple of $4x$ and $6x$ ?

     c)    Add $\dfrac{3}{4x} + \dfrac{11}{6x}$.

---

Recall that for a circle of radius $r$, its circumference, $C$, is $2\pi r$ and its area, $A$, is $\pi r^2$. Find the $\pi$ key on your scientific calculator and use it for computations.

---

GG-20.    A picture of an ice-cream cone is shown at right. Find the area of the picture. Assume the shape of the ice-cream creates a semi-circle. Show all subproblems.

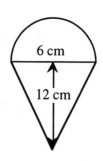

6 cm

12 cm

GG-21.    The diameter of a flattened Frisbee is 9.2 inches. Find its area and circumference. Be sure to draw pictures and identify any subproblems.

GG-22. Add or subtract and simplify, if possible.

a) $\dfrac{x}{2} + \dfrac{x-4}{2}$

b) $\dfrac{x}{x^2-2x-3} - \dfrac{3}{x^2-2x-3}$

GG-23. Solve for x. Check your solution.

a) $3x^2 = 12$

b) $\sqrt{x-5} = 7$

c) $|x-5| = 7$

d) $\sqrt{3-x} + 5 = 8$

GG-24. Find the roots (x-intercepts) of the parabola $y = \dfrac{1}{2}x^2 - 6$. Verify your solution by graphing.

GG-25. If $f(x) = \dfrac{2}{3}x + 11$, find f(-6), f(5) and f(300).

GG-26. Using complete sentences, write down what you know about adding and subtracting rational expressions. Use examples to demonstrate your knowledge.

GG-27. What is the effect of multiplying a number by one? By $\dfrac{3x}{3x}$ ? By $\dfrac{2-x}{2-x}$ ? Explain your reasoning.

GG-28. Use your results in part (a) below to help solve part (b).

a) What is the least common multiple of $(2x + 6)$ and $(x + 3)$ ?

b) Add and simplify: $\dfrac{4x}{2x+6} + \dfrac{3}{x+3}$

GG-29. Use your results in part (a) below to help solve part (b).

a) What would be the least common multiple of $x^2 - 1$ and $x + 1$ ? (Hint: first, factor $x^2 - 1$.)

b) Subtract and simplify: $\dfrac{x}{x^2-1} - \dfrac{2}{x+1}$.

The following box contains examples of adding and subtracting algebraic fractions with unlike denominators. Add this information to your tool kit.

### ADDING AND SUBTRACTING RATIONAL EXPRESSIONS

The Least Common Multiple of $(x + 3)(x + 2)$ and $(x + 2)$ is $(x + 3)(x + 2)$. **Why?**

$$\frac{4}{(x + 2)(x + 3)} + \frac{2x}{x + 2}$$

The denominator of the first fraction already is the Least Common Multiple. To get a common denominator in the <u>second</u> fraction, multiply the fraction by $\frac{x + 3}{x + 3}$, a form of one (1).

$$= \frac{4}{(x + 2)(x + 3)} + \frac{2x}{x + 2} \cdot \frac{(x + 3)}{(x + 3)}$$

Multiply the numerator and denominator of the second term:

$$= \frac{4}{(x + 2)(x + 3)} + \frac{2x(x + 3)}{(x + 2)(x + 3)}$$

Distribute the numerator.

$$= \frac{4}{(x + 2)(x + 3)} + \frac{2x^2 + 6x}{(x + 2)(x + 3)}$$

Add, factor, and simplify.

$$= \frac{2x^2 + 6x + 4}{(x + 2)(x + 3)} = \frac{2(x + 1)(x + 2)}{(x + 2)(x + 3)} = \frac{2(x + 1)}{(x + 3)}$$

GG-31. Some of the following algebraic fractions have common denominators and some do not. With your team, add or subtract the expressions and simplify them if possible.

a) $\dfrac{3}{(x - 4)(x + 1)} + \dfrac{6}{x + 1}$

d) $\dfrac{5}{2(x - 5)} - \dfrac{3x}{x - 5}$

b) $\dfrac{x}{x^2 - x - 2} - \dfrac{2}{x^2 - x - 2}$

e) $\dfrac{3x}{x^2 + 2x + 1} + \dfrac{3}{x^2 + 2x + 1}$

c) $\dfrac{y^2}{y + 4} - \dfrac{16}{y + 4}$

f) $\dfrac{x + 2}{x^2 - 9} - \dfrac{1}{x + 3}$

GG-32. Cleopatra rode an elephant to the outskirts of Rome at two kilometers per hour and then took a chariot back to camp at 10 kilometers per hour. If the total traveling time was 18 hours, how far was it from camp to the outskirts of Rome?

GG-33. Consider the following equations:

a) Solve for x. Check your solution. $2x - 5 = 3$

b) Clifford thinks $x = 4$ is a solution to $5x - 11 = 9$. Is he correct? Show why or why not.

GG-34. Fernando solved $4(3x - 12) = 16$ for x below. Justify each step of his solution with the appropriate Algebraic Property.

The problem: $4(3x - 12) = 16$

Step 1: $12x - 48 = 16$          Step 4: $\frac{1}{12} \cdot 12x = \frac{1}{12} \cdot 64$

Step 2: $12x - 48 + 48 = 16 + 48$     Step 5: $x = \frac{16}{3}$

Step 3: $12x = 64$

GG-35. Ms. Gerek recently bought a scooter for $6000. She estimates that over time the value of the scooter will depreciate (decrease) by $20 per month. Mr. Armentrout, on the other hand, bought a car for $8700. Studies show his car will depreciate at a rate of $80 per month. When will their vehicles be worth the same amount?

GG-36. Factor each of the following expressions.

a) $x^2 - 25$               d) $7x^2 - 49$

b) $x^2 + 25$               e) $100x^2 - 49y^2$

c) $4x^2 - 49$             f) $16y^2 - 1$

g) Which of the above problems are examples of the "Difference of Squares" ?

h) Compare part (b) with part (a). What was different?

i) Compare parts (c) and (d). They appear very similar, yet their answers are very different. Why?

GG-37. Find each of the following sums.

a) $\frac{1}{2} + \frac{1}{3}$       c) $\frac{x}{2} + \frac{x}{3}$       e) $\frac{1}{3} + \frac{1}{2x}$

b) $\frac{1}{2} + \frac{x}{3}$       d) $\frac{1}{2} + \frac{1}{x}$

GG-38. Solve for x. Check your solution.

a) $x - 6 = 4$            c) $(x - 6)^2 = 4$

b) $\sqrt{x - 6} = 4$          d) $|x - 6| = 4$

GG-39.    We introduced the symbols $\leq$ and $\geq$ in Unit 3. Review the definitions and then determine if the statements below are true or false.

| INEQUALITY NOTATION | |
| --- | --- |
| **Symbol** | **Translation** |
| < | less than |
| > | greater than |
| $\leq$ | less than or equal to |
| $\geq$ | greater than or equal to |

a)    $3 < 5$       c)    $2 \leq -5$       e)    $4 > 4$       g)    $-1 \leq -1$

b)    $9 > -3$      d)    $-2 \geq -6$      f)    $|-4| < |6|$      h)    $7 \geq |-10|$

GG-40.    Clifford is at it again! He thinks $x = 3$ is a solution to $2x + 1 > 5$.

a)    Is he correct? Show why or why not.

b)    Are there any other solutions? If so, name at least three. If not, explain why not.

GG-41.    This time, Clifford thinks $x = 7$ is a solution to $3(x - 2) \leq 4$. Is he correct? Show why or why not.

GG-42.    With your study team, find at least <u>five</u> x-values that make this inequality true:

$$2x - 5 \geq 3$$

a)    How many solutions are there?

b)    What is the smallest solution for x?

c)    What is the significance of the smallest solution from part (b)?

d)    On a number line, plot a point for each of your solutions for x.

GG-43.    Why did $2x - 5 = 3$ only have one solution, while $2x - 5 \geq 3$ had an infinite number of solutions? Discuss this with your study team and record all ideas on your paper.

**GG-44.** Find an x-value that makes $x - 4 > 2$ true.

    a)    Is $x = 6$ a solution? Why or why not?

    b)    Is $x = 7$ a solution? Is $x = 6.1$ a solution? Is $x = 6.01$ a solution? What about $x = 6.001$?

    c)    In your own words, describe which x-values are solutions to $x - 4 > 2$.

    d)    Using mathematical notation, write an expression that represents all solutions to the inequality $x - 4 > 2$.

**GG-45.** Simplify each expression:

    a)    $\dfrac{x^2}{x-2} \cdot \dfrac{x^2 - 3x + 2}{x}$
                    b)    $\dfrac{x^2 - 3x - 10}{x^2 - 8x + 15} \div \dfrac{x^2 + 8x + 12}{x^2 + 3x - 18}$

**GG-46.** Find the equation of the line:

    a)    with slope $-\dfrac{3}{5}$ passing through the point $(-6, 2)$.

    b)    perpendicular to the line in part (a) and passing through $(-6, 2)$.

**GG-47.** Add the following fractions using the same process you used in problem GG-31. Simplify your solution, if possible.

    a)    $\dfrac{2-x}{x+4} + \dfrac{3x+6}{x+4}$
                    d)    $\dfrac{3}{x-1} - \dfrac{2}{x-2}$

    b)    $\dfrac{x^2 - 4}{x-5} - \dfrac{x^2 - 4}{x-5}$
                  e)    $\dfrac{8}{x} - \dfrac{4}{x+2}$

    c)    $\dfrac{3}{(x+2)(x+3)} + \dfrac{x}{(x+2)(x+3)}$

**GG-48.** Solve each of the following quadratic equations. Although the Quadratic Formula will always work, factoring is sometimes faster.

    a)    $x^2 - 7x + 6 = 0$
                    b)    $y^2 + 6 = 7y$

**GG-49.** Solve the following systems of equations using any method.

    a)    $2x + y = 4$
                    b)    $x + y = 4$

        $3x - y = 16$
                        $2y + 3x = -39$

**GG-50.** Find the area and perimeter of this trapezoid. Show all subproblems.

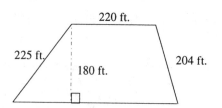

**GG-51.** Jethro and Mac were in a 24-hour bicycle race. Jethro biked at an average speed of 17 miles per hour and finished 60 miles ahead of Mac. What was Mac's average speed? If you need help getting started, draw a diagram.

**GG-52.** Farmer Fran is building a rectangular pig pen alongside her barn. She has 100 feet of fencing, and she wants the largest possible area in which the pigs can muck around. What should the dimensions of the pig pen be?

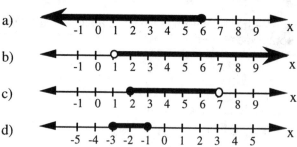

## SOLVING LINEAR INEQUALITIES

**GG-53.** Using complete sentences, explain why $x = 9$ is a solution to $x \leq 9$ but <u>not</u> a solution to $x < 9$.

**GG-54.** Write the inequality that represents the x-values highlighted on the number line below. On a number line graph, the **open endpoints** represent < or >, while **closed endpoints** represent ≤ and ≥.

a)

b)

c)

d)

**GG-55.** Read the information in the box below, add it to your tool kit, then complete parts (a) through (c).

> In the solutions of the inequality $2x - 5 \geq 3$ (problem GG-42), $x = 4$ is called the **DIVIDING POINT** because it divides the number line into two parts: the set of numbers less than four and the set of numbers greater than four.
>
> The dividing point is the solution to the **equality** $2x - 5 = 3$. Once we find the dividing point, we can test numbers on each side of our dividing point to determine the solution to our **inequality**. For $2x - 5 \geq 3$, the solution is $x \geq 4$, shown above right on the number line.
>
>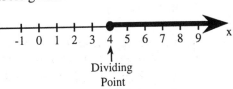
>
> a)  Find the dividing point for the inequality $2 + 3x \leq -4$ by solving the equation $2 + 3x = -4$. Plot this point on a number line.
>
> b)  Your solution to part (a) divides the set of numbers into two parts. Which part is the solution for this inequality? With your study team, test points on both side of your dividing point to help determine the solution to $2 + 3x \leq -4$.
>
> c)  In writing your solution, decide if your dividing point is part of your solution. If it is not part of your solution, $<$ and $>$ are the appropriate inequality symbols to use. Otherwise, $\leq$ and $\geq$ will indicate that you are including your dividing point. Write the solution as an algebraic inequality.

**GG-56.** Use the method from problem GG-55 to solve the following inequalities for x.

a)  $4x - 1 \geq 7$

b)  $2(x - 5) \leq 8$

c)  $3 - 2x < x + 6$

d)  $\frac{1}{2}x > 5$

**GG-57.** For the following problem, set up an inequality that shows the various numbers of cans Mr. Drucker could add to the machine, then solve it. Using an inequality allows for the possibility that he might restock the machine at less than its full capacity.

As Mr. Drucker prepared to restock the soda machine, he noticed there were already 20 cans of soda in the machine. If the soda machine can hold a maximum of 140 cans of soda, how many six-packs can he load in the machine?

**GG-58.** Carefully read the following information. Then add "Solving Inequalities" to your tool kit.

---

### SOLVING INEQUALITIES

To solve an inequality, we first treat the problem as an equality. The solution to the equality is called the **DIVIDING POINT**. For example, $x = 12$ is the Dividing Point of the inequality $3 + 2(x - 5) \leq 17$, as shown below:

Problem: $3 + 2(x - 5) \leq 17$

First change the problem to an equality and solve for x:

$$3 + 2(x - 5) = 17$$
$$3 + 2x - 10 = 17$$
$$2x - 7 = 17$$
$$2x = 24$$
$$x = 12$$

Since our original inequality <u>included</u> x = 12, we place our Dividing Point on our number line as a solid point. We then test one value on either side in the <u>original</u> inequality to determine which set of numbers makes the inequality true.

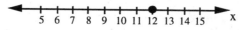

| Test: x = 8 | Test: x = 15 |
|---|---|
| $3 + 2(\mathbf{8} - 5) \leq 17$ | $3 + 2(\mathbf{15} - 5) \leq 17$ |
| $3 + 2 \cdot 3 \leq 17$ | $3 + 2 \cdot 10 \leq 17$ |
| $3 + 6 \leq 17$ | $3 + 20 \leq 17$ |
| **TRUE!** | **FALSE!** |

Therefore, the solution is $x \leq 12$.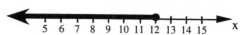

When the inequality is "<" or ">," then the Dividing Point is <u>not</u> included in the answer. On a number line, this would be indicated with an open circle at 12.

---

**GG-59.** Solve the following inequalities for x. Graph your solutions on a number line.

a) $5 < 8x - 3$

b) $9 + 4x \geq 6x + 15$

c) $\frac{x}{3} \leq \frac{6}{7}$

d) $5(x - 2) > -10$

**GG-60.** Complete each problem below. Look for similarities and differences in these two problems.

a) Add: $\frac{1}{x} + \frac{2}{3x}$

b) Solve for x: $\frac{1}{x} + \frac{2}{3x} = 10$

GG-61.    Tony managed to drive from Pittsburgh to Philadelphia at a speed of 70 miles per hour. About how long (in seconds) did it take Tony to drive one mile?

GG-62.    Add or subtract, then simplify if possible.

a)   $\dfrac{3}{8} - \dfrac{1}{8}$

c)   $\dfrac{x^2}{x-2} - \dfrac{2x+7}{x-2}$

b)   $\dfrac{2x}{5} - \dfrac{3y}{4}$

d)   $\dfrac{4}{2a} + \dfrac{-2}{6a}$

GG-63.    Solve for x. Check your solution.

a)   $|x| = 19$

c)   $|x+10| = 0$

b)   $|x-52| = 12$

d)   $|2x-1| = 7$

GG-64.    When a family with two adults and three children bought tickets for a movie, they paid a total of $27.75. The next family in line, with two children and three adults, paid $32.25 for the same movie. Find the adult and child ticket prices by writing a system of equations with two variables.

GG-65.    A grass playing field at Josie Smith Middle School is shaped as shown at right. The rounded pieces are each circular arcs of radius 35 yards. If two pounds of fertilizer are needed for every 100 square feet of grass, about how many pounds of fertilizer will be needed?

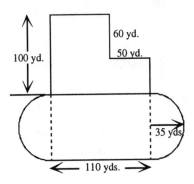

## SOLVING QUADRATIC INEQUALITIES

**GG-66.** In problem GG-55, we focused on linear inequalities. How can we use those ideas with non-linear inequalities? In this problem, we will focus on the quadratic inequality at right:   $x^2 - 3x - 18 \leq 0$

a) To find our dividing point(s), solve the equality $x^2 - 3x - 18 = 0$.

b) In the case of this parabola, we seem to have **two** dividing points! Plot these dividing points on a number line.

c) How many regions (sections or "pieces") do two different points create on the number line? Identify each region.

d) For what x-values is $x^2 - 3x - 18 \leq 0$? Test a number in each region. Be sure to consider whether the dividing points themselves are part of the solution.

e) Suppose we change the direction of the inequality symbol. Solve: $x^2 - 3x - 18 > 0$.

**GG-67.** Solve each inequality for x by finding the dividing points and testing a point in each region.

a) $(x + 2)(x - 4) < 0$

c) $x^2 - 4 \leq 0$

b) $x^2 + 5x + 4 > 0$

**GG-68.** For the following problem, set up an inequality and solve it.

Ms. Speedi's convertible can travel 32 miles per gallon of gasoline. If her gas tank already has 4 gallons of gas, how many gallons could she add in order to travel at least 280 miles?

**GG-69.** Solve the inequality for x:   $x^2 - 4x + 8 \geq 2$

**GG-70.** Examine the graph of the line at right. Write the equation of the line.

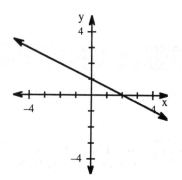

**GG-71.** Solve for x.

a) $\frac{2}{3} x \geq 16$

c) $4(6x - 1) < 40$

b) $1 - 3(x - 4) = -11$

d) $-12 < 3 + 8x$

GG-72. A piece of metal at 20°C is warmed at a steady rate of two degrees every minute. At the same time, another piece of metal at 240°C is cooled at a steady rate of three degrees every minute.

a) Write equations to describe how the temperature of each piece of metal is changing.

b) After how many minutes is the temperature of each piece of metal the same?

GG-73. Add or subtract and simplify. You may need to start by finding the common denominator.

a) $-\dfrac{1}{3} - \dfrac{1}{6}$

d) $\dfrac{x^2 - 2x + 1}{x^2 - 1} + \dfrac{x^2 + 2x - 3}{x^2 - 1}$

b) $\dfrac{x}{3} + \dfrac{-4}{5}$

e) Extension: $\dfrac{7}{x} - \dfrac{x-1}{y}$

c) $\dfrac{x+3}{4} + \dfrac{x-1}{4}$

GG-74. Solve for x. Check your solution.

a) $|x - 11| = 2$

c) $|x - 2| - 6 = -3$

b) $5|x - 2| = 15$

d) $|3x + 1| + 4 = 11$

GG-75. Review the Algebraic Properties in your tool kit. Then identify which property is being used below. Name two properties in parts (b) and (d).

a) $(8x + 5y) - 3y = 8x + (5y - 3y)$

c) If $x = 7$ and $y = 3x - 9$, then $y = 3(7) - 9$

b) $\dfrac{4}{3} \cdot (\dfrac{3}{4}x) = 24 \cdot \dfrac{4}{3}$

d) If $3x - 8 = 27$, then $3x - 8 + 8 = 27 + 8$

# SOLVING INEQUALITIES WITH ABSOLUTE VALUE

GG-76. Solve the inequality for x: $x^2 - x - 6 > 0$

GG-77. What happens when inequalities include absolute values? With your team, investigate the solutions for $|x| \le 4$. How many dividing points does this inequality have?

GG-78. Find the dividing points for the inequality $|x-3|>2$. Then, on a number line, test each region to determine the solution.

GG-79. Using Sherry's method from Unit 11, problem CM-84, $|x-3|=2$ translates as "The distance between x and three is equal to two units."

a) Similarly translate the inequality $|x-3|>2$.

b) The solution to $|x-3|>2$ is shown on the number line below. Using complete sentences, describe how the solution to this inequality relates to your translation from part (a).

c) Translate $|x-7|\geq 3$ and use a number line to quickly find its solution.

d) Write an inequality that represents the set of numbers that are less than 4 units away from 5. Then draw a number line that shows the solution to this inequality.

GG-80. Solve each inequality for x:

a) $|x|<3$

b) $x^2<9$

c) Compare parts (a) and (b) and their solutions. What do you notice? Is there any connection?

GG-81. Solve the following inequalities for x. Graph your solutions on a number line.

a) $3(x-6)\leq 12-2x$

b) $x^2-2x-15>0$

c) $2x^2-5x-3<0$

GG-82. Below is a mixture of rational expressions. Perform the indicated operation and simplify your solution, if possible.

a) $\dfrac{6}{x^2+8x+12}\cdot\dfrac{x+6}{3x-3}$

b) $\dfrac{4x}{5}-(x+1)$

c) $\dfrac{(x-2)(x+5)}{4(x+3)(x-2)}\div\dfrac{(x+1)(x+5)}{10(x+1)}$

d) $\dfrac{x^2-5x+10}{x^2+x-2}-\dfrac{x^2-8x+4}{x^2+x-2}$

e) $\dfrac{x+4}{2x^3}+\dfrac{5}{10x}$

GG-83. Solve each inequality for x:

a) $|x|-4>1$

b) $|x-4|>1$

c) Compare parts (a) and (b) and their solutions. What do you notice? Is there any connection?

GG-84. Review the Algebraic Properties in your tool kit. Then identify which property is being used below.

a) If $y = 4$ and $x = 2y - 1$,
then $x = 2(4) - 1$.

b) $\frac{2}{3} \cdot \frac{3}{2} = 1$

c) $3x \cdot 1 = 3x$

d) $x^3 = x^3$

GG-85. One leg of a right triangle is five inches shorter than the hypotenuse. The other leg is 15 inches long. How long is the hypotenuse?

GG-86. Solve for x: $\frac{4}{3x} + \frac{6}{x} = 9$

# GRAPHING LINEAR INEQUALITIES

GG-87. For the line $y = \frac{3}{2}x + 2$:

a) Does (-4, -4) lie on the line?

b) Does (6, 10) lie on the line? How can you tell?

c) Use graph paper and graph the line.

GG-88. With your study team, decide if the points listed below make the inequality $y > \frac{3}{2}x + 2$ true or false. If true, plot the point on your graph from the previous problem.

a) (2, 6)    b) (0, 0)    c) (4, 10)    d) (-1, 3)

GG-89. A point is called a **solution** to an inequality if it makes the inequality true.

a) Find three more solutions (in addition to those you found in problem GG-88) that make the inequality $y > \frac{3}{2}x + 2$ true.

b) How many solutions exist for $y > \frac{3}{2}x + 2$ ?

c) What do all the solutions to $y > \frac{3}{2}x + 2$ have in common?

d) How can we represent all the solutions to the equation?

The Grazing Goat: Problem Solving and Inequality

**GG-90.** Read the information in the box below, add it to your tool kit, then complete parts (a) through (d).

> To graph the linear inequality $y > \frac{3}{2}x + 2$, we must first graph $y = \frac{3}{2}x + 2$, referred to as the **DIVIDING LINE**. This dividing line is similar to a dividing point since it divides the graphing region into two parts.

The dividing line represents the points which satisfy the **equality** $y = \frac{3}{2}x + 2$. Once we graph the dividing line, we can test points on each side to determine the solution to our **inequality**. For $y > \frac{3}{2}x + 2$, the solution turned out to be all the points that lie above the line, as shown shaded at right.

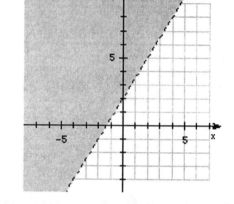

a) Why was the dividing line graphed at right dashed and not solid?

b) Find the dividing line for the inequality $y \le -2x - 3$ by graphing the line $y = -2x - 3$.

c) Your line from part (b) divides the graph into two parts. However, which part is the solution for $y \le -2x - 3$? With your study team, test points on both sides of the dividing line to help determine the solution to $y \le -2x - 3$.

d) Decide if your dividing line is part of your solution. If it is not part of your solution, your dividing line should be represented with a dashed line. Otherwise, your dividing line should be solid.

**GG-91.** On a new set of axes, graph and shade the region represented by the inequality at right:

$$y > \frac{3}{4}x - 5$$

**GG-92.** Solve for x. Check your solution.

a) $8 - 3x = 15$

b) $\frac{x-1}{5} = \frac{3}{x+1}$

c) $|x - 1| - 2 = 0$

d) $4 - 2(3x + 1) = 9x - 13$

**GG-93.** Solve the system of equations at right by graphing.

$$y = 2x - 3$$
$$y = -\frac{1}{3}x + 4$$

**GG-94.** Find the equation of the line parallel to $y = \frac{3}{4}x - 5$, and passing through the point (12, -2).

418

GG-95.   Solve each inequality for x:

a)   $6 - 3x > 2(3 + x)$

c)   $|x - 6| + 2 \leq 3$

b)   $x(x - 5) \geq 0$

d)   $|x - 1| < 0$

GG-96.   Simplify:

a)   $\dfrac{3x^2 + 6x + 3}{x + 2} \cdot \dfrac{x + 3}{x^2 + 4x + 3}$

b)   $\dfrac{(2x+1)(3x-7)}{(4x+11)(x-12)} \div \dfrac{(9x+7)(3x-7)}{(4x+11)(9x+7)}$

GG-97.   Find the area of the shaded region in each of the following figures.

a)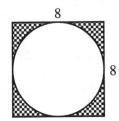

b)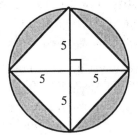

GG-98.   Cassie walked for awhile at three miles per hour and then continued her journey on a bus at 15 miles per hour. Her time on the bus was twice as long as her time walking. How long did she ride on the bus if the total distance she covered was 66 miles? If you need help getting started, draw a diagram.

## GRAPHING SYSTEMS OF LINEAR EQUATIONS

GG-99.   Match each graph below with the correct inequality.

a)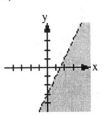

b)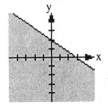

c)

d)

1)  $y > -x + 2$

2)  $y < 2x - 3$

3)  $y \geq \dfrac{1}{2}x$

4)  $y \leq -\dfrac{2}{3}x + 2$

GG-100.   What does a solution for a system of equations represent?

The Grazing Goat: Problem Solving and Inequality

**GG-101.** We have much experience with graphing systems of equations such as the one shown at right from problem GG-93. However, what would a solution to a system of inequalities look like?

Notice that we have slightly altered our equations from problem GG-93 to create the system of inequalities below.

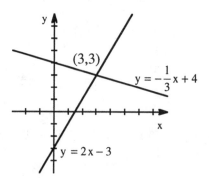

$$y \geq 2x - 3$$

$$y \leq -\frac{1}{3}x + 4$$

a) Sketch a copy of the graph (above right) on your paper. Then modify the graph (using the method in problem GG-90) to show the solution for _each_ inequality.

b) Since we have **two** dividing lines, the graph is divided into **four** regions. With your study team, test at least two points in each region of the graph. Decide which region(s) satisfy _both_ inequalities.

c) Compare your results from part (b) with the shadings in part (a). How does the shading of _each_ inequality lead to the solution for the system?

**GG-102.** On graph paper, graph and shade the solution for each of the systems of inequalities below. Describe each resulting region.

a) $y \leq \frac{2}{5}x$

$y > 5 - x$

b) $y \leq \frac{1}{4}x + 3$

$y \geq \frac{1}{4}x - 2$

**GG-103.** Write a system of inequalities represented by the graph at right.

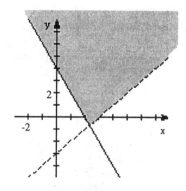

**GG-104.** Using complete sentences, describe your method for graphing systems of inequalities for a student who has missed class for the last couple of days. Be sure to include examples and important details.

**GG-105.** On graph paper, graph and shade the solution for the system of inequalities at right. Describe the resulting region.

$$y > 3x + 1$$

$$y < 3x - 4$$

GG-106.  Add the following fractions using the same process you used in problem GG-31. Simplify your solution, if possible.

a)  $\dfrac{6x}{x-3} - \dfrac{1}{x+2}$

d)  $\dfrac{3}{x} - \dfrac{x}{x+6}$

b)  $\dfrac{12x-11}{3x-1} - \dfrac{3x-8}{3x-1}$

e)  $\dfrac{x^2-3x-1}{4} + \dfrac{7x+5}{4}$

c)  $\dfrac{2x-18}{(2x-1)(x+8)} + \dfrac{2}{(2x-1)}$

GG-107.  Using complete sentences, explain why $|x| < -4$ cannot have a solution.

GG-108.  Solve the inequality for x:

a)  $11 + 4x - 3 < 6x$

c)  $|x-1| > 5$

b)  $x^2 - 6x + 8 \le 0$

d)  $|x-9| \ge -6$

GG-109.  Graph and shade the solution for the system of inequalities at right.

$y \ge \dfrac{3}{4}x - 2$

$y < -\dfrac{1}{2}x + 3$

GG-110.  Find the equation of the line perpendicular to $y = -2x$ and which passes through the point (6, 0).

GG-111.  What diameter pizza would you have to buy to get at least 100 square inches of pizza? Be sure to draw pictures and identify any subproblems.

GG-112.  A square with sides of length x centimeters has a circle of diameter x centimeters cut out of it. Find the fraction of the square that is left for the given values of x below. Hint: if you need help, review your solution to problem GG-97 (a).

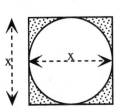

a)  $x = 2$

c)  $x = 10$

b)  $x = 20$

d)  For any x (in terms of x)

## APPLYING PROBLEM SOLVING STRATEGIES

GG-113. You have solved a great variety of problems using several different strategies presented to you, as well as using strategies you and your study team developed. Some of these strategies are listed below in no particular order. Add these problem solving strategies, as well as any others you developed, to your tool kit as necessary.

---

### PROBLEM SOLVING STRATEGIES

- Making a Guess and then Checking It (Guess And Check)
- Using Manipulatives such as Algebra Tiles
- Making Systematic Lists
- Graphing a Situation
- Drawing a Diagram
- Breaking a large problem into smaller Subproblems
- Writing and Solving an Equation

In problems GG-114 through GG-120, you will encounter a variety of problems that will require a problem solving strategy to solve. Remember to add new problem solving strategies to your tool kit as they are developed.

---

GG-114. Steven can look up 20 words in the dictionary in an hour. His teammate, Mary Lou, can look up 30 words per hour. Working together, how long will it take them to look up 100 words?

GG-115. Susan can paint her living room in 2 hours. Her friend, Jaime, estimates it would take him 3 hours to paint the same room. If they work together, how long will it take them to paint Susan's living room?

GG-116. How much coffee costing $6 a pound should be mixed with 3 pounds of coffee costing $4 per pound to create a mixture costing $4.75 per pound?

GG-117. A truck going 70 miles per hour passes a parked highway patrol car. When the truck is half a mile past the patrol car, the officer starts after it going 100 miles per hour. How long does it take the patrol car to overtake the truck?

GG-118. A rectangle is three times as long as it is wide. If the length and width are each decreased by four units, the area is decreased by 176 square units. What are the dimensions of the original rectangle?

GG-119. A square cake plate has area 150 square inches. Regina is baking a round cake. What is the maximum area the bottom of a round cake can have and still fit on the plate?

GG-120. Ms. Speedi's favorite recipe for fruit punch requires 12% apple juice. How much pure apple juice should she add to 2 gallons of punch that already contains 8% apple juice to meet her standards?

GG-121. Find the area of the remaining pizza if the figure at right was originally a 16" pizza.

GG-122. Find the equation of the line perpendicular to $y = \frac{1}{3}x - 5$ and which passes through the point (2, 1).

GG-123. On a new set of axes, graph and shade the region represented by the system at right.

$$y < -\frac{1}{3}x + 3$$
$$y \leq x + 1$$

GG-124. For the following problem, set up an inequality and solve it.

Baking dishes are three inches longer than they are wide. Susan is going to bake lasagna for six people and estimates that each person will want at least 18 square inches of lasagna. Help her decide which baking dishes she can use.

GG-125. Review the Algebraic Properties in your tool kit. Then identify which property is being used below.

a)    $3 + (5 + x) = (3 + 5) + x$

c)    $19 + 4x = 4x + 19$

b)    $8(9 - 4x) = 72 - 32x$

GG-126.  Solve for x and y.

a)   $x = 3y + 1$

   $5y - x = 3$

b)   $x + 3y = 4$

   $4x - 6y = 1$

GG-127.  THE GRAZING GOAT

Zoe the goat is tied by a rope to one corner of a 15 meter by 25 meter barn in the middle of a large, grassy field. Over what area of the field can Zoe graze if the rope is:

a)   10 meters long?   c)   30 meters long?

b)   20 meters long?   d)   40 meters long?

e)   Zoe is happiest when she has at least 400 m$^2$ to graze. What possible lengths of rope could be used?

GG-128.  UNIT 12 SUMMARY

With your study team, list 3 or 4 big ideas that you feel best represent Unit 12. Write a description of each main idea. For each topic, choose a problem that best demonstrates your understanding. Explain your solution as in previous unit summaries. Show all your work.

GG-129.  Using complete sentences, describe the different problem solving techniques you used during this unit.
It may help to look back through the unit, review your homework, or reflect on classwork.

GG-130.  On graph paper, graph and shade the solution for the system of inequalities at right.

$y \le 2x + 5$
$y > 3$

GG-131.  Solve the following inequalities for x. Graph your solutions on a number line.

a)   $3x - 5 \le 7 + 2x$

c)   $|x| - 3 < 7$

b)   $5(2 - x) + 6 > 16$

d)   $|x + 2| > 3$

GG-132. Add the following fractions using the same process you used in problem GG-31. Simplify your solution, if possible.

a) $\dfrac{5}{x-8} + \dfrac{3+x}{x-8}$

d) $\dfrac{x}{x+6} + \dfrac{6}{x-2}$

b) $\dfrac{x+2}{3x+6} - \dfrac{5}{3}$

e) $\dfrac{4}{2x-1} + 5$

c) $\dfrac{2(x-1)}{x^2+3x-10} + \dfrac{2(2x-5)}{x^2+3x-10}$

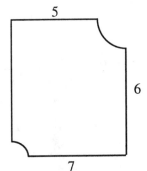

GG-133. In the figure at right, the curves are quarter circles cut out of a rectangle. The radius of the smaller circle in the lower left corner is one unit.

a) Find the dimensions of the original rectangle.

b) Find the area of the figure.

c) Find the perimeter of the figure.

GG-134. If two 10-inch pizzas cost the same as one 15-inch pizza, which choice gets you more pizza for your money? What if the crust is your favorite part of a pizza? Would you still make the same choice? Explain your answers.

GG-135. TOOL KIT CHECK-UP

Your tool kit contains reference tools for algebra. Return to your tool kit entries. You may need to revise or add entries.

Be sure that your tool kit contains entries for all of the items listed below. Add any topics that are missing to your tool kit NOW, as well as any other items that will help you in your study of algebra.

- Problem Solving Strategies

- Adding and Subtracting Rational Expressions

- Solving and Graphing Inequalities

- Graphing Systems of Linear Inequalities

## GM-23. BASIL'S BACKYARD (or THE CITY PERMIT)

Jerome has a problem. His pet schnauzer, Basil, has recently behaved very badly and your mail delivery will stop unless you can prevent Basil from reaching the mailbox. To make matters worse, a local city ordinance requires that you obtain a permit to leave a dog leashed during the day. In order to receive the permit, Jerome must fulfill the following requirements:

- The dog must have water.
- The dog must have access to shade.
- The dog must have at least 1,600 square feet to roam.

Jerome can attach the leash anywhere along the outside of his house as long as the requirements listed above are met. Basil's water dish is located below the water faucet, located two feet from the right front corner of Jerome's house, as shown in the diagram at right. The porch off the left side of Jerome's house provides shade. Jerome's mailbox is on the front of his house, 5 feet from the right-hand corner.

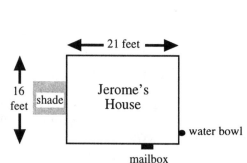

### Your Task:

- Decide where Jerome can attach Basil's leash, and how long the leash should be to meet the city's requirements, as well as please the mail deliverer. Since Jerome likes to spoil Basil, try to maximize the space Basil has to roam.

- Obtain a city permit from your teacher and fill it out for Jerome.

THE COOKIE CUTTER

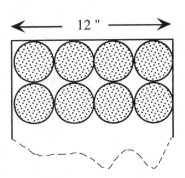

A cookie baker has an automatic mixer that turns out a sheet of dough 12 inches wide and $\frac{3}{8}$ inch thick. His cookie cutter cuts 3-inch diameter circular cookies as shown at right. The supervisor complained that too large a fraction of the dough had to be re-rolled each time and ordered the baker to use a 4-inch diameter cookie cutter.

**Your Task:**

• Analyze the percentage of dough that needs to be re-rolled for different sizes of cookies.

• Write a note to the supervisor explaining your results. Justify your conclusion.

# The Rocket Show

# More About Quadratic Equations

# Unit 13 Objectives
## *The Rocket Show:* **MORE ABOUT QUADRATIC EQUATIONS**

In past units, we were given linear and non-linear equations to graph and analyze. With the graph or the equation, we could answer questions about intercepts, slope and points of intersection. However, in this unit, we will start with data instead of equations. Finding the line or parabola that fits a trend will create a **model** with which to analyze the data.

We will also learn more about **parabolas**. We will study the connection between a graph and its equation, bringing together all of our skills from previous units.

In this unit you will have the opportunity to:

- work backwards from the x-intercepts of a parabola to write its equation and sketch its graph.

- use Algebra Tiles to learn the technique known as Completing the Square.

- examine the shape, location, and direction of parabolas.

- consider data points and trends for straight lines and parabolas.

- derive the Quadratic Formula using several of the skills you have learned this semester.

The course concludes with an opportunity to connect many of the concepts and skills you have learned all year, including data organization skills, graphing of data, detecting patterns and trends, all leading to writing equations that are reasonable representations of the data.

Read the problem below. **Do not try to solve it now.** Over the next few days you will learn what is needed to solve it.

---

RS-0.　THE ROCKET SHOW

It is the end of the year and the Math Club is going to have one last event. The students plan to have a rocket show. Jairo suggests that the rocket fly over the school building and land near the parking lot.

June, the Math Club president, needs your help to program the launch mechanism so that the rocket not only misses the building, but lands in a safe spot: the pond. June knows that a rocket that flies extremely high would miss the building, but she wants it as low as possible so it will be visible to the spectators. What path should the rocket follow?

---

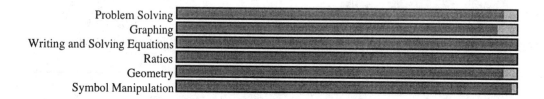

| | |
|---|---|
| Problem Solving | |
| Graphing | |
| Writing and Solving Equations | |
| Ratios | |
| Geometry | |
| Symbol Manipulation | |

# Unit 13

## The Rocket Show: MORE ABOUT QUADRATIC EQUATIONS

## TREND LINES

RS-1.    The Math Club has been fundraising for months in order
to buy the rocket. Bomani, the treasurer, expects an
excellent rocket to cost roughly $250 and wants to plan
ahead. Use the information shown below from the club's
bank statement for the first 10 weeks of school to estimate
when they will have enough money to buy the rocket.

   a)    Plot the data as ten ordered pairs $(x, y)$ with $x$
representing the week. Scale the axes carefully.

| week number | balance |
|:-----------:|:-------:|
| 0 | $ 7.50 |
| 1 | $ 53.00 |
| 2 | $ 60.22 |
| 3 | $ 85.64 |
| 4 | $ 92.88 |
| 5 | $ 99.41 |
| 6 | $ 116.67 |
| 7 | $ 122.72 |
| 8 | $ 134.60 |
| 9 | $ 150.53 |

   b)    Use a ruler to draw the line that best fits the data. Your line may not actually pass
through any of the data points. In particular, do not connect the dots with short
segments.

   c)    Write an equation for your line of best fit.

   d)    Use your equation from part (c) to predict when the Math Club will have enough
money to buy the rocket.

RS-2.    Is it always possible to fit a line to a set of data points?  Sketch a graph for which you
think it would be impossible to fit a line with any accuracy. Describe the situation that
might produce data that would create your graph.

RS-3.    On graph paper, graph the parabola $y = x^2 - 4x + 3$.  Label the x-intercepts.

RS-4.    Is (4, -6) on the graph of $y = x^2 - 3x - 10$? Explain how you know.

RS-5.    Simplify using positive exponents only.

a)    $(x^{-3})(y^0)$

c)    $2^{-4}$

b)    $(2xy^3)(-4x^2)$

d)    $(x^2)(2xy)^3$


RS-6.    Multiply or factor the following.

a)    $x^2 - 4x + 4$

d)    $x^2 - 5x + \frac{25}{4}$

b)    $3x^2 + 19x - 14$

e)    $(x + 31)^2$

c)    $(x - 9)^2$

f)    $(x - 7)(2x + 1)$


RS-7.    Solve each of the following equations. You may have more than one correct value of x.

a)    $|x - 6| = 12$

c)    $\sqrt{4x + 3} = 1$

b)    $\frac{2}{5x} + \frac{x + 1}{2x} = 1$

d)    $4x^2 + 3x = 1$


RS-8.    One of the most important skills needed to work with graphs is the ability to write an equation for a given line. Write an equation in the form $y = mx + b$ for each of the graphs shown. You may need to estimate to the nearest 0.5.

a)

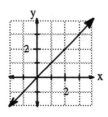

c)

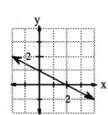

e)

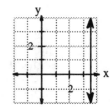

b)

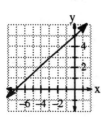

d)

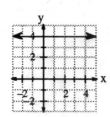

f)

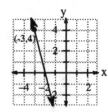


RS-9.    Solve the following inequalities for x. Graph your solutions on a number line.

a)    $3x - 5(4 - x) \geq 4$

b)    $|x - 6| < 3$

RS-10.    MATCH-A-GRAPH

One of the graphs at right is for the equation
$y = -2x(x - 6)$. Determine which graph corresponds
to $y = -2x(x - 6)$. Explain how you discovered your
solution.

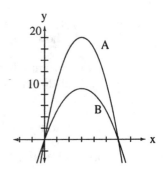

RS-11.    RETURN TO THE BEEBOPPER SHOE STORE

As she started to clear out her desk at the end of the school year, Ms. Speedi found
the data one of her classes compiled for the Beebopper Shoe Store problem from
Unit One, shown below. The shoe sizes were adjusted for the differences between
women's and men's shoe sizing.

| Student | height (inches) | shoe size |
|---------|-----------------|-----------|
| Dina | 70 | $11^1/_2$ |
| Max | 66 | 9 |
| Maxine | 68 | 9 |
| Janelle | 62 | 7 |
| Karen | 62 | 5 |
| Thu | 68 | 9 |
| Elizabeth | 60 | 4 |
| Arturo | 61 | 6 |
| Elaine | 67 | $7^1/_2$ |
| Judy | 65 | 7 |

| Student | height (inches) | shoe size |
|---------|-----------------|-----------|
| Tom | 76 | 14 |
| Bob | 69 | 12 |
| José | 65 | $8^1/_2$ |
| Alicia | 58 | 5 |
| Manuel | 70 | $10^1/_2$ |
| Henry | 75 | 14 |
| Brian | 67 | 10 |
| Leslie | 60 | $6^1/_2$ |
| Pat | 62 | 6 |
| Lim | 71 | 11 |

a)    Plot the data for Ms. Speedi's class. Use height as the  x  variable.

b)    Draw a line of best fit for the data.

c)    Write an equation for the line you drew in part (b).

d)    Ms. Speedi, who is  6'3"  tall, was absent the day the data was compiled.
      Predict her shoe size.

e)    Are you sure that Ms. Speedi's actual shoe size is what the graph indicated
      in part (d)?

The Rocket Show: More About Quadratic Equations                                                    433

RS-12.    Nine students did a science experiment by rolling a marble down a slanted board and
          timing how long it took.

          Adrián found that the marble took 10 seconds to roll 50 cm, but Mícheál's took only 8.9
          seconds to roll 40 cm. Monica's results were 14.1 seconds to roll 100 cm, while Karla's
          were 9.5 seconds to roll 45 cm. Tammy got 12.6 seconds to roll 80 cm. Allan reported 0
          seconds for 0 cm and George found the ball took 4.5 seconds to go 10 cm. Marni and
          Rebecca reported 11 seconds to roll 60 cm and 13.4 seconds to roll 90 cm, respectively.

          a)    Organize the information.

          b)    Plot the data as nine ordered pairs (x, y) with x representing time and y
                representing distance. Scale the axes carefully.

          c)    Draw a parabola of best fit for the data.

          d)    Use your graph to predict how long it will take the ball to roll 120 cm,  5 cm, and
                15 cm.

          e)    Use your graph to predict how far the ball will travel after 3 seconds, 6 seconds,
                and 15 seconds.

          f)    Write an equation for the parabola you drew in part (c).


RS-13.    Ms. Speedi's class measured some circular items to determine a relationship between
          the diameter and circumference. Their data is recorded in the table below.

| diameter (cm) | circumference (cm) |
|---------------|--------------------|
| 3             | 10                 |
| 5             | 16                 |
| 10.8          | 32.8               |
| 13            | 40                 |
| 10            | 32.3               |
| 6.8           | 21                 |
| 4.5           | 18                 |

          a)    Plot the data, fit a line, and write an equation for the line.

          b)    Compare your equation for the line of best fit to the equation which truly relates
                circumference and diameter. How close is your equation?  Other than measuring
                more accurately, what else could Ms. Speedi's class do to get a more precise
                description for the relationship from their data?

          c)    Explain the significance of the slope in this problem.

RS-14.     At 10:40 a.m., the time the math club meeting was scheduled to start, only four members of the math club had arrived! If an average of 7 students arrived every three minutes after that time, predict when all 53 members will be in attendance.

RS-15.     Solve each of the following equations. Some equations have **two** solutions.

a)     $2x + 1 = 7$                        d)     $\sqrt{x - 3} - 7 = 8$

b)     $2x^2 + 1 = 7$                      e)     $x^2 = 100$

c)     $5(x - 1) + 2[x + 3(x + 1)] = 25$

RS-16.     Solve each of the following systems for x and y.

a)     $0.7x - 0.3y = 1$                 b)     $y = x^2 - 7$
       $2x + y = 9$                              $y = 8 + 2x$

RS-17.     For the relation graphed at right:

a)     Find the domain and range.

b)     Is this relation a function? Explain why or why not.

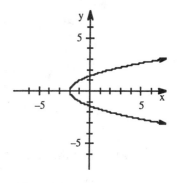

RS-18.     Solve the following inequalities for x. Graph your solutions on a number line.

a)     $5(9 - 3x) \le - 6(x + 9)$        b)     $|x + 2| + 2 > 1$

RS-19.     Identify which algebraic property allows you to change the expression on the left side of the equal sign to an equivalent expression on the right side.

a)     $8x + 1 = 1 + 8x$

b)     $32(2 - 9x) = 64 - 288x$

c)     $3 + (6 + 2x) = (3 + 6) + 2x$

# FINDING THE EQUATION OF A PARABOLA FROM ITS X-INTERCEPTS

**RS-20.** On graph paper, graph $y = x^2 - x - 12$.

a) Find the x-intercepts.

b) Solve the equation: $x^2 - x - 12 = 0$.

c) Using complete sentences, describe how you can find the x-intercepts of a parabola <u>without</u> graphing.

**RS-21.** Find an equation of a parabola with x-intercepts:

a) $(-2, 0)$ and $(1, 0)$.

b) $(6, 0)$ and the origin.

c) $(b, 0)$ and $(c, 0)$.

**RS-22.** Find a possible equation of a parabola with x-intercepts $(0, 0)$ and $(5, 0)$. Is there more than one answer?

**RS-23.** Find an equation for a parabola with x-intercepts $(-10, 0)$ and $(6, 0)$.

a) Latisha knows that the vertex of a parabola is $(6, -10)$. If one x-intercept is at $(4, 0)$, then where is the other?

b) Is there more than one solution? Explain how you know.

**RS-24.** The two solutions to $x^2 - 6x - 8 = 0$ are $3 + \sqrt{17}$ and $3 - \sqrt{17}$. Substitute each of them into the equation to show that they work.

**RS-25.** Solve the following problem. In complete sentences, describe your method, and be prepared to share with the class tomorrow.

For a food sale, the math club sold egg rolls and won tons. Ms. Speedi bought a combination plate of 2 egg rolls and 3 won tons for $1, while Latisha spent $2.30 for 4 egg rolls and 9 won tons. How much did the math club charge for an egg roll?

**RS-26.** Use algebraic methods to convert each of the following equations to slope-intercept form. State the slope.

a) $2y = 4x + 8$

b) $5x - y = 8$

c) $y - 8x = 7$

d) $x = \dfrac{2y - 1}{3}$

e) $6x + 3y - 5 = 0$

f) $\dfrac{2}{y} = \dfrac{6}{x + 3}$

g) Use the y-intercept and the slope to graph the equations in parts (a), (e) and (f) <u>without</u> making a table of values.

RS-27.  Find the equation of the line with y-intercept $(0, 6)$ through the point $(2, -1)$.

RS-28.  The slope of line AB is $\frac{5}{9}$ and the coordinates of point B are $(18, 6)$.

    a)  What is the y-intercept of line AB ?

    b)  Find the equation of the line perpendicular to line AB through the point B.

RS-29.  Factor each of the following expressions as far as possible.

    a)  $x^2 + 4xy + 4y^2$             c)  $x^3 + 4x^2 + 4x$

    b)  $6x^2 + 18x + 12$           d)  Extension:    $x^2 + 2y^2 + 3xy$

RS-30.  Solve each of the following equations for x.

    a)  $11 = |x + 1|$              c)  $x(x - 1)(x - 2) = 0$

    b)  $\frac{10}{x} + \frac{20}{x} = 5$          d)  $\sqrt{x + 4} = 10$

RS-31.  Ventura claims that if he knows the x-intercepts of a parabola, he also knows the x-coordinate of the vertex. Is he correct? If so, explain how.

RS-32.  What are the x-intercepts of $y = 3(x - 1)(x + 3)$? Plot them on axes using $-5 \leq x \leq 3$.

    a)  Find the x-coordinate of the vertex for $y = 3(x - 1)(x + 3)$.

    b)  Use the x-coordinate you discovered in part (b) to find the y-coordinate of the vertex. State the vertex as a point $(x, y)$.

    c)  Sketch the parabola using the x-intercepts and the vertex.

RS-33.  Make a large pair of coordinate axes on a sheet of graph paper by placing the origin at the center of the paper. Label your graph clearly. Graph $y = x^2$.

    a)  Each member of your study team should choose one of the equations from the list below. <u>Neatly</u> graph the parabolas on the <u>same set of axes as above</u> by making tables and assigning values to x for $-4 \leq x \leq 4$. Share the results of your graph with your team members.

         1)  $y = -x^2$     2)  $y = -\frac{1}{3}x^2$     3)  $y = \frac{1}{3}x^2$     4)  $y = 3x^2$

    b)  After verifying their accuracy, copy all the parabolas onto your graph. Label each parabola with its equation.

    c)  Write a few sentences to describe some patterns you see in the relationship between the quadratic equations and their graphs.

RS-34. Add or subtract the following fractions. Simplify your solution, if possible.

a) $\dfrac{2x}{3x-1} + \dfrac{x-1}{3x-1}$

c) $\dfrac{x+3}{5} - \dfrac{x+4}{2}$

b) $\dfrac{6}{x+3} + \dfrac{2x}{x+3}$

d) $\dfrac{2}{2x-1} + \dfrac{x+2}{3}$

RS-35. Bomani loves squares! In fact, he's trying to build one with Algebra Tiles. He has four large squares and 8 rectangles. How many small squares does he need to complete his square?

RS-36. Find the x-intercept, the y-intercept, and the slope of the line for each of the following equations.

a) $2x - 3y = 6$

c) $y - 3x = 5$

b) $y = 4$

d) $x + 44 = 0$

RS-37. Find the roots (x-intercepts) of the parabola $y = x^2 + 6x + 2$.

RS-38. How **long** is the line segment from the point $(4, 3)$ to the point $(-2, 7)$? Write your answer in simplified square root form and as a decimal. Then determine the slope of the line that connects these two points.

RS-39. Solve each of the following systems of equations.

a) $3x + 2y = 12$
$2x + 2y = 13$

b) $x + y = 1$
$2(x + y) = 5 + x$

RS-40. Use your conclusions from RS-33 to decide with your team how each graph differs from $x^2$.

a) $y = \dfrac{1}{2}x^2$

b) $y = -2x^2$

RS-41. Find an equation of a parabola with x-intercepts at $(0, 0)$ and $(6, 0)$.

a) Find the x-coordinate of the vertex.

b) Find a coefficient of your parabola so that the y-coordinate of the vertex is 3.

c) Sketch this parabola using the x-intercepts and the vertex.

RS-42.   Add this information to your tool kit:

> ## THE EQUATION OF A PARABOLA FROM ITS X-INTERCEPTS
>
> A parabola with x-intercepts (b, 0) and (c, 0) can be written in the form:
>
> $$y = a(x - b)(x - c)$$
>
> The coefficient, "a", determines the shape (wide or narrow) and direction (opens upward or downward) of the parabola. If we know the x-intercepts and one other point on the parabola, we can determine the equation.
>
> For example: suppose you have x-intercepts (2, 0) and (4, 0), and point (1, 18) on the parabola.
>
> Working backwards from the Zero Product Property, we know the equation is of the form y = a(x - 2)(x - 4).
>
> Substitute any other point on the parabola, in this case (1, 18), into the equation for x and y. Then solve for "a".
>
> $$y = a(x - 2)(x - 4)$$
> $$18 = a(1 - 2)(1 - 4)$$
> $$18 = a(-1)(-3)$$
> $$18 = 3a$$
> $$\frac{18}{3} = a$$
> $$6 = a$$
>
> Therefore, the equation of the parabola with x-intercepts (2, 0) and (4, 0) and passing through (1, 18) is:
>
> $$y = 6(x - 2)(x - 4)$$
>
> We can next find the **vertex** (the point at the top or bottom) of the parabola by using the average of (that is, halfway between) the x-intercepts. In the above example, x = 3 is midway between x = 2 and x = 4. Substitute x = 3 in the equation to find the y-coordinate of the vertex.
>
> $$y = 6(3 - 2)(3 - 4) = -6$$
>
> The vertex of the parabola is (3, -6).

RS-43.   Find the equation for the parabola with x-intercepts (3, 0) and (15, 0) that goes through (6, -162).

RS-44.   Find the vertex of the parabola $y = \frac{1}{2}(x - 2)(x + 6)$.

RS-45.   What are the x-intercepts of y = -2x(x - 5)? Plot them on axes using $-2 \le x \le 7$.

a)   Find the x-coordinate of the vertex for y = -2x(x - 5).

b)   Use the x-coordinate you discovered in part (a) to find the y-coordinate of the vertex. State the vertex as a point (x, y).

c)   Sketch the parabola using the x-intercepts and the vertex.

RS-46.   Find an equation of a parabola with x-intercepts (0, 0) and (10, 0). Find the value of "a" so that the vertex is at (5, 100). Refer to problem RS-42 if you need help.

RS-47.   If a parabola has its vertex at (1, 6) and one x-intercept at (5, 0), find its equation.

RS-48.   Suppose you are given one $x^2$ tile and 16 small square tiles.

   a)   Is it possible to use some rectangular tiles together with the square tiles you are given to get a composite rectangle which is a square? Use a diagram to show how this can be done.

   b)   Write the area of the composite square you formed in part (a) as a product and as a sum.

RS-49.   For the graph shown at right:

   a)   Estimate the x-intercept.

   b)   Find the slope of the line.

   c)   Find the equation of the line at right.

   d)   Use your equation to determine if your estimate of the x-intercept was accurate.

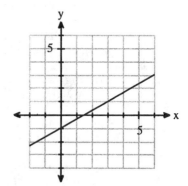

RS-50.   Find the equation of the parabola graphed at right.

RS-51.   Solve each of the following equations for x.

   a)   $4x^2 = 25$

   b)   $(x - 1)^2 + 3 = 7$

   c)   $x^2 - 2 = 14$

   d)   $2[2 - 3(5x + 4)] + 1 = 11$

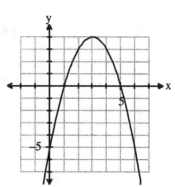

RS-52.   The math club purchased a 52" big screen TV for the math department from a catalog and it will be arriving soon. Alfredo built the cabinet, as shown at right, to store the TV. Now he is worried that it might not fit! His friend, Kate, has heard that the width of the screen is always $\sqrt{2}$ times as wide as it is tall. Will the new TV fit? (Note that the 52" refers to the diagonal of the television screen.)

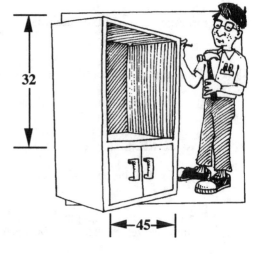

RS-53. Find the area of the shaded region. Show all subproblems.

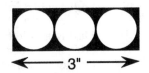

3"

# COMPLETING THE SQUARE

RS-54. Solve for x if $\sqrt{x} - 3 = 7$. How did you eliminate the square root?

RS-55. Solve for x if $x^2 = 25$. Explain why there are two solutions.

RS-56. Find all possible solutions to each of the following equations. Show your work clearly for each solution.

a) $x^2 = 9$

b) $x^2 = 7$

c) $(x - 5)^2 = 36$

d) $(x + 3)^2 = 49$

e) $x^2 + 8 = 51$

f) $(x - 4)^2 + 9 = 12$

RS-57. Suppose you are given one $x^2$ tile and twelve rectangles.

a) How many small squares will you need to make a composite rectangle which is a square?

b) Sketch the composite square you formed in part (a).

c) Write the area of the composite square as a product and as a sum.

d) Now do parts (a), (b) and (c) if you are given one $x^2$ tile and 10 rectangles.

RS-58. COMPLETING A SQUARE

The expression $x^2 + 6x$ can be represented by tiles as shown at right. To complete the diagram and make a **complete composite square**, we need to add nine unit (small) squares.

What number would you need to add to each of the following expressions to make each one represent the area of a complete composite square? Also write the dimensions of each square.

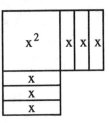

Example: $x^2 + 6x + \underline{\ 9\ } = (x + 3)^2$.

a) $x^2 + 10x +$ ____

b) $x^2 + 4x +$ ____

c) $x^2 - 2x +$ ____

d) $x^2 - 8x +$ ____

RS-59.    GOLD DIGGER'S GULCH

During a field trip to the Amusement Park,
Alfredo noticed that a portion of the roller
coaster was shaped like a parabola. Near the
base of the parabola, the track goes
underground into a gulch. A car on the track,
300 feet above the ground, sped toward the
gulch and emerged above ground 100 feet
later. How far below ground did the car
travel?

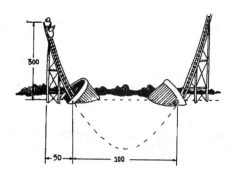

RS-60.    Factor each of the following polynomials completely. (Hint: remember to look for
the largest common factor first.)

a)    $3x^2 - 243$                    c)    $2x^2 + 9x + 10$

b)    $x^2 + 7x - 98$                 d)    $2x^2 + 9xy + 10y^2$

RS-61.    Solve each of the following systems for x and y.

a)    $2x + y = 7$                    b)    $y = 0.5x + 4$
       $3x - 2y = 7$                         $2x - 4y = 1$

c)    If you graphed the lines in part (b), where would they intersect?

RS-62.    To encourage club spirit, June decided to order
T-shirts and sweatshirts with the Math Club
logo. She called a T-shirt company and found
that she could order 40 T-shirts and 13
sweatshirts for $425.35. After surveying the
club membership, she changed her order to 30
T-shirts and 23 sweatshirts, for a total of
$477.35. What is the price of a single T-shirt?

RS-63.    Carefully graph $f(x) = |x - 3| + 1$.

a)    Evaluate f(3), f(0) and f(- 5).

b)    Use your graph to solve the equation for x:        $|x - 3| + 1 = 5$.

RS-64.   On a thermometer, $20°$ Celsius is equal to $68°$ Fahrenheit. Also, $10°$ Celsius is equal to $50°$ Fahrenheit. The conversion from Celsius to Fahrenheit degrees is linear.

a)   Use the data to plot the points. (Let the horizontal axis represent Celsius.)

b)   Draw a line through the points.

c)   Use the data to write an equation for the line.

d)   Use the equation to determine the temperature in degrees Fahrenheit for $30°$ Celsius. Check this with your graph. You have just written a conversion formula, which is simply a linear equation.

RS-65.   For the equation $2y - 4x = 6$:

a)   write the coordinates of the x- and y-intercepts.

b)   graph the intercepts and draw the line.

c)   find the slope of the line.

d)   find the distance between the x- and y-intercepts.

RS-66.   Solve these equations for x.

a)   $x^2 = 36$

b)   $(x + 2)^2 = 36$

c)   $(x + 4)^2 = 4$

d)   $x^2 + 8x + 12 = 0$

e)   Compare your answers for parts (c) and (d). They should be the same. Which part was easier to solve? Why?

RS-67.    Taking notes is always an important study tool. Take careful
notes and record sketches as your read this problem with your
study team.

---

### COMPLETING THE SQUARE

In problem RS-58, we added tiles to form a square. This changed the value of the
original polynomial. However, by using a neutral field, we can take any number
of tiles and create a square without changing the value of the original expression.
This technique is called **COMPLETING THE SQUARE**. For example, start
with the polynomial: $x^2 + 8x + 12$:

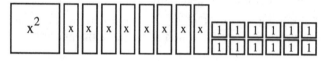

First, put these tiles together in the
usual arrangement and you can see a
"square that needs completing."

a)  How many small squares are
needed to complete this square?

b)  Draw a neutral field beside the
tiles. Does this neutral field affect
the value of our tiles?The
equation now reads:

$$x^2 + 8x + 12 + 0$$

c)  To complete the square, we are
going to need to move tiles from
the neutral field to the square.
When we take the necessary four
positive tiles that complete the
square, what is the value of the
formerly neutral field?

$$(x^2 + 8x + 12 + 4) + (-4)$$
complete square    neutral field

d)  Combining like terms,

$$x^2 + 8x + 16 + -4$$

e)  Factoring the trinomial square,

$$(x + 4)^2 - 4$$

So, $x^2 + 8x + 12 = (x + 4)^2 - 4$

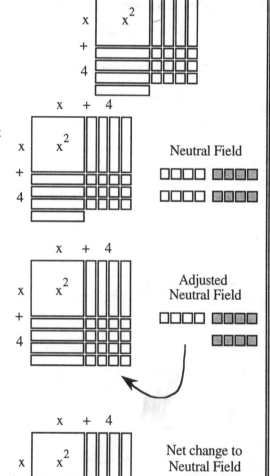

Neutral Field

Adjusted
Neutral Field

Net change to
Neutral Field

RS-68. You noted in problem RS-66 that parts (c) and (d) were the same equation in different forms. Completing the square is used to transform quadratic equations like $x^2 + 8x + 12 = 0$ into perfect squares like $(x + 4)^2 - 4 = 0$ and then into $(x + 4)^2 = 4$. Once the square is completed, we can solve by taking the square root of both sides. Complete the square and solve for x in each part below.

a)   $x^2 + 10x + 21 = 0$                c)   $x^2 + 4x + 3 = 0$

b)   $x^2 - 2x = 0$                        d)   $x^2 - 8x = -7$

RS-69. Find the equation of a parabola with x-intercepts at (5, 0) and the origin that passes through (2, -2).

RS-70. Explain how to determine what number to add and subtract to both sides of an equation of the form $x^2 + bx + c = 0$ when you complete the square. Use drawings and examples.

RS-71. Complete the square to solve for x.

a)   $x^2 + 2x - 3 = 0$                   b)   $x^2 + 8x = 5$

RS-72. Welded wire fencing is sold in rolls of 100 linear feet. A farmer intends to build a rectangular rabbit pen with an area of 481 square feet. The pen is two feet less than three times its width, and uses exactly one roll of wire.

a)   Draw a diagram of the pen and label its dimensions.

b)   Develop two equations to find the dimensions of the pen, one using area and one using perimeter.

c)   Find the dimensions of the pen.

RS-73. If the hundred-foot length of wire in the previous problem weighs 62 pounds, about how much will 240 feet of the same wire weigh?

RS-74. Solve the following inequalities for x. Graph your solutions on a number line.

a)    $- 2(x + 6) < 10$                   b)    $4 \geq -5 + |x|$

RS-75. On graph paper, graph and shade the solution for the systems of inequalities at right. Describe the resulting region.

$$y \geq 3x - 5$$
$$y < -\frac{1}{3}x + 2$$

RS-76.    Kristen has a box full of ping-pong balls numbered from 1 to 53. If she reaches in and pulls out one ball, find the probability that the ball has a number on it which is:

a)    even.

c)    a perfect square (1, 4, 9, …).

b)    less than or equal to 10.

d)    two digits.

RS-77.    THE ROCKET SHOW

It is the end of the year and the Math Club is going to have one last event. To celebrate, the club members plan to have a rocket show. Jairo suggested that the rocket fly over the school building and land near the parking lot. For safety reasons, the principal wants assurances that the students can control where it lands.

Since the rocket will be a fireball when it lands, the Math Club needs to aim the rocket so that it lands in the pond near the parking lot. Here are some facts about the school grounds. Use this data to sketch the path of the rocket on the resource page provided by your teacher.

The launcher will be placed on the football field, 60 meters from the school building. The school building is 40 meters wide and 30 meters tall. The parking lot on the other side of the school building is 15 meters wide. At the edge of the parking lot is a pond which is 10 meters wide.

June, the Math Club president, needs your help to program the launch mechanism so that it not only misses the building, but lands in a safe spot: the pond. June knows that a rocket that flies extremely high would miss the building, but she wants it as low as possible so that it will be visible to the spectators.

She has enlisted your help in programming the launcher. Find an equation that will tell the launcher where to send the rocket.

a)    On your resource page, draw the lowest path possible for the rocket that flies at least 5 meters over the building and lands in the pond.

b)    Name the intercepts of your parabola.

c)    Find a possible equation for the parabola using the x-intercepts from part (b).

d)    If a = -1, what will be the maximum height of the rocket?

e)    Does your equation of the rocket ensure that you will miss the building? Substitute an x-coordinate into your launching equation to find out if the rocket clears the building.

f)    June wants the lowest possible rocket trajectory so that it is visible to the crowd and wants at least a 5 meter clearance over the building. Double check your rocket's height on the top corner of the building nearest the parking lot. Find the x-coordinate that will help you determine whether you have proper clearance. What "a" value should your equation have to miss the building and yet be as low as possible? (Hint: figure out another point on the parabola you want to hit and use it in the equation to solve for "a".)

g)    Elmo, a reporter for the school newspaper, wants to know how high the rocket flies. Use your graph to estimate the height, then verify your estimate using your equation.

RS-78. Elizabeth fixed her tricycle and wants to race Leslie again. She now races 5 meters every 2 seconds, while Leslie rides 2 meters every second. If they start at the same place and time, and the race is 25 meters long, by how much of a margin does Elizabeth win?

RS-79. Factor the polynomial $4x^2 + 12x + 9$ by drawing a rectangle.

a) Label its dimensions and area(s).

b) The polynomial $4x^2 + 12x + 9$ is called a "perfect square" trinomial. Explain why this name is appropriate.

RS-80. During a camping trip, Cami forgot the poles to her tent! June suggested that the club search the vicinity for a tree branch that would work instead. When Cami measured the tent, she found that the base was 5 feet wide and the sides were 4.75 feet long. Determine how long the branch should be to properly hold up the tent.

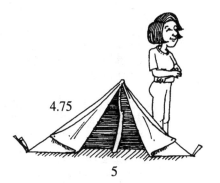

4.75

5

RS-81. The slope of line AB is 5, with points A (-3, -1) and B (2, n). Find the value of n.

RS-82. Write each of the following expressions as simply as possible.

a) $\dfrac{(x-1)(x+2)(x-3)(x+4)}{(x+2)(x+3)(x+4)(x+5)}$

b) $\dfrac{(x^2-1)(x^2-2x-3)}{(x-1)^2(x-2)(x-3)}$

RS-83. Complete the square. Solve parts (c) and (d).

a) $x^2 + 12x + 11$

c) $x^2 + 14x - 10 = 0$

b) $x^2 - 14x + 33$

d) $x^2 - 12x + 20 = 0$

RS-84. A rectangular garden has a perimeter of 100 meters and a diagonal of 40 meters. Find its dimensions.

# DERIVING THE QUADRATIC FORMULA

> We will now see how the Quadratic Formula is developed. We will approach the derivation of the Quadratic Formula as a series of subproblems. Look for <u>patterns</u> as you solve each problem and discuss the patterns you observe with your study team.

RS-85. **SUBPROBLEM 1**
Solve each of the following equations for y. Each equation has <u>two</u> solutions.

a) $y^2 = 25$

b) $y^2 = 19$

c) $y^2 = 45$

d) $y^2 = 16b^2$

e) $y^2 = 13b^2$

f) $y^2 = \frac{36}{49}$ (write solutions as fractions)

---

Stop to discuss with your study team any patterns you see developing in parts (a) through (f).
Use that pattern to solve parts (g), (h), and (i).

---

g) $y^2 = 4a^2$

h) $y^2 = \frac{b^2}{4a^2}$

i) $y^2 = \frac{b^2 - 4ac}{4a^2}$

RS-86. **SUBPROBLEM 2: COMPLETING A SQUARE**
Remember that the expression $x^2 + 6x$ can be represented by tiles.

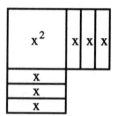

To complete the diagram and make a complete composite square, we would need to add unit (small) squares.

What number would you need to add to each of the following expressions to make each one represent the area of a composite square?

a) $x^2 + 2x +$ _____

b) $x^2 - 4x +$ _____

c) $x^2 + 7x +$ _____

d) $x^2 - 5x +$ _____

e) $x^2 + bx +$ _____

f) $x^2 + \frac{b}{a}x +$ _____

RS-87. **SUBPROBLEM 3**
What are the dimensions of each of the completed squares in RS-86? (Hint: think of a completed square, then use the factoring method you learned for rectangles.)

We know $x^2 + 6x + 9 = (x + 3)^2$, so the dimensions of the composite square are $x + 3$ by $x + 3$.

RS-88. **SUBPROBLEM 4**
Write each of the following sums as a single expression. ( Hint: common denominators are necessary in order to add fractions.)

a) $\frac{3}{4a} + \frac{5}{a}$

b) $\frac{b^2}{4a} + \frac{2}{a}$

c) $\frac{7}{4a^2} - \frac{c}{a}$

d) $\frac{b^2}{4a^2} - \frac{c}{a}$

RS-89.    DERIVATION OF THE QUADRATIC FORMULA

We are ready to derive the Quadratic Formula. To do this we will use the last part of each of the subproblems in problems RS-85 through RS-88 to solve the equation $ax^2 + bx + c = 0$  for  x. Our goal is to transform the equation into:

$$x = \frac{-b \pm \sqrt{b^2 - 4ac}}{2a}.$$

Fold a piece of lined paper in half vertically, make a crease, then unfold the paper. Copy the algebraic steps shown below onto the left-hand side of your paper. Write your answer to each question to the right of the corresponding algebraic step.

We want to solve the equation   $ax^2 + bx + c = 0$.

$$x^2 + \frac{b}{a}x + \frac{c}{a} = 0$$

What did we do to get this?

$$x^2 + \frac{b}{a}x = -\frac{c}{a}$$

What did we do to get this?

What do we do to get the next step?

$$x^2 + \frac{b}{a}x + \frac{b^2}{4a^2} = \frac{b^2}{4a^2} - \frac{c}{a}$$

Why do you think we chose $\frac{b^2}{4a^2}$ ?

Now we make a major replacement for the whole left side of the equation:

$$\left(x + \frac{b}{2a}\right)^2 = \frac{b^2}{4a^2} - \frac{c}{a}$$

Why is that possible?  What subproblem did we use?

This time we replace the right-hand side:

$$\left(x + \frac{b}{2a}\right)^2 = \frac{b^2 - 4ac}{4a^2}$$

What subproblem shows we can do this?

What operation do we need to do to get the next result?

$$x + \frac{b}{2a} = \pm\frac{\sqrt{b^2 - 4ac}}{2a}$$

On what subproblem are we relying?

$$x = -\frac{b}{2a} + \frac{\sqrt{b^2 - 4ac}}{2a}$$

What did we do to get this result?

Finally, we get to the long awaited solution:

$$x = \frac{-b \pm \sqrt{b^2 - 4ac}}{2a}$$

Which subproblem do we use to get this?

RS-90.   Find the equation of the line through the points (-6, 2) and (8, 9).


RS-91.   Solve the system of equations:

a)   $x = 7y - 3$                           b)   $3x - 5y = 4$
     $2x - 3y = 8$                                $x + 2y = 5$


RS-92.   Complete the square and solve for x.

a)   $x^2 - 6x = -5$                        b)   $x^2 - 6x + 7 = 0$


RS-93.   Solve the equation $2x^2 - 7x + 3 = 0$ by:

a)   factoring                             b)   using the Quadratic Formula

c)   How could you use your result in part (b) to write the factors of the equation?


RS-94.   Use the Quadratic Formula to find the roots of each equation. Use the roots to find the factors of each of the following polynomials.

a)   $6x^2 - 7x - 10 = 0$                   c)   $9x^2 + 11x + 2 = 0$

b)   $36x^2 - 37x - 48 = 0$


RS-95.   Simplify using positive exponents only.

a)   $(2x^3)(-3x)^2$                        c)   $\dfrac{x^3y^3}{xy}$

b)   $(-2x^2y)^3$                           d)   $\dfrac{x^3y^3}{x^{-1}y^{-1}}$


# UNIT SUMMARY AND REVIEW

RS-96.   UNIT THIRTEEN SUMMARY

With your study team, list 3 or 4 big ideas that you feel best represent Unit 13. Write a description of each main idea. For each topic, choose a problem that best demonstrates your understanding. Explain your solution as in previous unit summaries. Show all your work.

RS-97. MEMBERSHIP DRIVE

Each year, the math club has steadily grown in membership and members predict it will soon be the biggest club on campus! The science club, currently the largest, is growing as well. Some of the membership records for the last 17 years are shown below.

| Math Club | |
|---|---|
| Year | Membership |
| 1985 | 15 |
| 1987 | 27 |
| 1989 | 32 |
| 1992 | 36 |
| 1993 | 45 |
| 1995 | 45 |
| 1999 | 59 |

| Science Club | |
|---|---|
| Year | Membership |
| 1983 | 34 |
| 1986 | 35 |
| 1988 | 43 |
| 1990 | 50 |
| 1994 | 49 |
| 1997 | 61 |
| 1999 | 63 |

a) Plot the points on the same set of axes. Let x represent the year, and x = 0 for the year 1983. Use a different marking (or color) to distinguish the points for each club on your graph.

b) Find the equation of a line of best fit for each set of data.

c) Based on your graphs, estimate when the membership of the math club will surpass that of the science club.

d) Using the equations from part (b), solve the system of equations algebraically to determine when the math club will become the largest club on campus.

RS-98. Complete the square and use the resulting expression to solve for x. Then check your answer by factoring or by using the Quadratic Formula.

a) $x^2 - 4x + 3 = 0$

b) $x^2 - 10x + 14 = 0$

RS-99. Find the equation of the parabola shown in the graph at right.

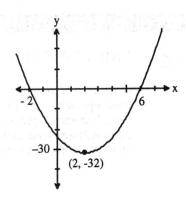

The Rocket Show: More About Quadratic Equations

451

RS-100. Below is a mixture of rational expressions. Perform the indicated operation and simplify your solution, if possible.

a) $\dfrac{x}{2} + \dfrac{x}{6}$

d) $5 - \dfrac{3}{2x}$

b) $\dfrac{3}{2x-1} \div \dfrac{x+5}{4x-2}$

e) $\dfrac{5}{x^2-4} + \dfrac{2}{x-2}$

c) $\dfrac{2x-2}{x^2+4x-5} \cdot \dfrac{x^2+2x-15}{x^2+x-12}$

RS-101. THE CAMPAIGN POSTER

Judy was running for math club president. She used an enlargement of a 3" by 5" photograph for her campaign poster. She surrounded the enlarged photo with a two-foot border. Including the border, the area of her poster was three times the area of the enlarged photograph. How large was Judy's poster?

RS-102. The point $(3, -7)$ is on line $k$ with slope $\dfrac{2}{3}$.

a) Find the equation of line $k$.

b) Find the equation of the line perpendicular to line $k$ that passes through $(3, -7)$.

RS-103. Solve each of the following equations.

a) $x^2 - 2x - 4 = 0$

d) $2x^2 - 7x - 4 = 0$

b) $3 - 2[3 - (x - 4)] = 10$

e) Extension: $(x^2 - 5)^2 - 3 = 13$

c) $3x^2 + 6x + 4 = 0$

RS-104. Simplify each of the following expressions.

a) $(x^2)^3 \cdot (3x^4)^2$

c) $\dfrac{2x^2 - x}{x} \cdot \dfrac{1}{2}$

b) $\dfrac{4x^3y}{12xy^3}$

RS-105.  Use what you know about the slopes of lines to show that points A, B, and C are on the same line:

$$A\ (4, 2) \quad B\ (17, 28) \quad C\ (7, 8)$$

(Hint: What is true about the slopes of line segments which are on the same line?)

RS-106.  Solve the equation $2x^2 + 3x - 9 = 0$.

a)  If you graph the equation $y = 2x^2 + 3x - 9$, where will the graph cross the x-axis?

b)  What equation would you have to solve if you wanted to know where the graph of $y = 2x^2 + 3x - 9$ would cross the line $y = 11$ ?

c)  Solve the equation in part (b).

RS-107.  A track around a soccer field is shown at right. All measurements represent distance in feet.

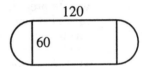

a)  Find the distance a jogger runs for one lap around the track.

b)  Find the area inside the track.

RS-108.  COURSE REFLECTION

You have arrived at the end of this algebra course. Reflect back on how much you have learned throughout this year. Write a paragraph addressing your year in this course. The questions below are merely suggestions to get you started.

What topics were difficult for you to learn at first? What learning are you most proud of? Is algebra what you thought it would be? Have the study teams helped your understanding? What talent are you most proud of? How have you helped others learn? Have your study habits changed? Have your feelings about math changed? What topics are still difficult for you? What are your goals for your next math course?

A LETTER OF ADVICE

Write a letter of advice to a student
entering CPM algebra for the first
time. Include in this letter how they
can be successful in this course. If
you could start over, what would
you do differently? What types of things helped you succeed in this class? What tools
were important? What general advice would you give this student?

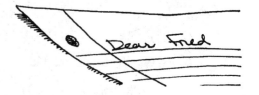

RS-110.   TOOL KIT CLEAN-UP

Examine the elements in your tool kit
from Units 7 - 13. You should create a
consolidated tool kit representing the
entire course of algebra.

Include items you value the most in your
tool kit. Spend time on this. It is a good
way to prepare for your final exam. You
may also want to use it as a resource tool
kit for next year!

a)   Examine the list of tool kit entries from this unit. Check to be sure you have all
of these entries. Add any you are missing.

b)   Identify which concepts in your complete tool kit (Units 7 - 13) you understand
well.

c)   Identify the concepts you still need to work on to master.

d)   Choose entries to create a Unit 0 - 13 tool kit that is shorter, clear, and useful.
You may want to consolidate or shorten some entries.

- Equation of a Parabola from its
  X-Intercepts

- Finding the Vertex of a
  Parabola

- Completing the Square

GM-25. CANDY SALES

For a fund-raiser, each math club member must sell 30 candy bars each day for a week. Although they all sell the same type of candy, the members may choose the sales price to help them compete for top sales member.

Alfredo decided to sell three candy bars for $1, earning $10 per day, while June priced hers at two for $1, earning her $15 per day.

One day, both Alfredo and June were on a field trip, so they asked Bomani to sell their candy bars for them. Bomani agreed and promised he would not change their prices. He decided that instead of offering three for $1 and two for $1, he would put them together and sell the 60 candy bars for five for $2.

When Alfredo and June returned, Bomani handed them the money he earned for the day, $24. Alfredo and June were angry and demanded the dollar they were sure Bomani stole! Bomani is now confused... what happened?

**Your Task:**

• Write a letter to Alfredo and June to explain what happened to the missing dollar.

# List of Symbols

| | | | |
|---|---|---|---|
| + | plus (addition) **SQ-18** | $\dfrac{P_{new}}{P_{original}}$ | enlargement (reduction) ratio of perimeter of new figure to perimeter of original figure **EF-9** |
| - | minus (subtraction) **SQ-18** | | |
| • | times (multiplication) **SQ-39** | | |
| ÷ | divide by (division) **SQ-29** | $\dfrac{A_{new}}{A_{original}}$ | enlargement (reduction) ratio of area of new figure to area of original figure **EF-9** |
| -1 | negative one (negative integer) **SQ-8** | | |
| = | equals | AB | length of the line segment AB **EF-44** |
| P(outcome) | probability of an outcome **GS-19** | A' | A prime **EF-9**, EF-44 |
| $f(x)$ | function notation **CM-60** | B" | B double-prime **EF-9** |
| $5^3$ | base 5 to the exponent 3 | △ABC | triangle ABC |
| $x^2$ | x squared **YS-26** | 90° | 90 degrees **EF-54** |
| (x, y) | the point x-y, coordinates of a point **BC-9**, BC-22, BC-37 | | right angle **EF-54** |
| ≥ | greater than or equal to **BC-55, GG-39** | 1:5 | 1 to 5 ratio **EF-7** |
| ≤ | less than or equal to **BC-55, GG-39** | % | percent **GS-9** |
| ... | ellipsis **BC-57** | π | pi **KF-91** |
| $\sqrt{\phantom{x}}$ | square root **KF-103** | y = mx + b | slope-intercept form of a linear equation **BR-51**, BP-35 |
| $\dfrac{S_{new}}{S_{original}}$ | enlargement (reduction) ratio of length of side of new figure to length of side of original figure **EF-9** | ∠A | angle A |
| | | ± | plus or minus **YS-86** |
| | | \| \| | absolute value **CM-71** |

# ALGEBRA 1 SKILL BUILDERS
## (Extra Practice)
### Introduction to Students and Their Teachers

Learning is an individual endeavor. Some ideas come easily; others take time--sometimes lots of time--to grasp. In addition, individual students learn the same idea in different ways and at different rates. The authors of this textbook designed the classroom lessons and homework to give students time--often weeks and months--to practice an idea and to use it in various settings. This section of the textbook offers students a brief review of 27 topics followed by additional practice with answers. Not all students will need extra practice. Some will need to do a few topics, while others will need to do many of the sections to help develop their understanding of the ideas. This section of the text may also be useful to prepare for tests, especially final examinations.

How these problems are used will be up to your teacher, your parents, and yourself. In classes where a topic needs additional work by most students, your teacher may assign work from one of the skill builders that follow. In most cases, though, the authors expect that these resources will be used by individual students who need to do more than the textbook offers to learn an idea. This will mean that you are going to need to do some extra work outside of class. In the case where additional practice is necessary for you individually or for a few students in your class, you should not expect your teacher to spend time in class going over the solutions to the skill builder problems. After reading the examples and trying the problems, if you still are not successful, talk to your teacher about getting a tutor or extra help outside of class time.

Warning! Looking is not the same as doing. You will never become good at any sport just by watching it. In the same way, reading through the worked out examples and understanding the steps are not the same as being able to do the problems yourself. An athlete only gets good with practice. The same is true of developing your algebra skills. How many of the extra practice problems do you need to try? That is really up to you. Remember that your goal is to be able to do problems of the type you are practicing on your own, confidently and accurately.

Another source for help with the topics in this course is the *Parent's Guide with Review to Math 1 (Algebra 1)*. Information about ordering this resource can be found inside the front page of the student text. It is also available free on the Internet at *www.cpm.org*.

### Skill Builder Topics

1. Arithmetic operations with numbers
2. Combining like terms
3. Order of operations
4. Distributive Property
5. Substitution and Evaluation
6. Tables, equations, and graphs
7. Solving Linear equations
8. Writing equations
9. Solving proportions
10. Ratio applications
11. Intersection of lines: substitution method
12. Multiplying polynomials
13. Writing and graphing linear equations
14. Factoring polynomials
15. Zero Product Property and quadratics
16. Pythagorean Theorem
17. Solving equations containing algebraic fractions
18. Laws of exponents
19. Simplifying radicals
20. The quadratic formula
21. Simplifying rational expressions
22. Multiplication and division of rational expressions
23. Absolute value equations
24. Intersection of lines: elimination method
25. Solving inequalities
26. Addition and subtraction of rational expressions
27. Solving mixed equations and inequalities

<< Skill Builders #1-8 are in Volume 1. <<

## SOLVING PROPORTIONS #9

A **proportion** is an equation stating that two ratios (fractions) are equal. To solve a proportion, begin by eliminating fractions. This means using the inverse operation of division, namely, multiplication. Multiply both sides of the proportion by one or both of the denominators. Then solve the resulting equation in the usual way.

### Example 1

$$\frac{x}{3} = \frac{5}{8}$$

Undo the division by 3 by multiplying both sides by 3.

$$(3)\frac{x}{3} = \frac{5}{8}(3)$$

$$x = \frac{15}{8} = 1\frac{7}{8}$$

### Example 2

$$\frac{x}{x+1} = \frac{3}{5}$$

Multiply by 5 and (x+1) on both sides of the equation.

$$5(x + 1)\frac{x}{x+1} = \frac{3}{5}(5)(x + 1)$$

Note that $\frac{(x+1)}{(x+1)} = 1$ and $\frac{5}{5} = 1$, so $5x = 3(x + 1)$

$$5x = 3x + 3 \quad \Rightarrow \quad 2x = 3 \quad \Rightarrow \quad x = \frac{3}{2} = 1\frac{1}{2}$$

Solve for x or y.

1. $\frac{2}{5} = \frac{y}{15}$   2. $\frac{x}{36} = \frac{4}{9}$   3. $\frac{2}{3} = \frac{x}{5}$   4. $\frac{5}{8} = \frac{x}{100}$

5. $\frac{3x}{10} = \frac{24}{9}$   6. $\frac{3y}{5} = \frac{24}{10}$   7. $\frac{x+2}{3} = \frac{5}{7}$   8. $\frac{x-1}{4} = \frac{7}{8}$

9. $\frac{4x}{5} = \frac{x-2}{7}$   10. $\frac{3x}{4} = \frac{x+1}{6}$   11. $\frac{9-x}{6} = \frac{24}{2}$   12. $\frac{7-y}{5} = \frac{3}{4}$

13. $\frac{1}{x} = \frac{5}{x+1}$   14. $\frac{3}{y} = \frac{6}{y-2}$   15. $\frac{4}{x} = \frac{x}{9}$   16. $\frac{25}{y} = \frac{y}{4}$

## Answers

1. 6   2. 16   3. $\frac{10}{3} = 3\frac{1}{3}$   4. $62\frac{1}{2}$   5. $\frac{80}{9}$   6. 4

7. $\frac{1}{7}$   8. $4\frac{1}{2}$   9. $\frac{-10}{23}$   10. $\frac{2}{7}$   11. -63   12. $\frac{13}{4}$

13. $\frac{1}{4}$   14. -2   15. ±6   16. ±10

Ratios and proportions are used to solve problems involving similar figures, percents, and relationships that vary directly.

## Example 1

ΔABC is similar to ΔDEF. Use ratios to find x.

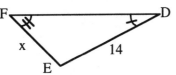

Since the triangles are similar, the ratios of the corresponding sides are equal.

$$\frac{8}{14} = \frac{4}{x} \quad \Rightarrow \quad 8x = 56 \quad \Rightarrow \quad x = 7$$

## Example 2

a) What percent of 60 is 45?

b) Forty percent of what number is 45?

In percent problems use the following proportion: $\frac{part}{whole} = \frac{percent}{100}$.

a) $\dfrac{45}{60} = \dfrac{x}{100}$       b) $\dfrac{40}{100} = \dfrac{45}{x}$

$60x = 4500$          $40x = 4500$

$x = 75 \ (75\%)$      $x = 112$

## Example 3

Amy usually swims 20 laps in 30 minutes. How long will it take to swim 50 laps at the same rate?

Since two units are being compared, set up a ratio using the unit words consistently. In this case, "laps" is on top (the numerator) and "minutes" is on the bottom (the denominator) in both ratios. Then solve as shown in Skill Builder #9.

$$\frac{laps}{minutes} : \quad \frac{20}{30} = \frac{50}{x} \quad \Rightarrow \quad 20x = 1500 \quad \Rightarrow \quad x = 75 \text{ minutes}$$

Each pair of figures is similar. Solve for the variable.

1.

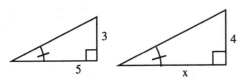

2.

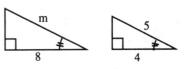

3.

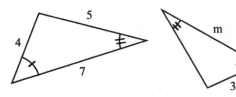

4.

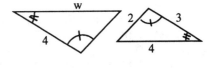

5.

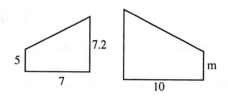

6.

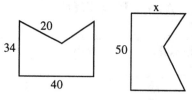

7.

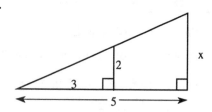

8.

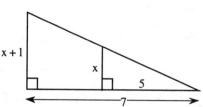

Write and solve a proportion to find the missing part.

9.  15 is 25% of what?

10. 12 is 30% of what?

11. 45% of 200 is what?

12. 32% of 150 is what?

13. 18 is what percent of 24?

14. What percent of 300 is 250?

15. What is 32% of $12.50?

16. What is 7.5% of $325.75?

Use ratios to solve each problem.

17. A rectangle has length 10 feet and width six feet. It is enlarged to a similar rectangle with length 18 feet. What is the new width?

18. If 200 vitamins cost $4.75, what should 500 vitamins cost?

19. The tax on a $400 painting is $34. What should the tax be on a $700 painting?

20. If a basketball player made 72 of 85 shots, how many shots could she expect to make in 200 shots?

21. A cookie recipe uses $\frac{1}{2}$ teaspoon of vanilla with $\frac{3}{4}$ cup of flour. How much vanilla should be used with five cups of flour?

22. My brother grew $1\frac{3}{4}$ inches in $2\frac{1}{2}$ months. At that rate, how much would he grow in one year?

23. The length of a rectangle is four centimeters more than the width. If the ratio of the length to width is seven to five, find the dimensions of the rectangle.

24. A class has three fewer girls than boys. If the ratio of girls to boys is four to five, how many students are in the class?

# Answers

1. $\frac{20}{3} = 6\frac{2}{3}$  2. 10  3. $5\frac{1}{4}$  4. $\frac{16}{3} = 5\frac{1}{3}$

5. $\frac{50}{7} = 7\frac{1}{7}$  6. 42.5  7. $\frac{10}{3} = 3\frac{1}{3}$  8. $2\frac{1}{2}$

9. 60  10. 40  11. 90  12. 48

13. 75%  14. $83\frac{1}{3}\%$  15. $4  16. $24.43

17. 10.8 ft.  18. $11.88  19. $59.50  20. About 169 shots

21. $3\frac{1}{3}$ teaspoons  22. $8\frac{2}{5}$ inches  23. 10 cm x 14 cm  24. 27 students

# USING SUBSTITUTION TO FIND THE POINT OF INTERSECTION OF TWO LINES

To find where two lines intersect we could graph them, but there is a faster, more accurate algebraic method called the **substitution method**. This method may also be used to solve systems of equations in word problems.

## Example 1

Start with two linear equations in y-form.

Substitute the equal parts.

Solve for x.

$$y = -2x + 5 \text{ and } y = x - 1$$
$$-2x + 5 = x - 1$$
$$6 = 3x \implies x = 2$$

The x-coordinate of the point of intersection is $x = 2$. To find the y-coordinate, substitute the value of x into either original equation. Solve for y, then write the solution as an ordered pair. Check that the point works in both equations.

$y = -2(2) + 5 = 1$ and $y = 2 - 1 = 1$, so (2, 1) is where the lines intersect.

Check: $1 = -2(2) + 5$ √ and $1 = 2 - 1$ √.

## Example 2

The sales of Gizmo Sports Drink at the local supermarket are currently 6,500 bottles per month. Since New Age Refreshers were introduced, sales of Gizmo have been declining by 55 bottles per month. New Age currently sells 2,200 bottles per month and its sales are increasing by 250 bottles per month. If these rates of change remain the same, in about how many months will the sales for both companies be the same? How many bottles will each company be selling at that time?

Let $x$ = months from now and $y$ = total monthly sales.

For Gizmo: $y = 6500 - 55x$; for New Age: $y = 2200 + 250x$.

Substituting equal parts: $6500 - 55x = 2200 + 250x \implies 3300 = 305x \implies 10.82 \approx x$.

Use either equation to find y: $y = 2200 + 250(10.82) \approx 4905$ and $y = 6500 - 55(10.82) \approx 4905$.

The solution is (10.82, 4905). This means that in about 11 months, both drink companies will be selling 4,905 bottles of the sports drinks.

Find the point of intersection (x, y) for each pair of lines by using the substitution method.

1.  $y = x + 2$
    $y = 2x - 1$

2.  $y = 3x + 5$
    $y = 4x + 8$

3.  $y = 11 - 2x$
    $y = x + 2$

4.  $y = 3 - 2x$
    $y = 1 + 2x$

5.  $y = 3x - 4$
    $y = \frac{1}{2}x + 7$

6.  $y = -\frac{2}{3}x + 4$
    $y = \frac{1}{3}x - 2$

7.  $y = 4.5 - x$
    $y = -2x + 6$

8.  $y = 4x$
    $y = x + 1$

For each problem, define your variables, write a system of equations, and solve them by using substitution.

9.  Janelle has $20 and is saving $6 per week.  April has $150 and is spending $4 per week.  When will they both have the same amount of money?

10.  Sam and Hector are gaining weight for football season.  Sam weighs 205 pounds and is gaining two pounds per week.  Hector weighs 195 pounds but is gaining three pounds per week.  In how many weeks will they both weigh the same amount?

11.  PhotosFast charges a fee of $2.50 plus $0.05 for each picture developed.  PhotosQuick charges a fee of $3.70 plus $0.03 for each picture developed.  For how many pictures will the total cost be the same at each shop?

12.  Playland Park charges $7 admission plus 75¢ per ride.  Funland Park charges $12.50 admission plus 50¢ per ride.  For what number of rides is the total cost the same at both parks?

Change one or both equations to y-form and solve by the substitution method.

13.  $y = 2x - 3$
     $x + y = 15$

14.  $y = 3x + 11$
     $x + y = 3$

15.  $x + y = 5$
     $2y - x = -2$

16.  $x + 2y = 10$
     $3x - 2y = -2$

17.  $x + y = 3$
     $2x - y = -9$

18.  $y = 2x - 3$
     $x - y = -4$

19.  $x + 2y = 4$
     $x + 2y = 6$

20.  $3x = y - 2$
     $6x + 4 = 2y$

# Answers

1.  (3, 5)

2.  (-3, -4)

3.  (3, 5)

4.  $\left(\frac{1}{2}, 2\right)$

5.  (4.4, 9.2)

6.  (6, 0)

7.  (1.5, 3)

8.  $\left(\frac{1}{3}, \frac{4}{3}\right)$

9.  13 weeks, $98

10.  10 weeks, 225 pounds

11.  60 pictures, $5.50

12.  22 rides, $23.50

13.  (6, 9)

14.  (-2, 5)

15.  (4, 1)

16.  (2, 4)

17.  (-2, 5)

18.  (7, 11)

19.  none

20.  infinite

We can use generic rectangles as area models to find the products of polynomials. A generic rectangle helps us organize the problem. It does not have to be drawn accurately or to scale.

## Example 1

Multiply $(2x + 5)(x + 3)$

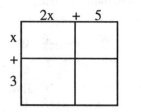
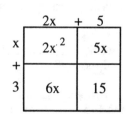

$(2x + 5)(x + 3) = 2x^2 + 11x + 15$

area as a product        area as a sum

## Example 2

Multiply $(x + 9)\left(x^2 - 3x + 5\right)$

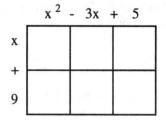

Therefore $(x + 9)\left(x^2 - 3x + 5\right) = x^3 + 9x^2 - 3x^2 - 27x + 5x + 45 = x^3 + 6x^2 - 22x + 45$

Another approach to multiplying binomials is to use the mnemonic "F.O.I.L." F.O.I.L. is an acronym for First, Outside, Inside, Last in reference to the positions of the terms in the two binomials.

## Example 3

Multiply $(3x - 2)(4x + 5)$ using the F.O.I.L. method.

| | | |
|---|---|---|
| **F**. | multiply the FIRST terms of each binomial | $(3x)(4x) = 12x^2$ |
| **O**. | multiply the OUTSIDE terms | $(3x)(5) = 15x$ |
| **I**. | multiply the INSIDE terms | $(-2)(4x) = -8x$ |
| **L**. | multiply the LAST terms of each binomial | $(-2)(5) = -10$ |

Finally, we combine like terms: $12x^2 + 15x - 8x - 10 = 12x^2 + 7x - 10$.

Multiply, then simplify each expression.

1. $x(2x - 3)$

2. $y(3y - 4)$

3. $2y(y^2 + 3y - 2)$

4. $3x(2x^2 - x + 3)$

5. $(x + 2)(x + 7)$

6. $(y - 3)(y - 9)$

7. $(y - 2)(y + 7)$

8. $(x + 8)(x - 7)$

9. $(2x + 1)(3x - 5)$

10. $(3m - 2)(2m + 1)$

11. $(2m + 1)(2m - 1)$

12. $(3y - 4)(3y + 4)$

13. $(3x + 7)^2$

14. $(2x - 5)^2$

15. $(3x + 2)(x^2 - 5x + 2)$

16. $(y - 2)(3y^2 + 2y - 2)$

17. $3(x + 2)(2x - 1)$

18. $-2(x - 2)(3x + 1)$

19. $x(2x - 3)(x + 4)$

20. $2y(2y - 1)(3y + 2)$

## Answers

1. $2x^2 - 3x$

2. $3y^2 - 4y$

3. $2y^3 + 6y^2 - 4y$

4. $6x^3 - 3x^2 + 9x$

5. $x^2 + 9x + 14$

6. $y^2 - 12y + 27$

7. $y^2 + 5y - 14$

8. $x^2 + x - 56$

9. $6x^2 - 7x - 5$

10. $6m^2 - m - 2$

11. $4m^2 - 1$

12. $9y^2 - 16$

13. $9x^2 + 42x + 49$

14. $4x^2 - 20x + 25$

15. $3x^3 - 13x^2 - 4x + 4$

16. $3y^3 - 4y^2 - 6y + 4$

17. $6x^2 + 9x - 6$

18. $-6x^2 + 10x + 4$

19. $2x^3 + 5x^2 - 12x$

20. $12y^3 + 2y^2 - 4y$

# WRITING AND GRAPHING LINEAR EQUATIONS ON A FLAT SURFACE #13

**SLOPE** is a number that indicates the steepness (or flatness) of a line, as well as its direction (up or down) left to right.

**SLOPE** is determined by the ratio: $\dfrac{\text{vertical change}}{\text{horizontal change}}$ between <u>any</u> two points on a line.

For lines that go **up** (from left to right), the sign of the slope is **positive.** For lines that go **down** (left to right), the sign of the slope is **negative**.

Any linear equation written as **y = mx + b**, where m and b are any real numbers, is said to be in **SLOPE-INTERCEPT FORM.** m is the **SLOPE** of the line. b is the **Y-INTERCEPT**, that is, the point (0, b) where the line intersects (crosses) the y-axis.

If two lines have the same slope, then they are parallel. Likewise, **PARALLEL LINES** have the same slope.

Two lines are **PERPENDICULAR** if the slope of one line is the negative reciprocal of the slope of the other line, that is, m and $-\dfrac{1}{m}$. Note that $m \cdot \left(\dfrac{-1}{m}\right) = -1$.

Examples: 3 and $-\dfrac{1}{3}$, $-\dfrac{2}{3}$ and $\dfrac{3}{2}$, $\dfrac{5}{4}$ and $-\dfrac{4}{5}$

Two distinct lines that are not parallel intersect in a single point. See "Solving Linear Systems" to review how to find the point of intersection.

## Example 1

Write the slope of the line containing the points (-1, 3) and (4, 5).

First graph the two points and draw the line through them.

Look for and draw a slope triangle using the two given points.

Write the ratio $\dfrac{\text{vertical change in } y}{\text{horizontal change in } x}$ using the legs of the right

triangle: $\dfrac{2}{5}$.

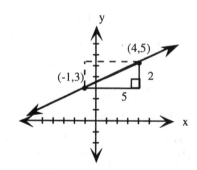

Assign a positive or negative value to the slope (this one is positive) depending on whether the line goes up (+) or down (–) from left to right.

If the points are inconvenient to graph, use a "Generic Slope Triangle", visualizing where the points lie with respect to each other.

## Example 2

Graph the linear equation $y = \frac{4}{7}x + 2$

Using $y = mx + b$, the slope in $y = \frac{4}{7}x + 2$ is $\frac{4}{7}$ and the
y-intercept is the point $(0, 2)$. To graph, begin at the
y-intercept $(0, 2)$. Remember that slope is $\frac{\text{vertical change}}{\text{horizontal change}}$ so go
up 4 units (since 4 is positive) from $(0, 2)$ and then move right 7
units. This gives a second point on the graph. To create the
graph, draw a straight line through the two points.

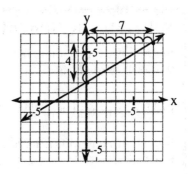

## Example 3

A line has a slope of $\frac{3}{4}$ and passes through $(3, 2)$. What is the equation of the line?

Using $y = mx + b$, write $y = \frac{3}{4}x + b$. Since $(3, 2)$ represents a point $(x, y)$ on the line, substitute

3 for x and 2 for y, $2 = \frac{3}{4}(3) + b$, and solve for b. $2 = \frac{9}{4} + b \Rightarrow 2 - \frac{9}{4} = b \Rightarrow -\frac{1}{4} = b$.

The equation is $y = \frac{3}{4}x - \frac{1}{4}$.

## Example 4

Decide whether the two lines at right are parallel, perpendicular, or neither (i.e., intersecting).

$5x - 4y = -6$ and $-4x + 5y = 3$.

First find the slope of each equation. Then compare the slopes.

| | | |
|---|---|---|
| $5x - 4y = -6$ <br> $-4y = -5x - 6$ <br> $y = \frac{-5x - 6}{-4}$ <br> $y = \frac{5}{4}x + \frac{3}{2}$ <br> The slope of this line is $\frac{5}{4}$. | $-4x + 5y = 3$ <br> $5y = 4x + 3$ <br> $y = \frac{4x + 3}{5}$ <br> $y = \frac{4}{5}x + \frac{3}{5}$ <br> The slope of this line is $\frac{4}{5}$. | These two slopes are not equal, so they are not parallel. The product of the two slopes is 1, not -1, so they are not perpendicular. These two lines are neither parallel nor perpendicular, but do intersect. |

## Example 5

Find two equations of the line through the given point, one parallel and one perpendicular to the
given line: $y = -\frac{5}{2}x + 5$ and $(-4, 5)$.

| | |
|---|---|
| For the parallel line, use $y = mx + b$ with the same slope to write $y = -\frac{5}{2}x + b$. <br><br> Substitute the point $(-4, 5)$ for x and y and solve for b. <br><br> $5 = -\frac{5}{2}(-4) + b \Rightarrow 5 = \frac{20}{2} + b \Rightarrow -5 = b$ <br><br> Therefore the parallel line through $(-4, 5)$ is $y = -\frac{5}{2}x - 5$. | For the perpendicular line, use $y = mx + b$ where m is the negative reciprocal of the slope of the original equation to write $y = \frac{2}{5}x + b$. <br><br> Substitute the point $(-4, 5)$ and solve for b. <br><br> $5 = \frac{2}{5}(-4) + b \Rightarrow \frac{33}{5} = b$ <br><br> Therefore the perpendicular line through $(-4, 5)$ is $y = \frac{2}{5}x + \frac{33}{5}$. |

Write the slope of the line containing each pair of points.

1. (3, 4) and (5, 7)  2. (5, 2) and (9, 4)  3. (1, -3) and (-4, 7)

4. (-2, 1) and (2, -2)  5. (-2, 3) and (4, 3)  6. (8, 5) and (3, 5)

Use a Generic Slope Triangle to write the slope of the line containing each pair of points:

7. (51, 40) and (33, 72)  8. (20, 49) and (54, 90)  9. (10, -13) and (-61, 20)

Identify the y-intercept in each equation.

10. $y = \frac{1}{2}x - 2$  11. $y = -\frac{3}{5}x - \frac{5}{3}$  12. $3x + 2y = 12$

13. $x - y = -13$  14. $2x - 4y = 12$  15. $4y - 2x = 12$

Write the equation of the line with:

16. slope $= \frac{1}{2}$ and passing through (4, 3).  17. slope $= \frac{2}{3}$ and passing through (-3, -2).

18. slope $= -\frac{1}{3}$ and passing through (4, -1).  19. slope $= -4$ and passing through (-3, 5).

Determine the slope of each line using the highlighted points.

20.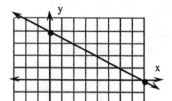

21.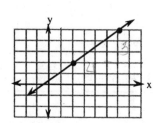

22.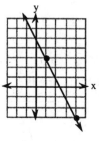

Using the slope and y-intercept, determine the equation of the line.

23.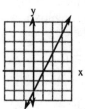

24.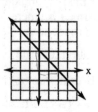

25.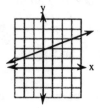

26.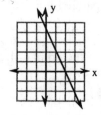

Graph the following linear equations on graph paper.

27. $y = \frac{1}{2}x + 3$  28. $y = -\frac{3}{5}x - 1$  29. $y = 4x$

30. $y = -6x + \frac{1}{2}$  31. $3x + 2y = 12$

State whether each pair of lines is parallel, perpendicular, or intersecting.

32. $y = 2x - 2$ and $y = 2x + 4$

33. $y = \frac{1}{2}x + 3$ and $y = -2x - 4$

34. $x - y = 2$ and $x + y = 3$

35. $y - x = -1$ and $y + x = 3$

36. $x + 3y = 6$ and $y = -\frac{1}{3}x - 3$

37. $3x + 2y = 6$ and $2x + 3y = 6$

38. $4x = 5y - 3$ and $4y = 5x + 3$

39. $3x - 4y = 12$ and $4y = 3x + 7$

Find an equation of the line through the given point and parallel to the given line.

40. $y = 2x - 2$ and (-3, 5)

41. $y = \frac{1}{2}x + 3$ and (-4, 2)

42. $x - y = 2$ and (-2, 3)

43. $y - x = -1$ and (-2, 1)

44. $x + 3y = 6$ and (-1, 1)

45. $3x + 2y = 6$ and (2, -1)

46. $4x = 5y - 3$ and (1, -1)

47. $3x - 4y = 12$ and (4, -2)

Find an equation of the line through the given point and perpendicular to the given line.

48. $y = 2x - 2$ and (-3, 5)

49. $y = \frac{1}{2}x + 3$ and (-4, 2)

50. $x - y = 2$ and (-2, 3)

51. $y - x = -1$ and (-2, 1)

52. $x + 3y = 6$ and (-1, 1)

53. $3x + 2y = 6$ and (2, -1)

54. $4x = 5y - 3$ and (1, -1)

55. $3x - 4y = 12$ and (4, -2)

Write an equation of the line parallel to each line below through the given point.

56.

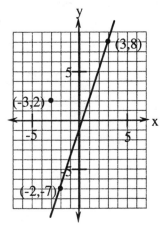

57.

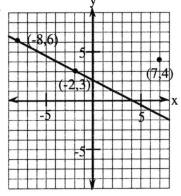

## Answers

1. $\dfrac{3}{2}$    2. $\dfrac{1}{2}$    3. $-2$    4. $-\dfrac{3}{4}$

5. $0$    6. $0$    7. $-\dfrac{16}{9}$    8. $\dfrac{41}{34}$

9. $\dfrac{-33}{71}$    10. $(0, -2)$    11. $\left(0, -\dfrac{5}{3}\right)$    12. $(0, 6)$

13. $(0, 13)$    14. $(0, -3)$    15. $(0, 3)$    16. $y = \dfrac{1}{2}x + 1$

17. $y = \dfrac{2}{3}x$    18. $y = -\dfrac{1}{3}x + \dfrac{1}{3}$    19. $y = -4x - 7$    20. $-\dfrac{1}{2}$

21. $\dfrac{3}{4}$    22. $-2$    23. $y = 2x - 2$    24. $y = -x + 2$

25. $y = \dfrac{1}{3}x + 2$    26. $y = -2x + 4$    27. line with slope $\dfrac{1}{2}$ and y-intercept $(0, 3)$

28. line with slope $-\dfrac{3}{5}$ and y-intercept $(0, -1)$    29. line with slope $4$ and y-intercept $(0, 0)$

30. line with slope $-6$ and y-intercept $\left(0, \dfrac{1}{2}\right)$    31. line with slope $-\dfrac{3}{2}$ and y-intercept $(0, 6)$

32. parallel    33. perpendicular    34. perpendicular    35. perpendicular

36. parallel    37. intersecting    38. intersecting    39. parallel

40. $y = 2x + 11$    41. $y = \dfrac{1}{2}x + 4$    42. $y = x + 5$    43. $y = x + 3$

44. $y = -\dfrac{1}{3}x + \dfrac{2}{3}$    45. $y = -\dfrac{3}{2}x + 2$    46. $y = \dfrac{4}{5}x - \dfrac{9}{5}$    47. $y = \dfrac{3}{4}x - 5$

48. $y = -\dfrac{1}{2}x + \dfrac{7}{2}$    49. $y = -2x - 6$    50. $y = -x + 1$    51. $y = -x - 1$

52. $y = 3x + 4$    53. $y = \dfrac{2}{3}x - \dfrac{7}{3}$    54. $y = -\dfrac{5}{4}x + \dfrac{1}{4}$    55. $y = -\dfrac{4}{3}x + \dfrac{10}{3}$

56. $y = 3x + 11$    57. $y = -\dfrac{1}{2}x + \dfrac{15}{2}$

# FACTORING POLYNOMIALS

Often we want to un-multiply or **factor** a polynomial P(x). This process involves finding a constant and/or another polynomial that evenly divides the given polynomial. In formal mathematical terms, this means $P(x) = q(x) \cdot r(x)$, where q and r are also polynomials. For elementary algebra there are three general types of factoring.

1) **Common term** (finding the largest common factor):

$6x + 18 = 6(x + 3)$ where 6 is a common factor of both terms.

$2x^3 - 8x^2 - 10x = 2x\left(x^2 - 4x - 5\right)$ where 2x is the common factor.

$2x^2(x - 1) + 7(x - 1) = (x - 1)\left(2x^2 + 7\right)$ where x - 1 is the common factor.

2) **Special products**

$a^2 - b^2 = (a + b)(a - b)$      $x^2 - 25 = (x + 5)(x - 5)$

$9x^2 - 4y^2 = (3x + 2y)(3x - 2y)$

$x^2 + 2xy + y^2 = (x + y)^2$      $x^2 + 8x + 16 = (x + 4)^2$

$x^2 - 2xy + y^2 = (x - y)^2$      $x^2 - 8x + 16 = (x - 4)^2$

3a) **Trinomials** in the form $x^2 + bx + c$ where the coefficient of $x^2$ is 1.

Consider $x^2 + (d + e)x + d \cdot e = (x + d)(x + e)$, where the coefficient of x is the <u>sum</u> of two numbers d and e AND the constant is the <u>product</u> of the same two numbers, d and e. A quick way to determine all of the possible pairs of integers d and e is to factor the constant in the original trinomial. For example, 12 is $1 \cdot 12$, $2 \cdot 6$, and $3 \cdot 4$. The signs of the two numbers are determined by the combination you need to get the sum. The "sum and product" approach to factoring trinomials is the same as solving a "Diamond Problem" in CPM's Algebra 1 course (see below).

$x^2 + 8x + 15 = (x + 3)(x + 5);\ \ 3 + 5 = 8,\ \ 3 \cdot 5 = 15$

$x^2 - 2x - 15 = (x - 5)(x + 3);\ \ -5 + 3 = -2,\ \ -5 \cdot 3 = -15$

$x^2 - 7x + 12 = (x - 3)(x - 4);\ \ -3 + (-4) = -7,\ \ (-3)(-4) = 12$

The sum and product approach can be shown visually using rectangles for an area model. The figure at far left below shows the "Diamond Problem" format for finding a sum and product. Here is how to use this method to factor $x^2 + 6x + 8$.

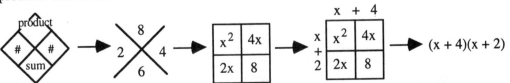

>> **Explanation and examples continue on the next page.** >>

3b) **Trinomials** in the form $ax^2 + bx + c$ where $a \neq 1$.

Note that the upper value in the diamond is no longer the constant. Rather, it is the <u>product</u> of a and c, that is, the coefficient of $x^2$ and the constant.

$2x^2 + 7x + 3$

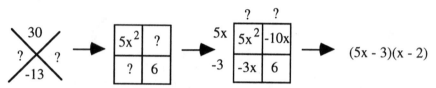

Below is the process to factor $5x^2 - 13x + 6$.

Polynomials with four or more terms are generally factored by grouping the terms and using one or more of the three procedures shown above. Note that polynomials are usually factored <u>completely</u>. In the second example in part (1) above, the trinomial also needs to be factored.

Thus, the complete factorization of $2x^3 - 8x^2 - 10x = 2x(x^2 - 4x - 5) = 2x(x - 5)(x + 1)$.

Factor each polynomial completely.

1. $x^2 - x - 42$     2. $4x^2 - 18$     3. $2x^2 + 9x + 9$     4. $2x^2 + 3xy + y^2$

5. $6x^2 - x - 15$     6. $4x^2 - 25$     7. $x^2 - 28x + 196$     8. $7x^2 - 847$

9. $x^2 + 18x + 81$     10. $x^2 + 4x - 21$     11. $3x^2 + 21x$     12. $3x^2 - 20x - 32$

13. $9x^2 - 16$     14. $4x^2 + 20x + 25$     15. $x^2 - 5x + 6$     16. $5x^3 + 15x^2 - 20x$

17. $4x^2 + 18$     18. $x^2 - 12x + 36$     19. $x^2 - 3x - 54$     20. $6x^2 - 21$

21. $2x^2 + 15x + 18$     22. $16x^2 - 1$     23. $x^2 - 14x + 49$     24. $x^2 + 8x + 15$

25. $3x^3 - 12x^2 - 45x$     26. $3x^2 + 24$     27. $x^2 + 16x + 64$

Factor completely.

28. $75x^3 - 27x$     29. $3x^3 - 12x^2 - 36x$     30. $4x^3 - 44x^2 + 112x$

31. $5y^2 - 125$     32. $3x^2y^2 - xy^2 - 4y^2$     33. $x^3 + 10x^2 - 24x$

34. $3x^3 - 6x^2 - 45x$     35. $3x^2 - 27$     36. $x^4 - 16$

Factor each of the following completely.  Use the modified diamond approach.

37. $2x^2 + 5x - 7$

38. $3x^2 - 13x + 4$

39. $2x^2 + 9x + 10$

40. $4x^2 - 13x + 3$

41. $4x^2 + 12x + 5$

42. $6x^3 + 31x^2 + 5x$

43. $64x^2 + 16x + 1$

44. $7x^2 - 33x - 10$

45. $5x^2 + 12x - 9$

## Answers

1. $(x + 6)(x - 7)$

2. $2(2x^2 - 9)$

3. $(2x + 3)(x + 3)$

4. $(2x + y)(x + y)$

5. $(2x + 3)(3x - 5)$

6. $(2x - 5)(2x + 5)$

7. $(x - 14)^2$

8. $7(x - 11)(x + 11)$

9. $(x + 9)^2$

10. $(x + 7)(x - 3)$

11. $3x(x + 7)$

12. $(x - 8)(3x + 4)$

13. $(3x - 4)(3x + 4)$

14. $(2x + 5)^2$

15. $(x - 3)(x - 2)$

16. $5x(x + 4)(x - 1)$

17. $2(2x^2 + 9)$

18. $(x - 6)^2$

19. $(x - 9)(x + 6)$

20. $3(2x^2 - 7)$

21. $(2x + 3)(x + 6)$

22. $(4x + 1)(4x - 1)$

23. $(x - 7)^2$

24. $(x + 3)(x + 5)$

25. $3x(x^2 - 4x - 15)$

26. $3(x^2 + 8)$

27. $(x + 8)^2$

28. $3x(5x - 3)(5x + 3)$

29. $3x(x - 6)(x + 2)$

30. $4x(x - 7)(x - 4)$

31. $5(y + 5)(y - 5)$

32. $y^2(3x - 4)(x + 1)$

33. $x(x + 12)(x - 2)$

34. $3x(x - 5)(x + 3)$

35. $3(x - 3)(x + 3)$

36. $(x - 2)(x + 2)(x^2 + 4)$

37. $(2x + 7)(x - 1)$

38. $(3x - 1)(x - 4)$

39. $(x + 2)(2x + 5)$

40. $(4x - 1)(x - 3)$

41. $(2x + 5)(2x + 1)$

42. $x(6x + 1)(x + 5)$

43. $(8x + 1)^2$

44. $(7x + 2)(x - 5)$

45. $(5x - 3)(x + 3)$

## ZERO PRODUCT PROPERTY AND QUADRATICS          #15

If $a \cdot b = 0$, then either $a = 0$ or $b = 0$.

Note that this property states that <u>at least</u> one of the factors MUST be zero. It is also possible that all of the factors are zero. This simple statement gives us a powerful result which is most often used with equations involving the products of binomials. For example, solve $(x + 5)(x - 2) = 0$.

By the Zero Product Property, since $(x + 5)(x - 2) = 0$, either $x + 5 = 0$ or $x - 2 = 0$. Thus, $x = -5$ or $x = 2$.

The Zero Product Property can be used to find where a quadratic crosses the x-axis. These points are the x-intercepts. In the example above, they would be (-5, 0) and (2, 0).

Here are two more examples. Solve each quadratic equation and check each solution.

## Example 1

$(x + 4)(x - 7) = 0$

By the Zero Product Property,
either $x + 4 = 0$ or $x - 7 = 0$
Solving, $x = -4$ or $x = 7$.

Checking,

$(-4 + 4)(-4 - 7) \overset{?}{=} 0$
$(0)(-11) = 0 \checkmark$

$(7 + 4)(7 - 7) \overset{?}{=} 0$
$(11)(0) = 0 \checkmark$

## Example 2

$x^2 + 3x - 10 = 0$

First factor $x^2 + 3x - 10 = 0$
into $(x + 5)(x - 2) = 0$
then $x + 5 = 0$ or $x - 2 = 0$,
so $x = -5$ or $x = 2$

Checking,

$(-5 + 5)(-5 - 2) \overset{?}{=} 0$
$(0)(-7) = 0 \checkmark$

$(2 + 5)(2 - 2) \overset{?}{=} 0$
$(7)(0) = 0 \checkmark$

Solve each of the following quadratic equations.

1. $(x + 7)(x + 1) = 0$
2. $(x + 2)(x + 3) = 0$
3. $x(x - 2) = 0$

4. $x(x - 7) = 0$
5. $(3x - 3)(4x + 2) = 0$
6. $(2x + 5)(4x - 3) = 0$

7. $x^2 + 4x + 3 = 0$
8. $x^2 + 6x + 5 = 0$
9. $x^2 - 6x + 8 = 0$

10. $x^2 - 8x + 15 = 0$
11. $x^2 + x = 6$
12. $x^2 - x = 6$

13. $x^2 - 10x = -16$
14. $x^2 - 11x = -28$

Without graphing, find where each parabola crosses the x-axis.

15. $y = x^2 - 2x - 3$
16. $y = x^2 + 2x - 8$
17. $y = x^2 - x - 30$

18. $y = x^2 + 4x - 5$
19. $x^2 + 4x = 5 + y$
20. $x^2 - 3x = 10 + y$

## Answers

1. $x = -7$ and $x = -1$
2. $x = -2$ and $x = -3$
3. $x = 0$ and $x = 2$

4. $x = 0$ and $x = 7$
5. $x = 1$ and $x = -\dfrac{1}{2}$
6. $x = \dfrac{-5}{2}$ and $x = \dfrac{3}{4}$

7. $x = -1$ and $x = -3$
8. $x = -1$ and $x = -5$
9. $x = 4$ and $x = 2$

10. $x = 5$ and $x = 3$
11. $x = -3$ and $x = 2$
12. $x = 3$ and $x = -2$

13. $x = 2$ and $x = 8$
14. $x = 4$ and $x = 7$
15. (-1, 0) and (3, 0)

16. (-4, 0) and (2, 0)
17. (6, 0) and (-5, 0)
18. (-5, 0) and (1, 0)

19. (1, 0) and (-5, 0)
20. (5, 0) and (-2, 0)

# PYTHAGOREAN THEOREM

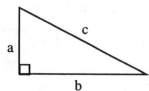

Any triangle that has a right angle is called a **right triangle**. The two sides that form the right angle, a and b, are called **legs**, and the side opposite (that is, across the triangle from) the right angle, c, is called the **hypotenuse**.

For any right triangle, the sum of the squares of the legs of the triangle is equal to the square of the hypotenuse, that is, $a^2 + b^2 = c^2$. This relationship is known as the **Pythagorean Theorem**. In words, the theorem states that:

$$(leg)^2 + (leg)^2 = (hypotenuse)^2.$$

## Example

Draw a diagram, then use the Pythagorean Theorem to write an equation or use area pictures (as shown on page 22, problem RC-1) on each side of the triangle to solve each problem.

a) Solve for the missing side.

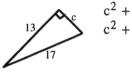

$$c^2 + 13^2 = 17^2$$
$$c^2 + 169 = 289$$
$$c^2 = 120$$
$$c = \sqrt{120}$$
$$c = 2\sqrt{30}$$
$$c \approx 10.95$$

b) Find x to the nearest tenth:

$$(5x)^2 + x^2 = 20^2$$
$$25x^2 + x^2 = 400$$
$$26x^2 = 400$$
$$x^2 \approx 15.4$$
$$x \approx \sqrt{15.4}$$
$$x \approx 3.9$$

c) One end of a ten foot ladder is four feet from the base of a wall. How high on the wall does the top of the ladder touch?

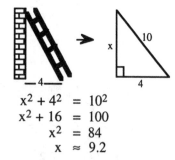

$$x^2 + 4^2 = 10^2$$
$$x^2 + 16 = 100$$
$$x^2 = 84$$
$$x \approx 9.2$$

The ladder touches the wall about 9.2 feet above the ground.

d) Could 3, 6 and 8 represent the lengths of the sides of a right triangle? Explain.

$$3^2 + 6^2 \stackrel{?}{=} 8^2$$

$$9 + 36 \stackrel{?}{=} 64$$

$$45 \neq 64$$

Since the Pythagorean Theorem relationship is not true for these lengths, they cannot be the side lengths of a right triangle.

Write an equation and solve for each unknown side. Round to the nearest hundredth.

1.

2.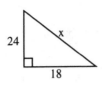

3.

4.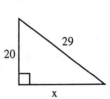

5.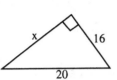

6.

7.

8.

9.

10.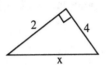

11.

12.

13.

14.

Be careful! Remember to square the whole side. For example, $(2x)^2 = (2x)(2x) = 4x^2$.

15.

16.

17.

18.

19.

20.

For each of the following problems draw and label a diagram. Then write an equation using the Pythagorean Theorem and solve for the unknown. Round answers to the nearest hundredth.

21. In a right triangle, the length of the hypotenuse is four inches. The length of one leg is two inches. Find the length of the other leg.

22. The length of the hypotenuse of a right triangle is six cm. The length of one leg is four cm. Find the length of the other leg.

23. Find the diagonal length of a television screen 30 inches wide by 20 inches long.

24. Find the length of a path that runs diagonally across a 53 yard by 100 yard field.

25. A mover must put a circular mirror two meters in diameter through a one meter by 1.8 meter doorway. Find the length of the diagonal of the doorway. Will the mirror fit?

Algebra 1                                                                                            SB37

26. A surveyor walked eight miles north, then three miles west. How far was she from her starting point?

27. A four meter ladder is one meter from the base of a building. How high up the building will the ladder reach?

28. A 12-meter loading ramp rises to the edge of a warehouse doorway. The bottom of the ramp is nine meters from the base of the warehouse wall. How high above the base of the wall is the doorway?

29. What is the longest line you can draw on a paper that is 15 cm by 25 cm?

30. How long an umbrella will fit in the bottom of a suitcase that is 2.5 feet by 3 feet?

31. How long a guy wire is needed to support a 10 meter tall tower if it is fastened five meters from the foot of the tower?

32. Find the diagonal distance from one corner of a 30 foot square classroom floor to the other corner of the floor.

33. Harry drove 10 miles west, then five miles north, then three miles west. How far was he from his starting point?

34. Linda can turn off her car alarm from 20 yards away. Will she be able to do it from the far corner of a 15 yard by 12 yard parking lot?

35. The hypotenuse of a right triangle is twice as long as one of its legs. The other leg is nine inches long. Find the length of the hypotenuse.

36. One leg of a right triangle is three times as long as the other. The hypotenuse is 100 cm. Find the length of the shorter leg.

## Answers

| | | | |
|---|---|---|---|
| 1. $x = 10$ | 2. $x = 30$ | 3. $x = 12$ | 4. $x = 21$ |
| 5. $x = 12$ | 6. $x = 40$ | 7. $x = 16$ | 8. $x = 20$ |
| 9. $x \approx 6.71$ | 10. $x \approx 4.47$ | 11. $x \approx 7.07$ | 12. $x \approx 9.9$ |
| 13. $x \approx 8.66$ | 14. $x \approx 5.66$ | 15. $x = 2$ | 16. $x = 2$ |
| 17. $x \approx 22.36$ | 18. $x \approx 3.16$ | 19. $x \approx 4.44$ | 20. $x \approx 4.33$ |
| 21. 3.46 inches | 22. 4.47 cm | 23. 36.06 inches | 24. 113.18 yards |
| 25. The diagonal is 2.06 meters, so yes. | | 26. 8.54 miles | 27. 3.87 meters |
| 28. 7.94 meters | 29. 29.15 cm | 30. 3.91 feet | 31. 11.18 meters |
| 32. 42.43 feet | 33. 13.93 miles | 34. The corner is 19.21 yards away so yes! | |
| 35. 10.39 inches | 36. 31.62 cm | | |

## SOLVING EQUATIONS CONTAINING ALGEBRAIC FRACTIONS     #17

Fractions that appear in algebraic equations can usually be eliminated in one step by multiplying each term on both sides of the equation by the common denominator for all of the fractions. If you cannot determine the common denominator, use the product of all the denominators. Multiply, simplify each term as usual, then solve the remaining equation. For more information, read the Tool Kit information on page 313 (problem BP-46) in the textbook. In this course we call this method for eliminating fractions in equations "fraction busting."

## Example 1

Solve for x: $\frac{x}{9} + \frac{2x}{5} = 3$

$45\left(\frac{x}{9} + \frac{2x}{5}\right) = 45(3)$

$45\left(\frac{x}{9}\right) + 45\left(\frac{2x}{5}\right) = 135$

$5x + 18x = 135$

$23x = 135$

$x = \frac{135}{23}$

## Example 2

Solve for x: $\frac{5}{2x} + \frac{1}{6} = 8$

$6x\left(\frac{5}{2x} + \frac{1}{6}\right) = 6x(8)$

$6x\left(\frac{5}{2x}\right) + 6x\left(\frac{1}{6}\right) = 48x$

$15 + x = 48x$

$15 = 47x$

$x = \frac{15}{47}$

Solve the following equations using the fraction busters method.

1. $\frac{x}{6} + \frac{2x}{3} = 5$

2. $\frac{x}{3} + \frac{x}{2} = 1$

3. $\frac{16}{x} + \frac{16}{40} = 1$

4. $\frac{5}{x} + \frac{5}{3x} = 1$

5. $\frac{x}{2} - \frac{x}{5} = 9$

6. $\frac{x}{3} - \frac{x}{5} = \frac{2}{3}$

7. $\frac{x}{2} - 4 = \frac{x}{3}$

8. $\frac{x}{8} = \frac{x}{12} + \frac{1}{3}$

9. $5 - \frac{7x}{6} = \frac{3}{2}$

10. $\frac{2x}{3} - x = 4$

11. $\frac{x}{8} = \frac{x}{5} - \frac{1}{3}$

12. $\frac{2x}{3} - \frac{3x}{5} = 2$

13. $\frac{4}{x} + \frac{2}{x} = 1$

14. $\frac{3}{x} + 2 = 4$

15. $\frac{5}{x} + 6 = \frac{17}{x}$

16. $\frac{2}{x} - \frac{4}{3x} = \frac{2}{9}$

17. $\frac{x+2}{3} + \frac{x-1}{6} = 5$

18. $\frac{x}{4} + \frac{x+5}{3} = 4$

19. $\frac{x-1}{2x} + \frac{x+3}{4x} = \frac{5}{8}$

20. $\frac{2-x}{x} - \frac{x+3}{3x} = \frac{-1}{3}$

## Answers

1. $x = 6$

2. $x = \frac{6}{5}$

3. $x = 26\frac{2}{3}$

4. $x = 6\frac{2}{3}$

5. $x = 30$

6. $x = 5$

7. $x = 24$

8. $x = 8$

9. $x = 3$

10. $x = -12$

11. $x = \frac{40}{9}$

12. $x = 30$

13. $x = 6$

14. $x = 1.5$

15. $x = 2$

16. $x = 3$

17. $x = 9$

18. $x = 4$

19. $x = -2$

20. $x = 1$

Algebra 1

**BASE, EXPONENT, AND VALUE**

In the expression $2^5$, 2 is the **base**, 5 is the **exponent**, and the **value** is 32.

$2^5$ means $2 \cdot 2 \cdot 2 \cdot 2 \cdot 2 = 32$ $\qquad\qquad$ $x^3$ means $x \cdot x \cdot x$

**LAWS OF EXPONENTS**

Here are the basic patterns with examples:

1) $x^a \cdot x^b = x^{a+b}$ $\qquad$ examples: $x^3 \cdot x^4 = x^{3+4} = x^7$; $\qquad$ $2^7 \cdot 2^4 = 2^{11}$

2) $\dfrac{x^a}{x^b} = x^{a-b}$ $\qquad$ examples: $x^{10} \div x^4 = x^{10-4} = x^6$; $\qquad$ $\dfrac{2^4}{2^7} = 2^{-3}$ or $\dfrac{1}{2^3}$

3) $(x^a)^b = x^{ab}$ $\qquad$ examples: $(x^4)^3 = x^{4 \cdot 3} = x^{12}$; $\qquad$ $(2x^3)^4 = 2^4 \cdot x^{12} = 16x^{12}$

4) $x^{-a} = \dfrac{1}{x^a}$ and $\dfrac{1}{x^{-b}} = x^b$ examples: $3x^{-3}y^2 = \dfrac{3y^2}{x^3}$; $\qquad$ $\dfrac{2x^5}{y^{-2}} = 2x^5y^2$

5) $x^0 = 1$ $\qquad$ examples: $5^0 = 1$; $\qquad$ $(2x)^0 = 1$

## Example 1

Simplify: $\left(2xy^3\right)\left(5x^2y^4\right)$

Multiply the coefficients: $2 \cdot 5 \cdot xy^3 \cdot x^2y^4 = 10xy^3 \cdot x^2y^4$

Add the exponents of x, then y: $10x^{1+2}y^{3+4} = 10x^3y^7$

## Example 2

Simplify: $\qquad\qquad$ $\dfrac{14x^2y^{12}}{7x^5y^7}$

Divide the coefficients: $\qquad$ $\dfrac{(14 \div 7)x^2y^{12}}{x^5y^7} = \dfrac{2x^2y^{12}}{x^5y^7}$

Subtract the exponents: $2x^{2-5}y^{12-7} = 2x^{-3}y^5$ OR $\dfrac{2y^5}{x^3}$

## Example 3

Simplify: $\qquad\qquad$ $\left(3x^2y^4\right)^3$

Cube each factor: $\qquad$ $3^3 \cdot \left(x^2\right)^3 \cdot \left(y^4\right)^3 = 27\left(x^2\right)^3\left(y^4\right)^3$

Multiply the exponents: $27x^6y^{12}$

# Example 4

Simplify: $\quad 3x^{-4}y^2z^{-3} \Rightarrow \dfrac{3y^2}{x^4z^3}$

Simplify each expression:

1. $y^5 \cdot y^7$

2. $b^4 \cdot b^3 \cdot b^2$

3. $8^6 \cdot 8^2$

4. $\left(y^5\right)^2$

5. $(3a)^4$

6. $\dfrac{m^8}{m^3}$

7. $\dfrac{12x^9}{4x^4}$

8. $\left(x^3y^2\right)^3$

9. $\dfrac{\left(y^4\right)^2}{\left(y^3\right)^2}$

10. $\dfrac{15x^2y^7}{3x^4y^5}$

11. $\left(4c^4\right)\left(ac^3\right)\left(3a^5c\right)$

12. $\left(7x^3y^5\right)^2$

13. $\left(4xy^2\right)(2y)^3$

14. $\left(\dfrac{4}{x^2}\right)^3$

15. $\dfrac{\left(2a^7\right)\left(3a^2\right)}{6a^3}$

16. $\left(\dfrac{5m^3n}{m^5}\right)^3$

17. $\left(3a^2x^3\right)^2\left(2ax^4\right)^3$

18. $\left(\dfrac{x^3y}{y^4}\right)^4$

19. $\left(\dfrac{6y^2x^8}{12x^3y^7}\right)^2$

20. $\dfrac{\left(2x^5y^3\right)^3\left(4xy^4\right)^2}{8x^7y^{12}}$

Write the following expressions without negative exponents.

21. $x^{-2}$

22. $y^{-3}y^2$

23. $\dfrac{x^5}{x^{-2}}$

24. $\left(y^{-2}\right)^5$

Note: More practice with negative exponents is available in Skill Builder #21.

# Answers

1. $y^{12}$

2. $b^9$

3. $8^8$

4. $y^{10}$

5. $81a^4$

6. $m^5$

7. $3x^5$

8. $x^9y^6$

9. $y^2$

10. $\dfrac{5y^2}{x^2}$

11. $12a^6c^8$

12. $49x^6y^{10}$

13. $32xy^5$

14. $\dfrac{64}{x^6}$

15. $a^6$

16. $\dfrac{125n^3}{m^6}$

17. $72a^7x^{18}$

18. $\dfrac{x^{12}}{y^{12}}$

19. $\dfrac{x^{10}}{4y^{10}}$

20. $16x^{10}y^5$

21. $\dfrac{1}{x^2}$

22. $\dfrac{1}{y}$

23. $x^7$

24. $\dfrac{1}{y^{10}}$

# SIMPLIFYING RADICALS                                      #19

Sometimes it is convenient to leave square roots in radical form instead of using a calculator to find approximations (decimal values). Look for perfect squares (i.e., 4, 9, 16, 25, 36, 49, ...) as **factors** of the number that is inside the radical sign (**radicand**) and take the square root of any perfect square factor. Multiply the root of the perfect square times the reduced radical. When there is an existing value that multiplies the radical, multiply any root(s) times that value.

For example:

$$\sqrt{9} = 3 \qquad\qquad\qquad 5\sqrt{9} = 5 \cdot 3 = 15$$

$$\sqrt{18} = \sqrt{9 \cdot 2} = \sqrt{9} \cdot \sqrt{2} = 3\sqrt{2} \qquad 3\sqrt{98} = 3\sqrt{49 \cdot 2} = 3 \cdot 7\sqrt{2} = 21\sqrt{2}$$

$$\sqrt{80} = \sqrt{16 \cdot 5} = \sqrt{16} \cdot \sqrt{5} = 4\sqrt{5} \qquad \sqrt{45} + 4\sqrt{20} = \sqrt{9 \cdot 5} + 4\sqrt{4 \cdot 5} = 3\sqrt{5} + 4 \cdot 2\sqrt{5} = 11\sqrt{5}$$

When there are no more perfect square factors inside the radical sign, the product of the whole number (or fraction) and the remaining radical is said to be in **simple radical form**.

Simple radical form does not allow radicals in the denominator of a fraction. If there is a radical in the denominator, **rationalize the denominator** by multiplying the numerator and denominator of the fraction by the radical in the original denominator. Then simplify the remaining fraction. Examples:

$$\frac{2}{\sqrt{2}} = \frac{2}{\sqrt{2}} \cdot \frac{\sqrt{2}}{\sqrt{2}} = \frac{2\sqrt{2}}{2} = \sqrt{2} \qquad\qquad \frac{4\sqrt{5}}{\sqrt{6}} = \frac{4\sqrt{5}}{\sqrt{6}} \cdot \frac{\sqrt{6}}{\sqrt{6}} = \frac{4\sqrt{30}}{6} = \frac{2\sqrt{30}}{3}$$

In the first example, $\sqrt{2} \cdot \sqrt{2} = \sqrt{4} = 2$ and $\frac{2}{2} = 1$. In the second example,

$\sqrt{6} \cdot \sqrt{6} = \sqrt{36} = 6$ and $\frac{4}{6} = \frac{2}{3}$.

The rules for radicals used in the above examples are shown below. Assume that the variables represent non-negative numbers.

(1) $\sqrt{x} \cdot \sqrt{y} = \sqrt{xy}$     (2) $\sqrt{x \cdot y} = \sqrt{x} \cdot \sqrt{y}$     (3) $\frac{\sqrt{x}}{\sqrt{y}} = \sqrt{\frac{x}{y}}$

(4) $\sqrt{x^2} = (\sqrt{x})^2 = x$     (5) $a\sqrt{x} + b\sqrt{x} = (a + b)\sqrt{x}$

Write each expression in simple radical (square root) form.

1. $\sqrt{32}$

2. $\sqrt{28}$

3. $\sqrt{54}$

4. $\sqrt{68}$

5. $2\sqrt{24}$

6. $5\sqrt{90}$

7. $6\sqrt{132}$

8. $5\sqrt{200}$

9. $2\sqrt{6} \cdot 3\sqrt{2}$

10. $3\sqrt{12} \cdot 2\sqrt{3}$

11. $\frac{\sqrt{12}}{\sqrt{3}}$

12. $\frac{\sqrt{20}}{\sqrt{5}}$

13. $\frac{8\sqrt{12}}{2\sqrt{3}}$

14. $\frac{14\sqrt{8}}{7\sqrt{2}}$

15. $\frac{2}{\sqrt{3}}$

16. $\frac{4}{\sqrt{5}}$

17. $\frac{6}{\sqrt{3}}$

18. $\frac{2\sqrt{3}}{\sqrt{6}}$

19. $2\sqrt{3} + 3\sqrt{12}$

20. $4\sqrt{12} - 2\sqrt{3}$

21. $6\sqrt{3} + 2\sqrt{27}$

22. $2\sqrt{45} - 2\sqrt{5}$

23. $2\sqrt{8} - \sqrt{18}$

24. $3\sqrt{48} - 4\sqrt{27}$

## Answers

1. $4\sqrt{2}$

2. $2\sqrt{7}$

3. $3\sqrt{6}$

4. $2\sqrt{17}$

5. $4\sqrt{6}$

6. $15\sqrt{10}$

7. $12\sqrt{33}$

8. $50\sqrt{2}$

9. $12\sqrt{3}$

10. 36

11. 2

12. 2

13. 8

14. 4

15. $\frac{2\sqrt{3}}{3}$

16. $\frac{4\sqrt{5}}{5}$

17. $2\sqrt{3}$

18. $\sqrt{2}$

19. $8\sqrt{3}$

20. $6\sqrt{3}$

21. $12\sqrt{3}$

22. $4\sqrt{5}$

23. $\sqrt{2}$

24. 0

# THE QUADRATIC FORMULA                                    #20

You have used factoring and the Zero Product Property to solve quadratic equations. You can solve <u>any</u> quadratic equation by using the **quadratic formula.**

If   $ax^2 + bx + c = 0$,        then   $x = \dfrac{-b \pm \sqrt{b^2 - 4ac}}{2a}$ .

For example, suppose $3x^2 + 7x - 6 = 0$. Here $a = 3$, $b = 7$, and $c = -6$.
Substituting these values into the formula results in:

$$x = \frac{-(7) \pm \sqrt{7^2 - 4(3)(-6)}}{2(3)} \quad \Rightarrow \quad x = \frac{-7 \pm \sqrt{121}}{6} \quad \Rightarrow \quad x = \frac{-7 \pm 11}{6}$$

Remember that non-negative numbers have both a positive and negative square root.
The sign $\pm$ represents this fact for the square root in the formula and allows us to write the equation <u>once</u> (representing two possible solutions) until later in the solution process.

Split the numerator into the two values:     $x = \dfrac{-7 + 11}{6}$ or $x = \dfrac{-7 - 11}{6}$

Thus the solution for the quadratic equation is:        $x = \dfrac{2}{3}$ or -3.

## Example 1

Solve: $x^2 + 7x + 5 = 0$

First make sure the equation is in standard form with zero on one side of the equation. This equation is already in standard form.

Second, list the numerical values of the coefficients a, b, and c. Since $ax^2 + bx + c = 0$, then $a = 1$, $b = 7$, and $c = 5$ for the equation $x^2 + 7x + 5 = 0$.

Write out the quadratic formula (see above). Substitute the numerical values of the coefficients a, b, and c in the quadratic

formula, $x = \dfrac{-7 \pm \sqrt{7^2 - 4(1)(5)}}{2(1)}$ .

Simplify to get the exact solutions.

$x = \dfrac{-7 \pm \sqrt{49 - 20}}{2} \Rightarrow x = \dfrac{-7 \pm \sqrt{29}}{2}$,

so  $x = \dfrac{-7 + \sqrt{29}}{2}$  or  $\dfrac{-7 - \sqrt{29}}{2}$

Use a calculator to get approximate solutions.

$x \approx \dfrac{-7 + 5.39}{2} \approx \dfrac{-1.61}{2} \approx -0.81$

$x \approx \dfrac{-7 - 5.39}{2} \approx \dfrac{-12.39}{2} \approx -6.20$

## Example 2

Solve: $6x^2 + 1 = 8x$

First make sure the equation is in standard form with zero on one side of the equation.

$\begin{array}{r} 6x^2 + 1 = 8x \\ -8x \quad -8x \\ \hline \end{array} \Rightarrow 6x^2 - 8x + 1 = 0$

Second, list the numerical values of the coefficients a, b, and c: $a = 6$, $b = -8$, and $c = 1$ for this equation.

Write out the quadratic formula, then substitute the values in the formula.

$x = \dfrac{-(-8) \pm \sqrt{(-8)^2 - 4(6)(1)}}{2(6)}$

Simplify to get the exact solutions.

$x = \dfrac{8 \pm \sqrt{64 - 24}}{12} \Rightarrow x = \dfrac{8 \pm \sqrt{40}}{12} \Rightarrow \dfrac{8 \pm 2\sqrt{10}}{12}$

so  $x = \dfrac{4 + \sqrt{10}}{6}$  or  $\dfrac{4 - \sqrt{10}}{6}$

Use a calculator with the original answer to get approximate solutions.

$x \approx \dfrac{8 + 6.32}{12} \approx \dfrac{14.32}{12} \approx 1.19$

$x \approx \dfrac{8 - 6.32}{12} \approx \dfrac{1.68}{12} \approx 0.14$

Use the quadratic formula to solve the following equations.

1. $x^2 + 8x + 6 = 0$

2. $x^2 + 6x + 4 = 0$

3. $x^2 - 2x - 30 = 0$

4. $x^2 - 5x - 2 = 0$

5. $7 = 13x - x^2$

6. $15x - x^2 = 5$

7. $x^2 = -14x - 12$

8. $6x = x^2 + 3$

9. $3x^2 + 10x + 5 = 0$

10. $2x^2 + 8x + 5 = 0$

11. $5x^2 + 5x - 7 = 0$

12. $6x^2 - 2x - 3 = 0$

13. $2x^2 + 9x = -1$

14. $-6x + 6x^2 = 8$

15. $3x - 12 = -4x^2$

16. $10x^2 + 2x = 7$

17. $2x^2 - 11 = 0$

18. $3x^2 - 6 = 0$

19. $3x^2 + 0.75x - 1.5 = 0$

20. $0.1x^2 + 5x + 2.6 = 0$

## Answers

1. $x \approx -0.84$ and $-7.16$

2. $x \approx -0.76$ and $-5.24$

3. $x \approx 6.57$ and $-4.57$

4. $x \approx 5.37$ and $-0.37$

5. $x \approx 12.44$ and $0.56$

6. $x \approx 14.66$ and $0.34$

7. $x \approx -0.92$ and $-13.08$

8. $x \approx 5.45$ and $0.55$

9. $x \approx -0.61$ and $-2.72$

10. $x \approx -0.78$ and $-3.22$

11. $x \approx 0.78$ and $-1.78$

12. $x \approx 0.89$ and $-0.56$

13. $x \approx -0.11$ and $-4.39$

14. $x \approx 1.76$ and $-0.76$

15. $x \approx 1.40$ and $-2.15$

16. $x \approx 0.74$ and $-0.94$

17. $x \approx -2.35$ and $2.35$

18. $x \approx -1.41$ and $1.41$

19. $x \approx 0.59$ and $-0.84$

20. $x \approx -0.53$ and $-49.47$

# SIMPLIFYING RATIONAL EXPRESSIONS #21

**Rational expressions** are fractions that have algebraic expressions in their numerators and/or denominators. To simplify rational expressions find **factors** in the numerator and denominator that are the same and then write them as fractions equal to 1. For example,

$$\frac{6}{6} = 1 \qquad \frac{x^2}{x^2} = 1 \qquad \frac{(x + 2)}{(x + 2)} = 1 \qquad \frac{(3x - 2)}{(3x - 2)} = 1$$

Notice that the last two examples involved binomial sums and differences. **Only** when sums or differences are **exactly** the same does the fraction equal 1. Rational expressions such as the examples below **cannot** be simplified:

$$\frac{(6 + 5)}{6} \qquad\qquad \frac{x^3 + y}{x^3} \qquad\qquad \frac{x}{x + 2} \qquad\qquad \frac{3x - 2}{2}$$

Most problems that involve rational expressions will require that you **factor** the numerator and denominator. For example:

$$\frac{12}{54} = \frac{2 \cdot 2 \cdot 3}{2 \cdot 3 \cdot 3 \cdot 3} = \frac{2}{9} \qquad \text{Notice that } \frac{2}{2} \text{ and } \frac{3}{3} \text{ each equal 1.}$$

$$\frac{6x^3y^2}{15x^2y^4} = \frac{2 \cdot 3 \cdot x^2 \cdot x \cdot y^2}{5 \cdot 3 \cdot x^2 \cdot y^2 \cdot y^2} = \frac{2x}{5y^2} \qquad \text{Notice that } \frac{3}{3}, \frac{x^2}{x^2}, \text{ and } \frac{y^2}{y^2} = 1.$$

$$\frac{x^2 - x - 6}{x^2 - 5x + 6} = \frac{(x + 2)(x - 3)}{(x - 2)(x - 3)} = \frac{x + 2}{x - 2} \qquad \text{where } \frac{x - 3}{x - 3} = 1.$$

All three examples demonstrate that **all parts** of the numerator and denominator--whether constants, monomials, binomials, or factorable trinomials--must be written as products **before** you can look for factors that equal 1.

One special situation is shown in the following examples:

$$\frac{-2}{2} = -1 \qquad \frac{-x}{x} = -1 \qquad \frac{-x - 2}{x + 2} = \frac{-(x + 2)}{x + 2} = -1 \qquad \frac{5 - x}{x - 5} = \frac{-(x - 5)}{x - 5} = -1$$

Note that in all cases we assume the denominator does not equal zero.

## Example 1

Simplify: $\dfrac{(a^3b^{-2})^2}{a^4}$

Rewrite the numerator and denominator without negative exponents and parentheses.

$$\dfrac{(a^3b^{-2})^2}{a^4} \Rightarrow \dfrac{a^6b^{-4}}{a^4} \Rightarrow \dfrac{a^6}{a^4b^4}$$

Then look for the same pairs of factors that equal one (1) when divided. Writing out all of the factors can be helpful.

$$\dfrac{a\cdot a\cdot a\cdot a\cdot a\cdot a}{a\cdot a\cdot a\cdot a\cdot b\cdot b\cdot b\cdot b} = 1\cdot 1\cdot 1\cdot 1\cdot \dfrac{a\cdot a}{b\cdot b\cdot b\cdot b}$$

Write the simplified expression with exponents.

$\dfrac{(a^3b^{-2})^2}{a^4} = \dfrac{a^2}{b^4}$, $b \neq 0$. Note that $\dfrac{a}{a} = 1$.

## Example 2

Simplify: $\dfrac{2x^2-13x-7}{x^2-4x-21}$

To simplify some rational expressions, the numerator and/or denominator may need to be factored before you may simplify the expression.

$$\dfrac{2x^2-13x-7}{x^2-4x-21} \Rightarrow \dfrac{(2x+1)(x-7)}{(x-7)(x+3)}$$

Then look for the same pairs of factors that equal one (1) when divided.

$$\dfrac{(2x+1)(x-7)}{(x+3)(x-7)} \Rightarrow \dfrac{2x+1}{x+3}\cdot 1 \Rightarrow \dfrac{2x+1}{x+3} \text{ for } x \neq \text{-3 or 7.}$$

Note that $\dfrac{(x-7)}{(x-7)} = 1$.

Simplify the following expressions. Assume that the denominator is not equal to zero.

1. $\dfrac{12x^2y^4}{3x^2y^3}$

2. $\dfrac{10a^6b^8}{40a^2b^2}$

3. $\dfrac{(x^5y^3)^3}{x^{12}y}$

4. $\dfrac{(a^5)^2}{a^{13}b^6}$

5. $\dfrac{(5x^3)^2y^3}{10xy^9}$

6. $\dfrac{3(a^3)^5b}{(3a^4)^3b^{10}}$

7. $\dfrac{4ab^{-5}}{a^8b}$

8. $\dfrac{2x^{-3}y^8}{4x^{-2}}$

9. $\dfrac{(x^8y^{-3})^{-2}}{x^2}$

10. $\dfrac{2x^3y^{-1}}{6(4x)^{-2}y^7}$

11. $\dfrac{(2x-1)(x+3)}{(x-5)(x+3)}$

12. $\dfrac{(5x-1)(x+2)}{(x+7)(5x-1)}$

13. $\dfrac{3x+1}{3x^2+10x+3}$

14. $\dfrac{x^2-x-20}{x-5}$

15. $\dfrac{3x-6}{x^2+4x-12}$

16. $\dfrac{2x^2-x-3}{10x-15}$

17. $\dfrac{3x^2+x-10}{x^2+6x+8}$

18. $\dfrac{x^2-64}{x^2+16x+64}$

19. $\dfrac{4x^2-x}{4x^3+11x^2-3x}$

20. $\dfrac{2x^3+2x^2-12x}{8x^2-8x-16}$

## Answers

1. $4y$

2. $\dfrac{a^4b^6}{4}$

3. $\dfrac{x^{15}y^9}{x^{12}y} = x^3y^8$

4. $\dfrac{a^{10}}{a^{13}b^6} = \dfrac{1}{a^3b^6}$

5. $\dfrac{25x^6y^3}{10xy^9} = \dfrac{5x^5}{2y^6}$

6. $\dfrac{3a^{15}b}{27a^{12}b^{10}} = \dfrac{a^3}{9b^9}$

7. $\dfrac{4a}{a^8b^6} = \dfrac{4}{a^7b^6}$

8. $\dfrac{2x^2y^8}{4x^3} = \dfrac{y^8}{2x}$

9. $\dfrac{x^{-16}y^6}{x^2} = \dfrac{y^6}{x^{18}}$

10. $\dfrac{32x^5}{6y^8} = \dfrac{16x^5}{3y^8}$

11. $\dfrac{2x-1}{x-5}$

12. $\dfrac{x+2}{x+7}$

13. $\dfrac{3x+1}{(x+3)(3x+1)} = \dfrac{1}{x+3}$

14. $\dfrac{(x-5)(x+4)}{x-5} = x+4$

15. $\dfrac{3(x-2)}{(x-2)(x+6)} = \dfrac{3}{x+6}$

16. $\dfrac{(2x-3)(x+1)}{5(2x-3)} = \dfrac{x+1}{5}$

17. $\dfrac{(3x-5)(x+2)}{(x+4)(x+2)} = \dfrac{3x-5}{x+4}$

18. $\dfrac{(x+8)(x-8)}{(x+8)(x+8)} = \dfrac{x-8}{x+8}$

19. $\dfrac{x(4x-1)}{x(4x-1)(x+3)} = \dfrac{1}{x+3}$

20. $\dfrac{2x(x+3)(x-2)}{8(x-2)(x+1)} = \dfrac{x(x+3)}{4(x+1)} = \dfrac{x^2+3x}{4x+4}$

## MULTIPLICATION AND DIVISION OF RATIONAL EXPRESSIONS    #22

To multiply or divide rational expressions, follow the same procedures used with numerical fractions. However, it is often necessary to factor the polynomials in order to simplify the rational expression.

## Example 1

Multiply $\dfrac{x^2+6x}{(x+6)^2} \cdot \dfrac{x^2+7x+6}{x^2-1}$ and simplify the result.

After factoring, the expression becomes:

$$\dfrac{x(x+6)}{(x+6)(x+6)} \cdot \dfrac{(x+6)(x+1)}{(x+1)(x-1)}$$

After multiplying, reorder the factors:

$$\dfrac{(x+6)}{(x+6)} \cdot \dfrac{(x+6)}{(x+6)} \cdot \dfrac{x}{(x-1)} \cdot \dfrac{(x+1)}{(x+1)}$$

Since $\dfrac{(x+6)}{(x+6)} = 1$ and $\dfrac{(x+1)}{(x+1)} = 1$, simplify:

$$1 \cdot 1 \cdot \dfrac{x}{x-1} \cdot 1 \;=>\; \dfrac{x}{x-1}.$$

Note: $x \neq$ -6, -1, or 1.

## Example 2

Divide $\dfrac{x^2-4x-5}{x^2-4x+4} \div \dfrac{x^2-2x-15}{x^2+4x-12}$ and simplify the result.

First, change to a multiplication expression by inverting (flipping) the second fraction:

$$\dfrac{x^2-4x-5}{x^2-4x+4} \cdot \dfrac{x^2+4x-12}{x^2-2x-15}$$

After factoring, the expression is:

$$\dfrac{(x-5)(x+1)}{(x-2)(x-2)} \cdot \dfrac{(x+6)(x-2)}{(x-5)(x+3)}$$

Reorder the factors (if you need to):

$$\dfrac{(x-5)}{(x-5)} \cdot \dfrac{(x-2)}{(x-2)} \cdot \dfrac{(x+1)}{(x-2)} \cdot \dfrac{(x+6)}{(x+3)}$$

Since $\dfrac{(x-5)}{(x-5)} = 1$ and $\dfrac{(x-2)}{(x-2)} = 1$, simplify:

$$\dfrac{(x+1)(x+6)}{(x-2)(x+3)}$$

Thus, $\dfrac{x^2-4x-5}{x^2-4x+4} \div \dfrac{x^2-2x-15}{x^2+4x-12} = \dfrac{(x+1)(x+6)}{(x-2)(x+3)}$ or $\dfrac{x^2+7x+6}{x^2+x-6}$. Note: $x \neq$ -3, 2, or 5.

Multiply or divide each expression below and simplify the result. Assume the denominator is not equal to zero.

1.   $\dfrac{3x+6}{5x} \cdot \dfrac{x+4}{x^2+2x}$

2.   $\dfrac{8a}{a^2-16} \cdot \dfrac{a+4}{4}$

3.   $\dfrac{x^2-1}{3} \cdot \dfrac{2}{x^2-x}$

4.   $\dfrac{x^2-x-12}{x^2} \cdot \dfrac{x}{x-4}$

5.   $\dfrac{x^2-16}{(x-4)^2} \cdot \dfrac{x^2-3x-18}{x^2-2x-24}$

6.   $\dfrac{x^2+6x+8}{x^2-4x+3} \cdot \dfrac{x^2-5x+4}{5x+10}$

7. $\frac{x^2-x-6}{x^2-x-20} \cdot \frac{x^2+6x+8}{x^2-x-6}$

8. $\frac{x^2-x-30}{x^2+13x+40} \cdot \frac{x^2+11x+24}{x^2-9x+18}$

9. $\frac{3x+12}{x^2} \div \frac{x+4}{x}$

10. $\frac{2a+6}{a^3} \div \frac{a+3}{a}$

11. $\frac{15-5x}{x^2-x-6} \div \frac{5x}{x^2+6x+8}$

12. $\frac{17x+119}{x^2+5x-14} \div \frac{9x-1}{x^2-3x+2}$

13. $\frac{x^2+8x}{9x} \div \frac{x^2-64}{3x^2}$

14. $\frac{x^2-1}{x^2-6x-7} \div \frac{x^3+x^2-2x}{x-7}$

15. $\frac{2x^2-5x-3}{3x^2-10x+3} \div \frac{4x^2+4x+1}{9x^2-1}$

16. $\frac{x^2+3x-10}{x^2+3x} \div \frac{x^2-4x+4}{4x+12}$

17. $\frac{x^2-x-6}{x^2+3x-10} \cdot \frac{x^2+2x-15}{x^2-6x+9} \cdot \frac{x^2+4x-21}{x^2+9x+14}$

18. $\frac{3x^2+21x}{x^2-49} \cdot \frac{x^2-x}{6x^3-9x^2} \cdot \frac{4x^2-9}{3x-3}$

19. $\frac{4x^3+7x-2x}{2x^2-162} \div \frac{4x^2+15x-4}{12x-60} \cdot \frac{x^2+9x}{x^2-3x-10}$

20. $\frac{10x^2-11x+3}{x^2-6x-40} \cdot \frac{x^2+11x+28}{2x^2-x} \div \frac{x+7}{2x^2-20x}$

## Answers

1. $\frac{3(x+4)}{5x^2} = \frac{3x+12}{5x^2}$

2. $\frac{2a}{a-4}$

3. $\frac{2(x+1)}{3x} = \frac{2x+2}{3x}$

4. $\frac{x+3}{x}$

5. $\frac{(x+3)}{(x-4)}$

6. $\frac{(x+4)(x-4)}{5(x-3)} = \frac{x^2-16}{5x-15}$

7. $\frac{(x+2)}{(x-5)}$

8. $\frac{(x+3)}{(x-3)}$

9. $\frac{3}{x}$

10. $\frac{2}{a^2}$

11. $\frac{-(x+4)}{x} = \frac{-x-4}{x}$

12. $\frac{17(x-1)}{9x-1} = \frac{17x-17}{9x-1}$

13. $\frac{x^2}{3(x-8)} = \frac{x^2}{3x-24}$

14. $\frac{1}{x(x+2)}$

15. $\frac{(3x+1)}{(2x+1)}$

16. $\frac{4(x+5)}{x(x-2)} = \frac{4x+20}{x^2-2x}$

17. $\frac{(x-3)}{(x-2)}$

18. $\frac{2x+3}{3(x-7)} = \frac{2x+3}{3x-21}$

19. $\frac{6x^2}{(x-9)(x+4)} = \frac{6x^2}{x^2-5x-36}$

20. $\frac{2(5x-3)}{1} = 10x - 6$

## ABSOLUTE VALUE EQUATIONS

Absolute value means the distance from a reference point. In the simplest case, the absolute value of a number is its distance from zero on the number line. Since absolute value is a distance, the result of finding an absolute value is zero or a positive number. All distances are positive.

## Example 1

Solve $|2x + 3| = 7$.

Because the result of $(2x + 3)$ can be 7 or -7, we can write and solve two different equations. (Remember that the absolute value of 7 and -7 will be 7.)

$$2x + 3 = 7 \text{ or } 2x + 3 = -7$$
$$2x = 4 \text{ or } 2x = -10$$
$$x = 2 \text{ or } x = -5$$

## Example 2

Solve $2|2x + 13| = 10$.

First the equation must have the absolute value isolated on one side of the equation.

$$2|2x + 13| = 10 \implies |2x + 13| = 5$$

Because the result of $2x + 13$ can be 5 or -5, we can write and solve two different equations.

$$2x + 13 = 5 \text{ or } 2x + 13 = -5$$
$$2x = -8 \text{ or } 2x = -18$$
$$x = -4 \text{ or } x = -9$$

Note that while some x-values of the solution are negative, the goal is to find values that make the original absolute value statement true. For $x = -5$ in example 1, $|2(-5) + 3| = 7 \implies |-10 + 3| = 7$ $\implies |-7| = 7$, which is true. Verify that the two negative values of $x$ in example 2 make the original absolute value equation true.

Solve for x.

1.  $|x + 2| = 4$

2.  $|3x| = 27$

3.  $|x - 5| = 2$

4.  $|x - 8| = 2$

5.  $\left|\frac{x}{5}\right| = 2$

6.  $|-3x| = 4$

7.  $|3x + 4| = 10$

8.  $|12x - 6| = 6$

9.  $|x| + 3 = 20$

10.  $|x| - 8 = -2$

11.  $2|x| - 5 = 3$

12.  $4|x| - 5 = 7$

13.  $|x + 2| - 3 = 7$

14.  $|x + 5| + 4 = 12$

15.  $|2x - 3| + 2 = 11$

16.  $-3|x| + 5 = -4$

17.  $-3|x + 6| + 12 = 0$

18.  $15 - |x + 1| = 3$

19.  $14 + 2|3x + 5| = 26$

20.  $4|x - 10| - 23 = 37$

# Answers

1.  x = 2, -6

2.  x = 9, -9

3.  x = 7, 3

4.  x = 10, 6

5.  x = 10, -10

6.  $x = -\frac{4}{3}, \frac{4}{3}$

7.  $x = 2, -\frac{14}{3}$

8.  x = 1, 0

9.  x = 17, -17

10. x = 6, -6

11. x = 4, -4

12. x = 3, -3

13. x = 8, -12

14. x = 3, -13

15. x = 6, -3

16. x = 3, -3

17. x = -2, -10

18. x = 11, -13

19. $x = \frac{1}{3}, -\frac{11}{3}$

20. x = 25, -5

## USING ELIMINATION (ADDITION) TO FIND     #24
## THE POINT OF INTERSECTION OF TWO LINES

The **elimination** method can be used to solve a system of linear equations. By adding or subtracting the two linear equations in a way that eliminates one of the variables, a single variable equation is left.

## Example 1

Solve: $\begin{array}{l} x + 2y = 16 \\ x + y = 2 \end{array}$

First decide whether to add or subtract the equations. Remember that the addition or subtraction should <u>eliminate</u> one variable. In the system above, the x in each equation is positive, so we need to subtract, that is, change all the signs of the terms in the second equation.

$$\begin{array}{l} x + 2y = 16 \\ -(x + y = 2) \end{array} \Rightarrow \begin{array}{l} x + 2y = 16 \\ -x - y = -2 \end{array} \Rightarrow y = 14$$

Substitute the solution for y into either of the original equations to solve for the other variable, x.

$$x + 2(14) = 16 \Rightarrow x = -12$$

Check your solution (-12, 14) in the second equation. You could also use the first equation to check your solution.

$$-12 + 14 = 2 \Rightarrow 2 = 2 \sqrt{}$$

## Example 2

Solve: $\begin{array}{l} 2x + 3y = 10 \\ 3x - 4y = -2 \end{array}$

Sometimes the equations need to be adjusted by multiplication before they can be added or subtracted to eliminate a variable. Multiply one or both equations to set them up for elimination.

Multiply the first equation by 3:
$$3(2x + 3y) = 10(3) \Rightarrow 6x + 9y = 30$$

Multiply the second equation by -2:
$$-2(3x - 4y) = -2 \cdot (-2) \Rightarrow -6x + 8y = 4$$

Decide whether to add or subtract the equations to eliminate one variable. Since the x-terms are additive opposites, add these equations.

$$\begin{array}{l} 6x + 9y = 30 \\ -6x + 8y = \phantom{0}4 \\ \hline \phantom{-6x + }17y = 34 \text{ so } y = 2. \end{array}$$

Substitute the solution for y into either of the original equations to solve for the other variable.

$$2x + 3(2) = 10 \Rightarrow 2x = 4 \Rightarrow x = 2 \sqrt{}$$

Check the solution (2, 2) in the second equation.
$$3(2) - 4(2) = -2 \Rightarrow 6 - 8 = -2 \Rightarrow -2 = -2 \sqrt{}$$

Solve each system of linear equations using the Elimination Method.

1.  $x + y = -4$
    $-x + 2y = 13$

2.  $3x - y = 1$
    $-2x + y = 2$

3.  $2x + 5y = 1$
    $2x - y = 19$

4.  $x + 3y = 1$
    $2x + 3y = -4$

5.  $x - 5y = 1$
    $x - 4y = 2$

6.  $3x - 2y = -2$
    $5x - 2y = 10$

7.  $x + y = 10$
    $15x + 28y = 176$

8.  $x + 2y = 21$
    $9x + 24y = 243$

9.  $4x + 3y = 7$
    $2x - 9y = 35$

10. $2x + 3y = 0$
    $6x - 5y = -28$

11. $7x - 3y = 37$
    $2x - y = 12$

12. $5x - 4y = 10$
    $3x - 2y = 6$

13. $x - 7y = 4$
    $3x + y = -10$

14. $y = -4x + 3$
    $3x + 5y = -19$

15. $2x - 3y = 50$
    $7x + 8y = -10$

16. $5x + 6y = 16$
    $3x = 4y + 2$

17. $3x + 2y = 14$
    $3y = -2x + 1$

18. $2x + 3y = 10$
    $5x - 4y = 2$

19. $5x + 2y = 9$
    $2x + 3y = -3$

20. $10x + 3y = 15$
    $3x - 2y = -10$

# Answers

1.  (-7, 3)

2.  (3, 8)

3.  (8, -3)

4.  (-5, 2)

5.  (6, 1)

6.  (6, 10)

7.  (8, 2)

8.  (3, 9)

9.  (4, -3)

10. (-3, 2)

11. (1, -10)

12. (2, 0)

13. (-3, -1)

14. (2, -5)

15. (10, -10)

16. (2, 1)

17. (8, -5)

18. (2, 2)

19. (3, -3)

20. (0, 5)

When an equation has a solution, depending on the type of equation, the solution can be represented as a point on a line or a point, line, or curve in the coordinate plane. Dividing points, lines, and curves are used to solve inequalities.

If the inequality has one variable, the solution can be represented on a line. To solve any type of inequality, first solve it as you would if it were an equation. Use the solution(s) as dividing point(s) of the line. Then test a value from each region on the number line. If the test value makes the inequality true, then that region is part of the solution. If it is false then the value and thus that region is not part of the solution. In addition, if the inequality is $\geq$ or $\leq$ then the dividing point is part of the solution and is indicated by a solid dot. If the inequality is $>$ or $<$, then the dividing point is not part of the solution and is indicated by an open dot.

## Example 1

Solve $-2x - 3 \geq x + 6$

Solve the equation
$$-2x - 3 = x + 6$$
$$-2x = x + 9$$
$$-3x = 9$$
$$x = -3$$

Draw a number line and put a solid dot at $x = -3$, which is the dividing point.

Test a value from each region. Here we test -4 and 0. Be sure to use the original inequality.

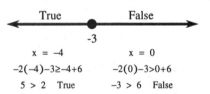

The region(s) that are true represent the solution. The solution is $-3$ and all numbers in the left region, written: $x \leq -3$.

## Example 2

Solve $x^2 - 2x + 2 < 5$

Solve the equation
$$x^2 - 2x + 2 = 5$$
$$x^2 - 2x - 3 = 0$$
$$(x - 3)(x + 1) = 0$$
$$x = 3 \quad \text{or} \quad x = -1$$

Draw a number line and put open dots at $x = 3$ and $x = -1$, the dividing points.

Test a value from each region in the original inequality. Here we test -3, 0, and 4.

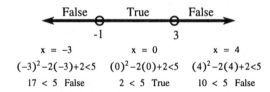

The region(s) that are true represent the solution. The solution is the set of all numbers greater than $-1$ but less than 3, written: $-1 < x < 3$.

If the inequality has two variables, then the solution is represented by a graph in the xy-coordinate plane. The graph of the inequality written as an equation (a line or curve) divides the coordinate plane into regions which are tested in the same manner described above using an ordered pair for a point on a side of the dividing line or curve. If the inequality is $>$ or $<$, then the boundary line or curve is dashed. If the inequality is $\geq$ or $\leq$, then the boundary line or curve is solid.

# Example 3

Graph and shade the solution to this system of inequalities $\begin{cases} y \le \dfrac{2}{5}x \\ y > 5 - x \end{cases}$

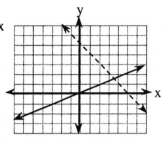

Graph each equation. For $y = \dfrac{2}{5}x$ the slope of the solid line is $\dfrac{2}{5}$ and y-intercept is 0. For $y = 5 - x$ the slope of the dashed line is $-1$ and the y-intercept is 5.

Test a point from each region in <u>both</u> of the original inequalities.

| (0, 2) | (2, 0) | (4, 5) | (5, 1) |
|---|---|---|---|
| False in both | True in first, False in second | False in first, True in second | True in both |

The region that makes <u>both</u> statements (inequalities) true is the solution.

The solution is the region below the solid line $y = \dfrac{2}{5}x$ and above the dashed line $y = 5 - x$.

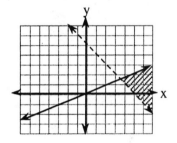

Solve and graph each inequality.

1. $x + 12 \ge 2x - 5$

2. $-16 + 4x > 10 - x$

3. $7x - 2x - x \ge 24 + 3x$

4. $3(x - 4) - 9x \ge 2x - 4$

5. $|x - 1| < 5$

6. $|x + 10| > 5$

7. $|12x| \ge 24$

8. $\left|\dfrac{x}{3}\right| < 8$

9. $x^2 + 3x - 10 \le 0$

10. $x^2 - 7x + 6 > 0$

11. $x^2 + 2x - 8 \le 7$

12. $x^2 - 5x - 16 > -2$

13. $y < 2x + 1$

14. $y \le -\dfrac{2}{3}x + 3$

15. $y \ge \dfrac{1}{4}x - 2$

16. $2x - 3y \le 5$

17. $y \ge -2$

18. $-3x - 4y > 4$

19. $y \le \dfrac{1}{2}x + 2$ and $y > -\dfrac{2}{3}x - 1$.

20. $y \le -\dfrac{3}{5}x + 4$ and $y \le \dfrac{1}{3}x + 3$

21. $y < 3$ and $y \le -\dfrac{1}{2}x + 2$

22. $x \le 3$ and $y < \dfrac{3}{4}x - 4$

23. $y \le x^2 + 4x + 3$

24. $y > x^2 - x - 2$

## Answers

1.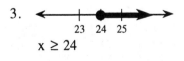

x ≤ 17

2. 

x > 5$\dfrac{1}{5}$

3. 

x ≥ 24

4.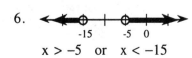

x ≤ −1

5. 

−4 < x < 6

6. 

x > −5   or   x < −15

7.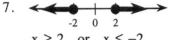

   x ≥ 2   or   x ≤ −2

8.

   −24 < x < 24

9.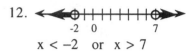

   −5 ≤ x ≤ 2

10.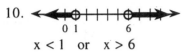

   x < 1   or   x > 6

11.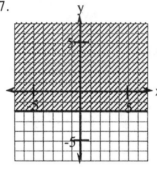

   −5 ≤ x ≤ 3

12.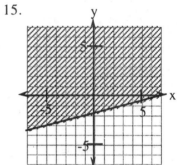

   x < −2   or   x > 7

13.
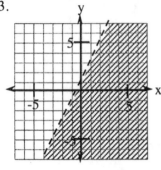

14.
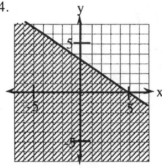

15.

16.
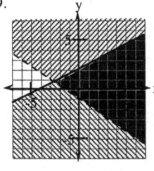

17.
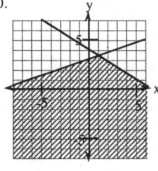

18.
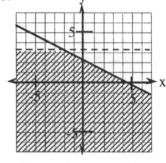

19.
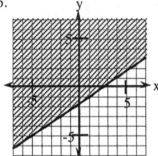

20.
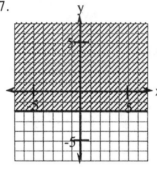

21.
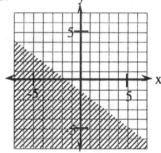

22.
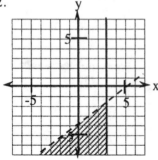

23.
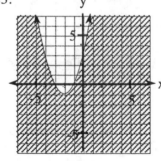

24.
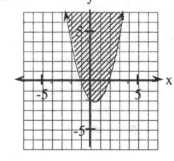

## ADDITION AND SUBTRACTION OF RATIONAL EXPRESSIONS     #26

Addition and subtraction of rational expressions is done the same way as addition and subtraction of numerical fractions. Change to a common denominator (if necessary), combine the numerators, and then simplify.

## Example 1

The Least Common Multiple (lowest common denominator) of $(x + 3)(x + 2)$ and $(x + 2)$ is $(x + 3)(x + 2)$.

$$\frac{4}{(x+2)(x+3)} + \frac{2x}{x+2}$$

The denominator of the first fraction already is the Least Common Multiple. To get a common denominator in the <u>second</u> fraction, multiply the fraction by $\frac{x+3}{x+3}$, a form of one (1).

$$= \frac{4}{(x+2)(x+3)} + \frac{2x}{x+2} \cdot \frac{(x+3)}{(x+3)}$$

Multiply the numerator and denominator of the second term:

$$= \frac{4}{(x+2)(x+3)} + \frac{2x(x+3)}{(x+2)(x+3)}$$

Distribute in the second numerator.

$$= \frac{4}{(x+2)(x+3)} + \frac{2x^2+6x}{(x+2)(x+3)}$$

Add, factor, and simplify. Note: $x \neq -2$ or $-3$.

$$= \frac{2x^2+6x+4}{(x+2)(x+3)} = \frac{2(x+1)(x+2)}{(x+2)(x+3)} = \frac{2(x+1)}{(x+3)}$$

## Example 2

Subtract $\frac{3}{x-1} - \frac{2}{x-2}$ and simplify the result.

Find the lowest common denominator of $(x - 1)$ and $(x - 2)$. It is $(x - 1)(x - 2)$.

In order to change each denominator into the lowest common denominator, we need to multiply each fraction by factors that are equal to one.

$$\frac{(x-2)}{(x-2)} \cdot \frac{3}{x-1} - \frac{2}{(x-2)} \cdot \frac{(x-1)}{(x-1)}$$

Multiply the denominators.

$$\frac{3(x-2)}{(x-2)(x-1)} - \frac{2(x-1)}{(x-2)(x-1)}$$

Multiply and distribute the numerators.

$$\frac{3x-6}{(x-2)(x-1)} - \frac{2x-2}{(x-2)(x-1)}$$

When adding fractions, the denominator does not change. The numerators need to be added or subtracted and like terms combined.

$$\frac{3x-6-(2x-2)}{(x-2)(x-1)} \Rightarrow \frac{3x-6-2x+2}{(x-2)(x-1)} \Rightarrow \frac{x-4}{(x-2)(x-1)}$$

Check that both the numerator and denominator are completely factored. If the answer can be simplified, simplify it. This answer is already simplified. Note: $x \neq 1$ or $2$.

$$\frac{x-4}{(x-2)(x-1)} = \frac{x-4}{x^2-3x+2}$$

Add or subtract the expressions and simplify the result.

1. $\dfrac{x}{(x+2)(x+3)} + \dfrac{2}{(x+2)(x+3)}$

2. $\dfrac{x}{x^2+6x+8} + \dfrac{4}{x^2+6x+8}$

3. $\dfrac{b^2}{b^2+2b-3} + \dfrac{-9}{b^2+2b-3}$

4. $\dfrac{2a}{a^2+2a+1} + \dfrac{2}{a^2+2a+1}$

5. $\dfrac{x+10}{x+2} + \dfrac{x-6}{x+2}$

6. $\dfrac{a+2b}{a+b} + \dfrac{2a+b}{a+b}$

7. $\dfrac{3x-4}{3x+3} - \dfrac{2x-5}{3x+3}$

8. $\dfrac{3x}{4x-12} - \dfrac{9}{4x-12}$

9. $\dfrac{6a}{5a^2+a} - \dfrac{a-1}{5a^2+a}$

10. $\dfrac{x^2+3x-5}{10} - \dfrac{x^2-2x+10}{10}$

11. $\dfrac{6}{x(x+3)} + \dfrac{2}{x+3}$

12. $\dfrac{5}{x-7} + \dfrac{3}{4(x-7)}$

13. $\dfrac{5x+6}{x^2} - \dfrac{5}{x}$

14. $\dfrac{2}{x+4} - \dfrac{x-4}{x^2-16}$

15. $\dfrac{10a}{a^2+6a} - \dfrac{3}{3a+18}$

16. $\dfrac{3x}{2x^2-8x} + \dfrac{2}{(x-4)}$

17. $\dfrac{5x+9}{x^2-2x-3} + \dfrac{6}{x^2-7x+12}$

18. $\dfrac{x+4}{x^2-3x-28} - \dfrac{x-5}{x^2+2x-35}$

19. $\dfrac{3x+1}{x^2-16} - \dfrac{3x+5}{x^2+8x+16}$

20. $\dfrac{7x-1}{x^2-2x-3} - \dfrac{6x}{x^2-x-2}$

## Answers

1. $\dfrac{1}{x+3}$

2. $\dfrac{1}{x+2}$

3. $\dfrac{b-3}{b-1}$

4. $\dfrac{2}{a+1}$

5. $2$

6. $3$

7. $\dfrac{1}{3}$

8. $\dfrac{3}{4}$

9. $\dfrac{1}{a}$

10. $\dfrac{x-3}{2}$

11. $\dfrac{2}{x}$

12. $\dfrac{23}{4(x-7)} = \dfrac{23}{4x-28}$

13. $\dfrac{6}{x^2}$

14. $\dfrac{1}{x+4}$

15. $\dfrac{9}{(a+6)}$

16. $\dfrac{7}{2(x-4)} = \dfrac{7}{2x-8}$

17. $\dfrac{5(x+2)}{(x-4)(x+1)} = \dfrac{5x+10}{x^2-3x-4}$

18. $\dfrac{14}{(x+7)(x-7)} = \dfrac{14}{x^2-49}$

19. $\dfrac{4(5x+6)}{(x-4)(x+4)^2}$

20. $\dfrac{x+2}{(x-3)(x-2)} = \dfrac{x+2}{x^2-5x+6}$

Solve these various types of equations.

1. $2(x - 3) + 2 = -4$

2. $6 - 12x = 108$

3. $3x - 11 = 0$

4. $0 = 2x - 5$

5. $y = 2x - 3$
   $x + y = 15$

6. $ax - b = 0$
   (solve for x)

7. $0 = (2x - 5)(x + 3)$

8. $2(2x - 1) = -x + 5$

9. $x^2 + 5^2 = 13^2$

10. $2x + 1 = 7x - 15$

11. $\frac{5 - 2x}{3} = \frac{x}{5}$

12. $2x - 3y + 9 = 0$
    (solve for y)

13. $x^2 + 5x + 6 = 0$

14. $x^2 = y$
    $100 = y$

15. $x - y = 7$
    $y = 2x - 1$

16. $x^2 - 4x = 0$

17. $x^2 - 6 = -2$

18. $\frac{x}{2} + \frac{x}{3} = 2$

19. $x^2 + 7x + 9 = 3$

20. $y = x + 3$
    $x + 2y = 3$

21. $3x^2 + 7x + 2 = 0$

22. $\frac{x}{x + 1} = \frac{5}{7}$

23. $x^2 + 2x - 4 = 0$

24. $\frac{1}{x} + \frac{1}{3x} = 2$

25. $3x + y = 5$
    $x - y = 11$

26. $y = -\frac{3}{4}x + 4$
    $\frac{1}{4}x - y = 8$

27. $3x^2 = 8x$

28. $|x| = 4$

29. $\frac{2}{3}x + 1 = \frac{1}{2}x - 3$

30. $x^2 - 4x = 5$

31. $3x + 5y = 15$
    (solve for y)

32. $(3x)^2 + x^2 = 15^2$

33. $y = 11$
    $y = 2x^2 + 3x - 9$

34. $(x + 2)(x + 3)(x - 4) = 0$

35. $|x + 6| = 8$

36. $2(x + 3) = y + 2$
    $y + 2 = 8x$

37. $2x + 3y = 13$
    $x - 2y = -11$

38. $2x^2 = -x + 7$

39. $1 - \frac{5}{6x} = \frac{x}{6}$

40. $\frac{x - 1}{5} = \frac{3}{x + 1}$

41. $\sqrt{2x + 1} = 5$

42. $2|2x - 1| + 3 = 7$

43. $\sqrt{3x - 1} + 1 = 7$

44. $(x + 3)^2 = 49$

45. $\frac{4x - 1}{x - 1} = x + 1$

Solve these various types of inequalities.

46. $4x - 2 \le 6$

47. $4 - 3(x + 2) \ge 19$

48. $\frac{x}{2} > \frac{3}{7}$

49. $3(x + 2) \ge -9$

50. $-\frac{2}{3}x < 6$

51. $y < 2x - 3$

52. $|x| > 4$

53. $x^2 - 6x + 8 \le 0$

54. $|x + 3| > 5$

55. $2x^2 - 4x \ge 0$

56. $y \le -\frac{2}{3}x + 2$

57. $y \le -x + 2$
$y \le 3x - 6$

58. $|2x - 1| \le 9$

59. $5 - 3(x - 1) \ge -x + 2$

60. $y \le 4x + 16$
$y > -\frac{4}{3}x - 4$

## Answers

1. 0

2. -8.5

3. $\frac{11}{3}$

4. $\frac{5}{2}$

5. (6, 9)

6. $x = \frac{b}{a}$

7. $\frac{5}{2}$, -3

8. $\frac{7}{5}$

9. $\pm 12$

10. $\frac{16}{5}$

11. $\frac{25}{13}$

12. $y = \frac{2}{3}x + 3$

13. -2, -3

14. $(\pm 10, 100)$

15. (-6, -13)

16. 0, 4

17. $\pm 2$

18. $\frac{12}{5}$

19. -1. -6

20. (-1, 2)

21. $-\frac{1}{3}$, -2

22. $\frac{5}{2}$

23. $\frac{-2 \pm \sqrt{20}}{2}$

24. $\frac{2}{3}$

25. (4, -7)

26. (12, -5)

27. 0, $\frac{8}{3}$

28. $\pm 4$

29. -24

30. 5, -1

31. $y = -\frac{3}{5}x + 3$

32. $\approx \pm 4.74$

33. $(-4, 11)$ and $\left(\frac{5}{2}, 11\right)$

34. -2, -3, 4

35. 2, -14

36. (1, 6)

37. (-1, 5)

38. $\frac{1 \pm \sqrt{57}}{4}$

39. 1, 5

40. $\pm 4$

41. 12

42. $\frac{3}{2}$, $-\frac{1}{2}$

43. $\frac{37}{3}$

44. 4, -10

45. 0, 4

46. $x \le 2$

47. $x \le -7$

48. $x > \frac{6}{7}$

49. $x \ge -5$

50. $x > -9$

51. below

52. x>4, x<-4

53. $2 \le x \le 4$

54. x>2 or x< -8

55. x≤0 or x≥2

56. below

57. below

58. $-4 \le x \le 5$

59. $x \le 3$

60. below

**51.**

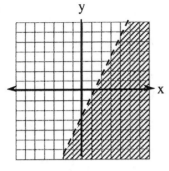

**56.**

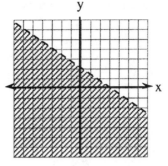

**57.**

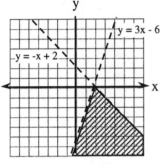

**60.**

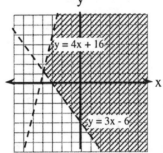

# Glossary

**absolute value**   The absolute value of a number is the distance of the number from zero. Since the absolute value represents a distance, without regard to direction, it is always non-negative. (381)

**additive identity**   The Additive Identity Property states that any term added to zero (0) remains unchanged; a + 0 = a. (393)

**additive inverse**   The Additive Inverse Property states that when opposites are added, the result is always zero: a + (-a) = 0. (393)

**additive property of equality**    The Additive Property of Equality states that equality is maintained if you add the same amount to both sides of an equation.  If a = b, then a + c = b + c. (393)

**algebra tiles**    The algebra tiles used in this course consist of large squares with dimensions  x by x, rectangles with dimensions  x by 1, and small squares with dimensions  1 by 1.  The areas of these tiles are $x^2$, x and 1 respectively.  We call the smallest squares unit squares.  (42)

**area**   For this course, area is the number of square units needed to fill up a region on a flat surface. The idea can be extended to cones, spheres, and more complex surfaces. (63)

**area of a triangle**    To find the area of a triangle, multiply the length of the base (b) by the height (h) and divide by two.  $A = \frac{1}{2}bh$.

**associative property**    The Associative Property states that if a sum or product contains terms that are grouped, then the sum or product can be grouped differently with no effect on the result; a + (b + c) = (a + b) + c  and  a(bc) = (ab)c. (393)

**average**   See mean.

**base**   In the expression $2^5$, 2 is called the base.  Also, 5 is the exponent and 32 is the value. The term "base" may also refer to sides of a triangle, rectangle, parallelogram, trapezoid, prism, cylinder, pyramid, and cone. (340)

**binomial**    The sum or difference of two monomials is called a binomial. (217, 269)

**circle**   A circle is the set of all points that are the same distance  r  from a fixed point  P.  The fixed point is called the center of the circle and the distance from the center to the points on the circle is called the radius. (61)

**circle (area of)**    $A = \pi r^2$, where r is the length of the radius of the circle. See area. (63)

**circumference**    The circumference C of a circle is its perimeter, that is, the distance around the circle.  $C = 2\pi r = \pi d$ (r = radius, d = 2r = diameter). (63)

**coefficient (numerical)**    The numeral part of a term, such as 6 in 6x. (350)

**common factor**    Factors which are the same for two or more terms. (137, 291)

**common term factoring** Factoring out a common (term) factor means identifying the common factor of the terms of a polynomial and then writing it outside the parentheses containing the sum of the factored terms. For example, $6x^2y - 9xy^2 = 3xy(2x - 3y)$. Factoring usually means using the Distributive Property: $ab + ac = a(b + c)$. (137, 291)

**Commutative Property** The Commutative Property states that if two terms are added or multiplied, the order is reversible. $a + b = b + a$ and $ab = ba$. (393)

**complete graph** A complete graph has the following components: (1) the x-axis and y-axis labeled, clearly showing the scale. (2) Equation of the graph written near the line or curve. (3) Line or curve extended as far as possible on the graph. (4) x- and y-intercepts labeled. (5) Coordinates of points stated in (x, y) form. (96)

**completing the square** A method for solving quadratic equations or writing quadratic functions in graphing form. (444)

**congruent** Two shapes (for example, triangles) are congruent if they have exactly the same size and shape.

**conjecture** An educated guess, based on data, patterns, and relationships. Scientists use the term hypothesis. (161)

**constant** A symbol representing a value that does not change. For example, in the equation $y = 2x + 5$, "5" is referred to as the constant. (202)

**coordinate** The number paired with a point on the number line or an ordered pair (x, y) that corresponds to a point in xy-coordinate system. (96)

**coordinate system** A system of graphing ordered pairs of numbers in relation to axes (horizontal and vertical) that intersect at right angles at their zero points (origin). (96)

**corresponding parts** Points, edges (sides), or angles in congruent or similar figures that are arranged in similar ways. For instance if $\triangle ABC$ is similar to $\triangle XYZ$, side $\overline{AB}$ corresponds to (matches) the side $\overline{XY}$. (158)

**degree (of a polynomial)** (1) The degree of a monomial is the sum of the exponents of its variables, such as $3x^2y^5$ has degree 7; (2) The degree of a polynomial is: (a) in one variable, the degree of the term with the highest exponent, such as $3x^5 - 4x^2 - x + 7$ has degree 5; (b) in more than one variable, the highest sum of the exponents among the terms, such as $2x^5y^3 - 4x^2x^4z^3 - xy^5 + 3y^2z -12$ has degree 9.

**dependent variable** The output variable, y, of a relation or function is called the dependent variable because its values are determined by the value of x that is used in the relation or function. (378)

**diagram** A problem-solving technique based on drawing a picture or diagram representing the problem. Including all the known information on the diagram helps us to see what is important and necessary in solving the problem. (308)

**diameter** A line segment drawn through the center of the circle with both endpoints on the circle is called a diameter of the circle, usually denoted d. Note: $d = 2r$, where r is the radius of the circle. (61)

**difference of squares** A special polynomial that can be factored as the product of the sum and difference of two terms. The general pattern is $x^2 - y^2 = (x + y)(x - y)$. (287)

**discriminant**   For quadratic equations in standard form $ax^2 + bx + c = 0$, the discriminant is $b^2 - 4ac$.

**distributive property**   For any numbers or expressions a, b, and c, $a(b + c) = ab + ac$. (74, 391, 393)

**dividing line (or boundary line)**   A line on a two dimensional graph that divides the graph into two regions. We use a dividing line or boundary line when graphing linear inequalities such as $y > 3x - 1$. (418)

**dividing point**   The endpoint of a segment on a number line where an inequality is true. For strict inequalities, that is, < or >, the point is not part of the solution. (411)

**domain**   The set of all input values for a relation or function. For variables, the set of numbers the variable may represent. For ordered pairs (x, y), all x-values. (111-12, 363, 378)

**elimination method**   (systems of equations)  A method for solving a system of equations by adding or subtracting the equations to eliminate one of the variables. (367, 370)

**ellipsis**   The symbol "..." is called an ellipsis. It indicates that certain values in an established pattern have not been written, although they are part of the pattern. (110)

**enlargement ratio**   The ratio of similarity comparing a figure to a similar larger one is often called the enlargement ratio. This number tells you by what factor the first figure is enlarged by to get the second. (165)

**equation**   A mathematical sentence with an equal sign (=).

**evaluate**   To evaluate an expression, substitute the value(s) given for the variable(s) and perform the operations according to the order of operations. (63)

**exponent**   In the expression $2^5$, 5 is called the exponent. Also, 2 is the base and 32 is the value. The exponent indicates how many times to use the number 2 as a multiplier, in this case, 5 times, $2 \cdot 2 \cdot 2 \cdot 2 \cdot 2 = 32$. (340)

**exponents (laws of)**   There are several basic laws of exponents:  (1) $x^a \cdot x^b = x^{a+b}$ ;
(2) $\dfrac{x^a}{x^b} = x^{a-b}$ ;  (3) $(x^a)^b = x^{ab}$. (342)

**exponents (negative)**   For any number $x \neq 0$, $x^{-n} = \dfrac{1}{x^n}$ and $\dfrac{1}{x^{-n}} = x^n$ . (343)

**exponents (zero)**   For any number $x \neq 0$, $x^0 = 1$. (343)

**expression**   An algebraic expression consists of one or more variables. It may also contain some constants. Each part of the expression separated by addition or subtraction signs is called a term. (42)

**factor**   (1) In arithmetic: when two or more numbers are multiplied, each of the numbers is a factor of the product. (2) In algebra: where two or more algebraic expressions are multiplied together, each of the expressions is a factor of the product.

**factored completely**   A polynomial is factored completely if none of the resulting factors can be factored further. (291)

**Fibonacci Numbers**   The numbers in the sequence 1, 1, 2, 3, 5, 8, 13, ... are called the Fibonacci Numbers. (201)

**F.O.I.L.**   An approach for multiplying two binomials is to use the mnemonic "F.O.I.L." which stands for "First, Outer, Inner, Last." It describes the order in which to multiply the terms of two binomials to be sure to get all the products. (324)

**fraction busters**   A method of simplifying equations involving fractions that uses the Multiplication Property of Equality to rearrange the equation so that no fractions remain. (313)

**function**   A function is a relation in which for each input value there is one and only one output value. In terms of ordered pairs (x, y), no two ordered pairs have the same first member (x). (378)

**function notation**   Functions are given names, most commonly "f", "g" or "h." The notation f(x) represents the output of a function, named f, when x is the input. It is pronounced "f of x". The notation g(2) is pronounced "g of 2" and represents the output of the function g when x = 2. (378)

**generic rectangle**   In this course, used as an organizational device for multiplying polynomials. For example, the figure below shows how to use generic rectangles to multiply binomials. (215-17)

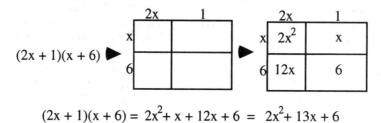

$$(2x + 1)(x + 6) = 2x^2 + x + 12x + 6 = 2x^2 + 13x + 6$$

**greatest common factor**   (1) For integers, the greatest positive integer that is a common factor of two or more integers. (2) For two or more algebraic monomials, the product of the greatest common integer factor of the coefficients of the monomials and the variable(s) in each algebraic term with the greatest degree of that variable in every term. For example, the greatest common factor of $12x^3y^2$ and $8xy^4$ is $4xy^2$. (3) For a polynomial, the greatest common monomial factor of its terms. For example, the greatest common factor of $16x^4 + 8x^3 + 12x$ is $4x$. (279)

**guess and check**   Guess and check is a problem solving strategy in which you begin by making a guess and then check whether or not your guess is correct. In the process of checking, you gain information about how close your guess might be and make adjustments to your guess. The second guess is then tested. This continues until the correct answer is discovered. Being organized is crucial to the success of this method, as well as writing a usable table. Guess and check also leads us to writing equations to represent word problems. (37, 127)

**horizontal lines**   Horizontal lines are "flat" and run left to right in the same direction as the x-axis. All horizontal lines have equations of the form y = b, where b can be any number. Their slope is 0. The x-axis has the equation y = 0 because y = 0 everywhere on the x-axis. (174)

**hypotenuse**   In a right triangle, the longest side of the triangle, opposite the right angle, is called the hypotenuse. (303)

**hypothesis**   A conjecture is what mathematicians call an educated guess, based on data, patterns, and relationships. Scientists use the term hypothesis. (161)

**identity element**   The identity element for addition is 0 because adding 0 leaves the number unchanged: a + 0 = 0. The identity element for multiplication is 1, because multiplying by 1 leaves a number unchanged: a(1) = a. (393)

**independent variable**   The input variable, x, of a relation or function is called the independent variable. (378)

**inequality symbols**   The symbol "≤" read from left to right means "less than or equal to."   The symbol "≥" read from left to right means "greater than or equal to."   The symbols < and > mean "less than: and "greater than" respectively. (110, 408)

**input value**   In a relation or function where y = f(x), the values used for x (the domain) and substituted into the relationship are the input values. The input values are the numbers represented by the independent variables, the first numbers in ordered pairs (x, y). (93, 378)

**integers**   The set of numbers { . . . -3, -2, -1, 0, 1, 2, 3, . . . }.

**inverse operations**   Addition and subtraction are inverse operations, as are multiplication and division. (139, 393)

**irrational numbers**   The set of numbers that cannot be expressed in the form $\frac{a}{b}$ where a and b are integers and b ≠ 0.  For example, $\pi$ and $\sqrt{2}$ are irrational numbers.

**justify**   To use facts, definitions, rules, and/or previously proven statements in an organized way to convince your audience that what you claim (or your answer) is valid (true). (161)

**legs of a right triangle**   The two sides of a right triangle which are not the hypotenuse are called the legs of the triangle. Note that the legs meet to form the right angle of the triangle.

**like terms**   Two or more terms that contain the same variable(s), with corresponding variables raised to the same power are called like terms. For example,  5x and 2x are like terms. Combine like terms by adding them: 5x + 2x = (5 + 2)x = 7x. (67)

**linear equation**   Any equation equivalent to  ax + by = c  (standard form), where  a, b, and c  are real numbers and  a  and  b  are not both zero. Slope-intercept form,  y = mx + b, is one equivalent form. (250, 292)

**linear graphs**   Graphs that are straight lines are called linear graphs. (108)

**line segment**   A portion of a line between two points. We name a line segment by its endpoints, A and B, and write $\overline{AB}$. (167)

**mean**   The mean (average) of several numbers (or data points) is a statistical measurement that describes one way of defining the middle of the numbers.  It is found by adding the numbers together and dividing by the number of data points in the set. (144)

**monomial**   An expression with only one term. It can be a numeral, a variable, or the product of a number and a one or more variables.  for example,  7, 3x, -4ab, or $3x^2y$. (269)

**multiplicative identity**   The Multiplicative Identity Property states that any term multiplied by one (1) remains unchanged; a(1) = a. (393)

**multiplicative inverse**   The Multiplicative Inverse Property states that when multiplying a term by its reciprocal, the result is always one: $a \cdot \frac{1}{a} = 1$  and  $\frac{a}{b} \cdot \frac{b}{a} = 1$ for a (not equal) 0. (393)

**multiplying binomials**   See generic rectangle. (217)

**neutral field**   The number 0 can be represented by the same number of positive and negative tiles, known as a neutral field. (24)

**numeral**   A symbol that names a number.

**numerical coefficient**   See coefficient.

**opposite**   The opposite of a number is its additive inverse. For example, -5 is the opposite of 5.

**ordered pairs**   Points on the x-y coordinate grid written as (x, y).  The first coordinate, x, represents the horizontal distance and direction from the origin; the second coordinate, y, represents the vertical distance and direction from the origin. (104)

**order of operations**   We use the order of operations to simplify complex arithmetic and algebraic expressions, by performing certain operations in a specific order.  The order is parentheses (or other grouping symbols), exponents (powers or roots), multiplication and division (left to right) and addition and subtraction (left to right). (77)

**origin**   The point assigned to zero on the number line or the point where the x- and y-axes intersect in a coordinate system. (96)

**output values**   In a relation or function where y = f(x), the y-values (range) are the output values. (93, 378)

**parabola (equation from its x-intercepts)**   A parabola with x-intercepts (b, 0) and (c, 0) can be written in the form:  y = a(x - b)(x - c). The coefficient a determines the shape (wide or narrow) and the direction (open upward or downward) of the parabola. (439)

**parabolic graphs**   Graphs of quadratic equations are parabolas and are called parabolic. (108)

**percent**   A notation for a ratio with the denominator 100.

**perfect square trinomials**   Trinomials of the form $x^2 + 2ax + a^2$ are known as perfect square trinomials and factor as $(x + a)^2$. (289)

**perimeter**   Perimeter is the distance around a figure on a flat surface. (10, 101)

**perpendicular**   Two lines or segments on a flat surface meet (intersect) to form a 90° angle. (387)

**pi ($\pi$)**   Pi is the name for the ratio of the circumference (c) of a circle, to its diameter (d), so $\pi = \frac{c}{d}$. (63)

**polynomial**   The sum or difference of two or more monomials.  (269)

**power**   A number or variable raised to an exponent in the form $x^n$. See exponent. (340)

**probability**   Probability is a mathematical way to predict how likely it is that an event will occur. If all the outcomes of an event are equally likely to occur, then the probability (or likelihood) that a specified result occurs is expressed by the fraction:

$$P(event) = \frac{\text{number of outcomes in the specified event}}{\text{total number of possible outcomes}}$$   (15)

**problem solving strategies**   This course deals with numerous problem solving strategies. Specifically, Making a Guess and Checking It, Using Manipulatives (such as algebra tiles), Making Systematic Lists, Graphing, Drawing a Diagram, Breaking a Large Problem into Smaller Subproblems, Working Backward, and Writing and Solving an Equation. (422)

**proportion**  An equation stating that two fractions (or ratios) are equal. (169)

**Pythagorean Theorem**  In a right triangle with legs of length a and b and hypotenuse of length c, $a^2 + b^2 = c^2$. This can also be written as $(leg)^2 + (leg)^2 = (hypotenuse)^2$. (305)

**quadratic**  A polynomial is quadratic if the largest exponent in the polynomial is two (that is, the polynomial has degree 2). (269)

**quadratic equation (standard form)**  A quadratic equation is in standard form if it is written as $ax^2 + bx + c = 0$. (350)

**quadratic formula**  If $ax^2 + bx + c = 0$ and $a \neq 0$, then $x = \dfrac{-b \pm \sqrt{b^2 - 4ac}}{2a}$ . (353)

**radical**  An expression in the form $\sqrt{a}$ (square root). Other roots, such as cube root, will be studied in other courses. (319, 326)

**radical (simplified form)**  A number $r\sqrt{s}$ is in simple radical form if no square of an integer divides s and s is not a fraction; that is, there are no more perfect square factors (square numbers such as 4, 9, 16, etc.) under the radical sign and no radicals in the denominator. For example, $5\sqrt{12}$ is not in simple radical form since 4 (the square of 2) divides 12. But $5\sqrt{12} = 10\sqrt{3}$ is in simple radical form. (319, 326)

**radicand**  The expression under the radical sign.

**radius**  The distance from the center to the points on the circle is called the radius, usually denoted r. (61)

**range**  The set of all second members of a function or relation, that is, all possible output values for a relation or function. For ordered pairs (x, y), all output (y) values. (378)

**ratio**  A ratio is a comparison of two quantities by division. (158-59)

**ratio of similarity**  The ratio of similarity between any two similar figures is the ratio of any pair of corresponding sides. In this course ratios will always be listed in the order that compares the "new" to the "original" figure. (158-59)

**rational expressions**  A rational expression is a fraction in which the numerator and/or denominator contain polynomials. (348)

**rational numbers**  Numbers that can be expressed in the form $\dfrac{a}{b}$ where a and b are integers, $b \neq 0$.

**ratio of similar figures**  The ratio of similarity between any two similar figures is the ratio of any pair of corresponding sides. This means that once it is determined that two figures are similar, all of their pairs of corresponding sides have the same ratio. (165)

**real numbers**  Irrational numbers together with rational numbers form the set of the real numbers. All real numbers are represented on the number line.

**reciprocal**  The reciprocal of a non-zero number is its multiplicative inverse. For x, the reciprocal is $\dfrac{1}{x}$; for $\dfrac{a}{b}$, the reciprocal is $\dfrac{b}{a}$.

**rectangular numbers**   The numbers in the pattern 2, 6, 12, 20, ... are known as the rectangular numbers. (40)

**reduction ratio**   The ratio of similarity comparing a figure to a similar smaller one is often called the reduction ratio. This number tells you by what factor the first figure is reduced to get the second. (165)

**reference point**   When solving equations involving absolute values, it is sometimes useful to start with a reference point. For an equation such as $|x - a| = b$, a is the reference point. After locating the point  a  on a number line, we find the numbers which are a distance of b from a. This usually gives us the two solutions to the equation. (384)

**reflexive property**   The Reflexive Property states that a term is always equal to itself: $a = a$. (393)

**relation**   An equation which relates inputs to outputs is called a relation. As such, a relation is a set of ordered pairs. The set of first values is the domain, the set of second values is the range. (363)

**right angle**   A right angle is an angle that measures 90°. (171)

**right triangle**   A right triangle is a triangle with one right angle. (171)

**roots of an equation**   A solution of the equation. The x-intercepts of a parabola are also referred to as the roots of the quadratic equation. (284)

**scientific notation**   A number is expressed in scientific notation when it is in the form $a \times 10^n$, where  $1 \le a < 10$  and n is an integer. (78)

**similar figures**   Similar geometric figures are figures that have the same shape but are not necessarily the same size. In similar figures, the measures of corresponding angles are equal <u>and</u> the lengths of corresponding sides have the same ratio. (158)

**simplest form (of a numerical expression)**   Replacing a numerical expression by the simplest form of its value.

**simplest form (of a variable expression)**   A variable expression in simplest form has no like terms and no parentheses. (42, 348, 373)

**slope**   The slope of a line is a ratio that describes how steep (or flat) the line is.  Slope can be positive, negative, or even zero, but a straight line has only one slope.  Slope is the ratio $\frac{\text{change in y value}}{\text{change in x value}}$ or $\frac{\text{vertical change}}{\text{horizontal change}}$. The symbol used to represent slope is the letter "m."  Some texts refer to slope as the ratio of the "rise over the run."
A line has positive slope if it slopes upward from left to right on a graph; negative slope if it slopes downward from left to right. A vertical line has undefined or no slope. (243)

**slope-intercept form**   Any non-vertical line can be described by an equation written in the form $y = mx + b$. The "m" represents the slope of the line (it is the coefficient of x). The "b" represents the y-value of the y-intercept (where $x = 0$). Ordered pairs (x, y) that make the equation true are coordinates of points on that line. (250)

**slope triangle**   A slope triangle is a right triangle drawn on a graph of a line so that the hypotenuse of the triangle is part of the line. The vertical leg length is the change in the y-value; the horizontal leg length is the change in the x-value. The length of the legs of the triangle are the values used in the slope ratio (change in  y  and change in  x). (252)

**solution**   A replacement for the variable that makes an open sentence (equation) true.

**solve**   Find the solution(s) of equations or inequalities. (134, 142, 205, 283, 387, 412)

**square numbers**   The numbers in the pattern 1, 4, 9, 16, 25, ..., that is, the squares of the counting numbers 1, 2, 3, 4, 5, ...,  are known as square numbers. (39-40)

**standard form (of a linear equation)**   See linear equation.

**standard notation**   A number written out completely, showing all digits and without use of exponents is written in standard notation. (39)

**subproblem**   Breaking down problems into smaller, simpler parts is a technique for solving problems.  The smaller, simpler problems are called subproblems.  Solving the simpler, smaller problems first allows us to then put the results together to complete a larger problem. (54)

**substitution**   Replacing one symbol by another (a number, a variable, or other algebraic expression) without changing the value of the expression. (63)

**substitution method (systems of equations)**   A method of solving a system of equations by replacing one variable with an expression involving the remaining variable(s). One variable is expressed in terms of the other variable, such as y-form, that is, $y = mx + b$, then the expression $mx + b$  replaces that variable (y) in a second equation involving x and y. (206, 254)

**substitution property**   If $a = b$, then either a or b can be replaced by the other. (392-93)

**symmetric property**   The Symmetric Property states that if two terms are equal it does not matter which is stated first. If $a = b$ then $b = a$. (393)

**systems of linear equations**   For this course, two equations in two variables that describe lines that may or may not intersect. The equations together are called a system of equations and the process of finding where, if at all, the lines intersect is called solving the system. (206)

**term**   Each part of the expression separated by addition or subtraction signs is called a term. (42)

**triangular numbers**   The numbers in the pattern 1, 3, 6, 10, 15, ... are known as triangular numbers. (41)

**transitive property of equality**   The Transitive Property of Equality states that if $a = b$ and $b = c$, then $a = c$. (393)

**trinomial**   A polynomial of three terms. (269)

**two-point graphing method**   Using only two points to graph a linear equation.  Often one of the points is the y-intercept, but it does not necessarily need to be. (203)

**value**   In the expression $2^5$, 32 is the value.  Also, 5 is the exponent and 2 is the base. (340)

**variable**   For this course a variable is a symbol used in a mathematical sentence to represent a number. (74)

**vertex (of a parabola)**   The highest point or lowest point on a parabola (depending on its orientation) is called the vertex. (439)

**vertical lines**    Vertical lines run up and down in the same direction as the y-axis and parallel to it. All vertical lines have equations of the form x = a, where a can be any number. The y-axis has the equation x = 0 because x = 0 everywhere on the y-axis. Vertical lines have undefined slope. (174)

**working backward**    In many cases, to solve a problem we must "undo" something that has been "done." This is true when we solve equations. The notion of being able to "undo" something is part of the problem solving strategy of working backward and the mathematical operation is called an inverse operation. Working backwards uses inverse operations to find the original form of an expression or value(s) of a variable. Solving an equation is an example of this process. (139)

**x-axis**    The horizontal axis on a coordinate plane (graph) is called the x-axis. (96)

**x-coordinate**    The first component (coordinate) in an ordered pair.

**x-intercepts**    The point(s) where a graph crosses the x-axis is (are) called the x-intercepts. The x-intercept always has coordinates (x, 0). (96, 106, 239, 284)

**y-axis**    The vertical axis on a coordinate plane (graph) is called the y-axis. (96)

**y-coordinate**    The second component (coordinate) in an ordered pair.

**y-form**    An equation is written in y-form if the equation is solved for y, and so is written as "y = _____". For example, the y-form of a linear equation is  y = mx + b. (202, 205)

**y-intercepts**    The point(s) where the graph crosses the y-axis is (are) called the y-intercepts. The y-intercept always has a coordinate (0, y). (96, 106, 239)

**zero product property**    The Zero Product Property states that when the product of two or more factors is zero, one of these factors must equal zero; that is, if a • b = 0 then either a = 0 or b = 0. Note that we can use the Zero Product Property to solve quadratic equations that are factorable. (283, 285)

# Unit Prefixes

Many of the problems listed here contain definitions or examples of the topic listed. It may be necessary, however, to read text preceding or following the problem, or additional problems to fully understand the topic. Also, some problems listed here are "good examples" of the topic and may not offer any explanation. It is very important, therefore, for you to be sure you correct and complete your homework and keep it organized. Your record of the problem may be your best index to understanding the mathematics of this course.

# THIS BOOK IS THE PROPERTY OF:

Book No._____

| ISSUED TO | Year Used | CONDITION | |
|---|---|---|---|
| | | ISSUED | RETURNED |
| Jameela J. | 2005 | Ripped | Same |
| | | | |
| | | | |
| | | | |
| | | | |
| | | | |
| | | | |
| | | | |

PUPILS to whom this textbook is issued must not write on any page or mark any part of it in any way, unless otherwise instructed by the teacher.